J...
DA...

A
COLLECTION

Janet Dailey An author of international status, Janet Dailey is one of the most powerful names in the world of women's fiction. Since publication of her first book in 1974, Dailey has penned more than 80 novels which have sold over 100 million copies worldwide. A name that frequently appears on bestseller lists, her string of successful novels include *Heiress, Rivals, Aspen Gold* and *Tangled Vines* (all Michael Joseph).

Worldwide Books are proud to bring back three of this outstanding author's previous titles with *A Collection*. Vintage Dailey, these novels are as fresh and exciting as when first published, giving new fans a unique chance to sample some of her earlier works and longtime readers a collector's edition to treasure.

CONTENTS:

CONTENTS

THE IVORY CANE

BY
JANET DAILEY

WORLDWIDE BOOKS
LONDON • SYDNEY • TORONTO

*All the characters in this book have no existence outside the imagina-
tion of the Author, and have no relation whatsoever to anyone bearing the same name or names. They are not even distantly inspired by
any individual known or unknown to the Author, and all the incidents
are pure invention.*

*First published in Great Britain in 1977
Reprinted in Great Britain in 1994
by Worldwide Books, Eton House,
18-24 Paradise Road, Richmond, Surrey TW9 1SR*

© Janet Dailey 1977

ISBN 0 373 59201 9

99-9405

*Printed and bound in Great Britain by
BPCC Paperbacks Ltd
Member of BPCC Ltd*

CHAPTER ONE

OVERHEAD a seagull screeched. The blustery wind off the Pacific Ocean swirled around the boats docked at the Yacht Harbour of San Francisco Bay. Distantly came the clang of a cable car, the one climbing the steep hill of Hyde Street.

A light blue Continental with a leather-grained top of dark blue was wheeled expertly into the parking lot in front of the harbour. The driver, a stunningly beautiful woman with titian hair in her mid-thirties, braked the car precisely between the white parking lines and switched off the motor. As she reached for the door handle, emerald green eyes flicked to the silent girl in the passenger seat.

'It's quite chilly outside, Sabrina. It probably would be best if you waited in the car while I see if your father is back.' It was a statement, not a suggestion that the woman made.

Sabrina Lane opened her mouth to protest. She was tired of being treated as an invalid. With a flash of insight, she realised that Deborah was not concerned about her health as much as she was about spending some time alone with Sabrina's father.

'Whatever you say, Deborah,' she submitted grudgingly, her right hand closing tightly over the smooth handle of her oak cane.

The silent moments following Deborah's departure grated at Sabrina's already taut nerves. It was difficult enough to endure her own physical restric-

5

tions without having her father's girl-friend place others on her, regardless of the motive.

Her father's girl-friend. One corner of her wide mouth turned up wryly at the phraseology. Her father had had many women friends since her mother had died when Sabrina was seven. But Deborah Mosley was not just another woman. If it had not been for Sabrina's accident some eight months ago, Deborah would have already been her new stepmother.

Prior to the accident, Sabrina had thought it was terrific that her father had found someone he wanted to marry. Deborah Mosley wouldn't have been Sabrina's choice, although she liked her, but that hadn't mattered not as long as her father was happy.

That was before the accident, when Sabrina had been totally independent. She had had a place of her own, a very small apartment, but it had been hers. She had had a career, not a lucrative one, but she could have supported herself.

Now—the word screamed with its own despairing wail. It would be a long time, if ever, before Sabrina could say any of that again.

'Why me?' a sobbing, self-pitying voice asked silently. 'What did I ever do to deserve this? Why me?'

Her throat tightened with pain at the unanswerable question. There was simply too much time to think. Too much time to think about the 'what-might-have-beens' and the 'if-onlys'. The damage was done and irreparable, as specialist after specialist had told Sabrina and her father. She would be incapacitated for the rest of her life and there was

6

nothing, barring a miracle, that could ever be done to change it.

A seed of rebellion stirred to life. An anger seethed to the surface that she might forever sit in cars and stay at home while someone else decided what was best for her.

A sickening thought sprang to mind. Suppose, Sabrina thought, that Deborah's wish to be alone with her father was not prompted by a desire for some romantic moments but part of a plan to persuade him to send her away to that rehabilitation home? Rehabilitation—the word always made her feel like a criminal.

'Please, God,' Sabrina prayed, 'don't let Daddy listen to her. I don't want to go to that place. Surely there must be an alternative besides another school.'

She felt guilty praying to God for help. It hurt to need anyone to help her. She had always been so completely self-sufficient. Now she was constantly depending on someone. At this very minute, Deborah might be persuading her father to send her to another school and she was sitting in the car, accepting her fate by the very fact that she was not participating in the discussion but calling on someone else to intercede on her behalf.

Thousands of times Sabrina had walked from the parking lot of the harbour to the slip where her father tied his boat. It wasn't that great a distance. If she remained calm and took her time, there was no reason why she couldn't traverse it again.

Artistically long fingers tightened the cord of the striped tunic and adjusted the rolled collar of the navy dark turtleneck she wore underneath. The wind whistled a warning outside. She ran a smoothing hand up to the back of her head to be certain her mink-brown hair was securely fastened in its knot atop her head.

Taking a deep breath to still the quivering excitement racing through her, Sabrina opened the door and swung her long legs on to the pavement. With the car door closed behind her and the cane firmly in her grasp, she moved slowly in the direction of the harbour fence. The icy tendrils of fear dancing down her spine added to the adventurous thrill of her small journey.

Emboldened by her initial success, Sabrina unconsciously began to hurry. She stumbled over a concrete parking stop and couldn't regain her balance. The cane slipped from her hand, skittering away as she sprawled on to the pavement.

Excitement disappeared immediately, leaving only black fear. Her shaking fingers reached for the cane, but it was out of her grasp. Except for the shock to her senses, there was no pain. She wasn't hurt, but how was she going to make her way to the dock without the cane?

'Damn, damn, damn!' Sabrina cursed her own foolishness for making the attempt in the first place.

If her father found her like this, it would only increase the apparent validity of Deborah's argument that Sabrina needed more professional help. Propping herself up on one elbow, she tried to check the rising terror that was leading her towards panic and think her way out of this predicament rationally.

8

'Are you all right?' The low, masculine voice offering concern was laced with amusement.

Sabrina's head jerked in the direction from which it had come, embarrassed red surging into her cheeks that a stranger should find her and humiliation that she was forced to seek his help.

The triangular line of her chin, tapering from prominent cheekbones and square jaw, tilted to a proud angle. 'I'm not hurt,' she asserted quickly, then grudgingly, 'My cane, would you get it for me?'

'Of course.' The amusement disappeared.

The instant the cane was retrieved Sabrina reached out to take it from him, not wanting to endure the mortification of his pity and hoping a quick 'thank you' would send him on his way. As her outstretched hand remained empty, her cheeks flamed darker.

A pair of strong hands slipped under her arms and bodily lifted her to her feet before she could gasp a protest. Her fingers touched the hard flesh of his upper arms, covered by the smooth material of his windbreaker. The salty tang of the ocean breeze mingled with the spicy after-shave cologne and his virile masculine scent. Sabrina was tall, nearly five foot seven, but the warm breath from his mouth stirred the fringe covering her wide forehead, making him easily six inches taller than she.

Her cane, hooked over his arm, tapped the side of her leg. 'Please let me go,' she said crisply while her fingers closed over the cane and lifted it from his arm.

'Nothing sprained but your pride, is that it?' the

9

man mocked gently, loosening his grip on her slim waist and letting his hands fall away.

Sabrina smiled tautly, keeping her luminous brown eyes that sometimes seemed too large for her face, averted from the man's face. His pity she didn't need.

'Thank you for your help,' she murmured unwillingly as she took a hesitant step backwards.

Turning away, she waited for interminable seconds for him to continue wherever it was that he was going. She could feel his eyes on her back and guessed that he was waiting to be certain she hadn't hidden an injury from the fall.

Afraid that he might feel compelled because of her need for the cane to offer further assistance, Sabrina stepped out boldly. The shocking blare of a horn simultaneously accompanied by the squeal of car brakes paralysed her. A steel band circled her waist and roughly pulled her back.

The husky male voice was still low, but there was nothing gentle and concerned about its tone as he growled in her ear. 'Were you trying to kill yourself? Didn't you see that car coming?'

'How could I?' Sabrina muttered bitterly, unable to tug the steel-hard arm from around her waist. 'I'm blind!'

She heard and felt his swift intake of breath a split second before he spun her around, her upper arms now prisoners of his hands. His eyes burned over her face. Her downcast chin was seized by his fingers and jerked up. Sabrina knew her sightless eyes were gazing into his face. For once she was blessedly glad she couldn't see. The pity that would be in his ex-

10

pression would have been unbearable.

'Why the hell didn't you say so!' There was a savage snap to his angry voice that caught her off guard. Anger she had not expected. 'And why the blazes isn't your cane white?'

Stung, Sabrina retorted in kind. 'Why am I supposed to have a white cane? Why am I expected to wear dark glasses? Should I run around with a little tin cup, too, crying "alms for the blind"? Why does being blind make me different from anyone else? Why do I have to be singled out? I hate it when parents point their fingers at me and tell their children to let the blind lady go first. My cane isn't white because I don't want any special consideration or any pity!'

'And your abhorrence of white canes nearly got you killed,' the stranger said grimly. 'Had the driver of the car that almost ran you down seen a white cane in your hand, he might have taken extra precautions, slowed down to give you the right of way or perhaps honked his horn to be sure you knew he was there. You go right on being a proud fool. You won't live long. Just keep on stepping in front of cars and sooner or later one of them will hit you. It might not trouble your conscience, but I'm sure the driver who ultimately runs you down will have difficulty understanding the pride that kept you from carrying a white cane that could have saved your life.'

'It's not difficult to understand,' Sabrina replied in a strangled voice. 'If the man had ever lost his sight, he'd know how grating it is to advertise your blindness.'

11

'It's very obvious why you reject pity from others,' the man taunted. 'You're much too busy wallowing in a pool of your own self-pity.'

'Of all the arrogant——' Sabrina didn't bother to finish the statement as her hand accurately judged the distance and height before connecting with a resounding slap against the man's jaw and cheek.

The trajectory of her hand had not completed its arc when she felt a stinging hand against her own cheek. It was no more than a reproving tap, but her shock at his reaction magnified it tenfold.

'How dare you strike a blind person!' she exclaimed in an outraged whisper.

'I thought you didn't want any special privileges?' he mocked. 'Or doesn't that extend to slapping another person, secure in the belief that he wouldn't retaliate against a blind girl? You'll have to make up your mind whether the kid gloves should be on or off.'

Sabrina gasped sharply, caught in the trap of her own words. 'You are insufferable!' she breathed, and turned away.

'Not so fast.' The hand digging into her shoulder and neck effectively halted her steps. 'You're worse than a toddler,' he muttered impatiently. 'Do you hear any cars coming? Do you know where you're going? Have you got your directions straight?'

'Just leave me alone!' Sabrina demanded. 'My well-being is nobody's responsibility but my own!'

'I'm sorry.' There was no apology in his harsh tone. 'But I was raised to believe that all of us are our brother's keeper, or sister's as the case may be. So, whether you like it or not, I'm going to see that you safely arrive at whatever destination you have. Go ahead and walk away.' Sabrina could sense his shrug of indifference. 'I'll be walking right behind you.'

She wanted to scream her frustration, but the stranger's unrelenting manner seemed to say that even that would be a waste of energy. She could not go on the docks, not with this man as an unwanted bodyguard. The last thing she wanted was to have her father feel that it wasn't safe to leave her alone even for a few minutes. The minute her father saw this man at her side there would be all sorts of questions and the entire embarrassing story would be told.

Reluctantly she turned back in the direction she had just come. 'You don't need to trouble yourself,' she said stiffly. 'I'm only going to the car.'

'And drive, I suppose.' Satirical amusement was back in the man's low-pitched voice.

Sabrina chose to ignore his laughing jibe. Embarrassment and anger had all but erased her sense of humour. She tried to step past the tall stranger, but he moved to block her way.

'Which car?' he asked softly.

'The blue Continental behind you in the next row.'

'That isn't where you were headed when I first saw you.'

She gritted her teeth. 'I had intended to go out on the docks to meet my father and Deborah. Since you insist on accompanying me, I prefer to wait for them in the car.' There was a saccharine quality to her carefully enunciated words.

'They're out sailing and left you here in the car?'

13

His tone seemed to indicate that her father and Deborah possessed as little sense as she did.

'No, my father went sailing. Deborah and I came down to pick him up. She's somewhere out on the dock now and I was going to see what was keeping them,' Sabrina retorted.

'Deborah is your sister?'

'You seem determined to pry into my personal life,' she sighed impatiently. 'Deborah will quite likely be my new mother—if it's any of your business!'

His hand closed over her elbow, the firm hold guiding her steps in the direction Sabrina knew the car to be. Several steps later, the end of the cane clunked against the side fender of the car.

'Which slip does your father use? I'll go see what's keeping him for you,' the man offered.

'No, thank you,' she refused curtly. 'He's nearly convinced already that I need a permanent baby-sitter. If you go carrying tales to him, I'll never be able to persuade him that I don't want anybody wiping my nose for me.' Exasperation ringed her voice. 'If I give you my word that I won't leave the car, will you go away and leave me alone?'

'I'm afraid it's too late to keep our meeting a secret from your father,' the man said.

'What do you mean?' Sabrina frowned.

'Is Deborah a redhead?'

'Yes.'

'Well, there's a man walking towards the harbour gates with a redhead at his side. He's looking this way with a rather anxious frown on his face,' was the reply.

14

'Please go quickly before he gets here,' she pleaded.

'Since he's already seen me, if I were your father I would be very suspicious if a strange man was talking to my daughter and left when he saw me coming. It's better that I stay,' the man stated.

'No.' Sabrina whispered her protest. With this man, words held little persuasion.

There was the clink of the harbour fence gates opening and closing. Time had run out.

'Stop looking as if I'd made some indecent proposition to you. Smile.' The sound of the man's low voice held a smile, warm and faintly amused at her apparent discomfort. Her reluctance was obvious as the corners of her mouth stretched into a slow smile.

'Sabrina.' Her father's voice hailed her, an undertone of concern in his otherwise warmly happy use of her name. 'Were you getting tired of waiting?'

Nervously she turned, trying to keep the faltering smile in place, knowing how perceptively discerning the scrutiny of his hazel eyes could be.

'Hello, Dad.' She forced a casualness into her voice. 'Did you have a good sail?'

'What else?' he laughed his assertion.

Sabrina sensed almost the exact instant when her father's inquisitive gaze was turned on the man at her side. She had been so busy trying to get rid of him that she hadn't thought of a single excuse to explain his presence.

The problem was taken out of her hands. 'You must be Sabrina's father. She was just asking me if I'd seen the *Lady Sabrina* come in while I was at the docks. I have the ketch down the way from yours,

15

Dame Fortune. The name is Bay Cameron,' the stranger introduced.

'Grant Lane,' her father countered, the vague wariness leaving his voice at the introduction.

Unconsciously Sabrina had been holding her breath. She let it out in a silent sigh. The stranger, now identified as Bay Cameron, could think on his feet, she decided with relief. Of course she was certain there wasn't another boat in the harbour named *Lady Sabrina*, but the man had been quick to put two and two together simply from her father's use of her name. And it sounded like such a plausible excuse for her to be talking to him.

Her father's hand touched her shoulder and she turned her face to him with an easy smile. 'You weren't worrying about me, were you, Sabrina?' he teased.

'Not a bit. Not a salty old sailor like you. Of course, you were minus the best deckhand you ever had,' she laughed.

'Yes, well——' His stumbling agreement made Sabrina wish she could bite off her tongue. She had not meant to remind him of the many hours they had spent together sailing these very same waters before the accident that had left her permanently blind.

'Women always worry when their men are at sea,' the stranger named Bay Cameron filled in the awkward gap.

'It's our nature,' Deborah spoke up in her best purring voice. 'You men wouldn't like it any other way.'

'Quite right, Deborah,' her father agreed. 'Mr

16

Cameron, this is my fiancée, Deborah Mosely.'

'Miss Mosely, it's a pleasure, but I shouldn't keep you any longer. I'm sure you all have plans of some kind,' Bay Cameron responded.

'Thank you for keeping Sabrina company.' There was sincere gratitude in her father's offer of thanks.

'Yes, Mr Cameron,' Sabrina added, reluctantly acknowledging the fact that he had not given her away. 'I appreciated your thoughtfulness.'

'Yes, I know.' Lack of sight made Sabrina's hearing more acute. She caught the mocking inflection in his words that quite likely escaped her father and Deborah's ears. He knew very well what she was thanking him for. 'Perhaps we'll all see each other again some time. Good afternoon.'

After their answering chorus of goodbyes, Sabrina listened to his footsteps fading away to another area of the parking lot. She wondered why he had not seen fit, in his arrogance, to tell her father the way they had really met. Pity, most likely, although he had certainly exhibited a remarkable lack of it earlier. In fact he had been downright rude and tyrannical.

The car door was opened behind her, bringing an abrupt end to her wandering thoughts as her father's guiding hand helped her into the back seat.

'I thought you were going to wait in the car,' Deborah said in a faintly reproving tone after they were all seated.

'It got stuffy, so I decided to get some fresh air,' Sabrina lied.

'It did put some colour in your cheeks,' Grant Lane observed. 'You probably should get out more.'

17

Was that an innocent comment or a remark prompted by a discussion with Deborah concerning that new school for the blind she had heard about? It was impossible to tell. Sabrina crossed her fingers.

'This Mr Cameron,' Deborah said, 'had you met him before?'

'No. Why?' Sabrina stiffened, vaguely on the defensive.

'It's not like you to talk to total strangers, that's all,' the redhead replied.

'You mean, not since I've been blind,' Sabrina corrected sharply. 'I've never been exactly shy. Besides, all I did was ask about Dad.'

There was a moment of uneasy silence. Her reply hadn't needed to be so cutting, but sometimes Deborah's air of solicitude and apparent concern got on Sabrina's nerves. For that matter, anyone's did.

'Do you suppose,' Deborah covered the silence, 'he's one of the real estate Camerons?'

'I can't visualise any other having a ketch in the Yacht Harbour,' her father replied. 'The Camerons are one of the founding families of San Francisco.'

A native San Franciscan, Sabrina was well aware of the city's colourful history. Until gold was discovered in 1849, it had been a nothing little settlement on San Francisco Bay called Yerba Buena, 'good herb'. The bay was a perfect harbour for the ships racing around the tip of South America to join in the rush for California gold. The natural entrance into the bay truly became 'golden gates' for a lot of pioneers.

Few actually found the precious metal in any

quantity, but the real treasure had been in the goods and services they brought with them. The great bulk of the gold was possessed by a very small number of men. The majority of it from the California and Nevada lodes built San Francisco, the City by the Bay.

The Cameron family was one of the less publicised of the original founders. It was laughingly said that they once owned all of San Francisco, and now they possessed only a quarter of the city. Hardly a step down in this day and age, Sabrina thought wryly, and it certainly accounted for the man's arrogance.

Oh, well, she sighed, what was the use in thinking about him? He was not the kind of man a person would run into very often, not with his background.

She had rather liked his voice, though. Sabrina qualified the thought quickly. She had liked it when he hadn't been dictatorially telling her what to do. The low baritone pitch had been warm and vaguely caressive, mature, too. She wondered how old he was.

That was one of the problems of not being able to see. She had to rely so heavily on the other senses to judge the new people she met. Still, she was becoming rather good at it. She began a quick exercise of the impressions she had gained in her brief meeting with Bay Cameron.

He was tall, over six foot by at least an inch. When he had pulled her out of the oncoming car's path, she had had the sensation of wide shoulders, a flat stomach and lean hips. Judging by the solidness of his muscles he was in excellent physical condition.

19

The salty ocean spray that had clung to him at least verified that he often journeyed forth in the ketch tied up in the harbour and probably had that day since the scent had been predominant. That indicated an affection for the sea or at least, the outdoors, possibly both. His clean male scent and the fragrantly spicy after-shave cologne told her a bit about his personal habits.

At the time she had been too angry to appreciate his sense of humour, but she guessed it was there, somewhere beneath his amused mockery. His intelligence was in some ways measured by his educated manner of speaking and the quick thinking that had immediately assimilated the facts and come up with a reasonable excuse for her father as to why Sabrina had been talking to him. On the business side, he would probably be very shrewd and astute. The family fortune would be safe with him, if not increased.

She settled back into her seat with smug triumph. That was a great deal of information to glean from one meeting. There were only two things about him she didn't know. His age she could only narrow as being somewhere between thirty and fifty, judging by the maturity of his voice and his physical condition. The second was a detailed description of his looks—the colour of his hair, his eyes, that type of thing. Sabrina was really quite pleased with herself.

For an instant she was motionless. There was one other thing she didn't know—his marital status. That was something she couldn't be certain of even if she could see, unless he was one of those men who faithfully wore his wedding ring. She couldn't recall the sensation of anything metal on his fingers.

Not that she cared one way or the other whether he was married or not. She had merely been conducting an exercise of her senses, a satisfactory one at that.

CHAPTER TWO

call the sensation of anything resting on his fingers. Not that she cared one way or the other whether he was mollified. She was simply keen on enduring an amount of her stress, a satisfactory one

SABRINA licked the vanilla icing from her fingers, then painstakingly ran the knife across the top of every centimetre of the cake. No matter what kind of cake she made, her father invariably called it a fingerprint cake. Sabrina was never totally confident that the frosting covered the entire cake. The only way she could be certain was by feeling, hence the telltale impressions of her fingers across the icing.

Placing the knife on the formica counter, she set the cake platter towards the back, refusing to give in to the sensation that there was a gaping hole somewhere exposing the dark devil's food cake. Before the accident that had left her blinded, Sabrina had taken the simplest task in the kitchen for granted.

Now, washing dishes was a study in diligence, let alone cooking a meal. She had mastered nearly everything but eggs. There was only one type she could cook. Invariably they turned out to be scrambled omelettes. For the sake of their stomachs, breakfast had become the meal her father prepared.

Sunday was the day that Deborah did all the cooking, as had been the case this last weekend. She was a gourmet cook. Sabrina had always been mediocre at best, which made her doubly conscious of the occasionally charred or rare meals she placed on the table during the week compared to the perfection of Deborah's. Yet her father had never complained once, ignoring the less appetising to compliment the good.

Except for a daily woman who came in twice a week to do the more thorough cleaning, Sabrina took care of the house herself, dusting and vacuuming. It took her longer than the average sighted person, but she had discovered that, with patience, there was very little she couldn't do. But patience was the key.

Without the benefit of sunlight, the passage of time was nearly impossible to judge. It seemed to slip through her fingers at times, five minutes turning out to be ten. Sometimes when the loneliness of her dark world caved in about her, the opposite was true. The empty, desolate sensation invariably occurred after a great surge of creative energy that she was unable to release.

Sabrina had learned to endure the myriad inconveniences that came from being sightless. She could even keep the bitterness in check until she thought about the career that had come to such an abrupt halt after the accident.

Since almost the first time a watercolour brush had been put in her hand, art and more specifically painting had been her special love. Her natural talent, enhanced by skill taught by some of the best teachers around, had made her a relatively successful artist at the early age of twenty-two, thanks to nearly fifteen years of training. Recognition had been achieved in portraits, not necessarily commissioned sittings but more often interesting faces she had seen along Fisherman's Wharf or Little Italy.

That had been the cruelty in the accident that had taken her sight. It had been a car accident. Even to this day Sabrina didn't know what had happened. She had been driving home very late at night after a weekend spent with a girl friend in Sacramento. She had fallen asleep at the wheel.

Looking back, her haste to return home seemed so senseless, considering the month she had spent in the hospital recovering from broken ribs and a concussion—not to mention the evident blow to her head that had irreparably damaged the optic nerves.

Giving her head a firm shake, Sabrina resolutely tried to push such memories to the back of her mind. Her survival lay in the future not in looking over her shoulder at the past. At the moment the future looked empty, but seven months ago Sabrina had not believed she would accomplish as much as she had.

Her next obstacle was walking from her home to the drugstore to buy a bottle of shampoo. It was only five blocks, but it was five blocks of San Francisco traffic and four intersections. Only in the last two months had she had sufficient confidence in her ability to attempt such a journey without accompaniment. Her pride always kept the humiliation of getting lost uppermost in her mind.

The pale green sweater jacket Sabrina took from the closet complemented the dark green of her slacks. She touched the handle of her oak cane in the umbrella stand, the smooth finish of the wood reminding her instantly of the arrogant stranger Bay Cameron that she had met at the Yacht Harbour last Sunday. She didn't care what he thought. She preferred the anonymity of a wooden cane. It was bad enough blundering about in her permanent darkness without drawing attention to her plight.

Entering into the stairway, Sabrina walked down the steps to the front door, carefully locking it behind her. The grillework gates just a few feet away creaked noisily as she opened and locked them. The sidewalk sloped abruptly downward. Sabrina counted the paces slowly, accurately turning at the front door of the neighbouring Victorian house.

Pressing the intercom buzzer, she waited for her neighbour's response. As a precaution, her father insisted that she always let someone know where she was going and when she had safely returned, whether it was Peggy Collins, their neighbour for nearly fifteen years, or himself at his office.

'Yes, who is it?' a briskly sharp female voice answered the buzz.

'It's me, Sabrina. I'm on my way to the drugstore. Do you need anything?'

'How about three more hands? Or better yet, a plane ticket to South America?' the woman replied with amused exasperation.

'It's as bad as that, is it?' Sabrina laughed.

'Ken called me an hour ago and is bringing a couple of very important clients home for cocktails and dinner. Naturally there's not a thing in the house to eat and I'm also defrosting the refrigerator and have the contents of half the closets strewn through the house. It looks as if a cyclone had hit this place. Of all days to get ambitious, I had to pick today.'

'I'll be back in an hour or so.' Sabrina smiled at the intercom. There always seemed to be an impending crisis at Peggy's house that was invariably weathered with commendable aplomb. 'If we have anything you need—ice, drink, food—you just let me know.'

'My best solution is to find a husband with a better sense of timing,' Peggy sighed. 'Take care, Sabrina. I'll let you know if I need anything when you get back.'

Humming softly, Sabrina started out again. Her neighbour's droll humour had restored her somewhat dampened spirits. The trip to the drugstore became more of an adventure than an obstacle. There was a nip in the wind racing down the hill, but there always seemed to be a nip in the winds wandering through San Francisco.

There was no warmth on her cheeks as she crossed to the normally more sunny side of the street. The sun had evidently not burned through the fog yet. Instantly a vision of the fog swirling about the spans of the Golden Gate bridge sprang to her mind.

Her concentration broke for a moment and she had to pause to get her bearings. It was so difficult not to daydream. The end of her cane found the drop box for the mail and she knew which block she was on.

Crossing the street, she began counting her steps. She didn't want to walk into the barbershop instead of the drugstore as she had done the last time. A funny, prickly sensation started down the back of her neck. She ran a curious finger along the back collar of her sweater jacket and frowned at the unknown cause of the peculiar feeling.

'No white cane, I see,' a familiarly husky voice

26

said from behind her. 'You're a stubborn girl, Miss Lane.'

A disbelieving paralysis took hold of her limbs for a fleeting second before Sabrina pivoted towards the male voice.

'Mr Cameron,' she acknowledged him coolly. 'I didn't expect to see you again.'

'The city isn't as large as it seems. Here I am driving down the street and see a girl walking with a cane. I start wondering if you've been run down yet. Then, lo and behold, I realise the young girl with the cane is you. Are you in search of your father again?' Bay Cameron asked in that faintly amused tone she remembered.

'I was just going into the drugstore here.' Sabrina motioned absently over her shoulder in the general direction of her destination. 'You were driving?'

'Yes, I parked my car up the street. Do you live near here?'

'A few blocks,' she answered, tilting her head curiously and wishing she could see the expression on his face. 'Why did you stop?'

'To see if you would have a cup of coffee with me,' he replied smoothly.

'Why?' She couldn't keep the wariness out of her voice.

Bay Cameron laughed softly. 'Do I have to have an ulterior motive? Why can't it just be a friendly gesture on my part?'

'I just don't understand why you should want to have coffee with'—Sabrina nearly said 'with a blind girl'. The haughtiness left her voice as she ended lamely with—'me.'

27

'It seems to me, Sabrina, that you not only suffer from a persecution complex but a feeling of inferiority as well,' he suggested mockingly.

'That's absurd!' The sightless brown eyes that had been directed blankly at his face were sharply averted to the traffic in the street.

'Good.' Strong fingers closed over her elbow, turning her towards the drugstore. 'Where would you like to have the coffee? I know a little café in the next block we could go to.'

'I'm sure your wife would much prefer you spend your free time with her.' She made another feeble protest.

'I'm sure she would—if I had a wife.'

'I—I have an errand in the drugstore,' Sabrina protested again.

'Will it take long?'

Hopelessly she wished it would take an hour. She was simply reluctant to spend any time with him. That air of confidence that surrounded him did make her feel inferior.

'No,' she admitted with a downcast chin, 'it shouldn't take very long.'

'Your lack of enthusiasm isn't very flattering,' Bay Cameron taunted softly. 'Would you feel more comfortable if I waited outside for you?'

Just knowing he was in the vicinity unnerved her. Sabrina shook her head. 'It doesn't make any difference.'

'In that case, I'll go in with you. I need some cigarettes.'

She felt the brush of his arm against her shoulder as he reached around her to open the door. Her

28

elbow was released and she entered the store more or less on her own. She tapped her way to the rear counter, sighing as she heard Bay Cameron's footsteps heading towards the tobacco section.

'Is there something I can help you find?' a woman clerk's voice asked.

Before Sabrina could reply, another gruffly happy voice broke in, male this time. 'Sabrina, I was beginning to think you had forgotten where my store was. I have not seen you in nearly two weeks.'

'Hello, Gino.' She smiled widely in the direction of the reproachful voice.

'It is all right, Maria, I will help Sabrina. You go see what that man at the prescription counter wants,' he dismissed the clerk that had initially approached Sabrina. As the woman's footsteps moved away, Gino Marchetti whispered, 'Maria is new, a cousin of my wife's sister's husband. This is only her first week, so she doesn't know my regular customers.'

Those who worked in Gino's drugstore pharmacy were always related to him in some way, Sabrina had learned over the years. But she knew the information had been offered to gently apologise for the woman not knowing Sabrina was blind.

'She has a very nice voice. I'm sure she'll soon learn,' she replied.

'What is it that you need this day? Name it and I will get it for you.'

'Some shampoo.' Sabrina gave him the brand name she wanted.

While he went to get it, she carefully felt through the paper money in her wallet, marked by a certain

29

fold to distinguish the denominations, for the amount she owed him.

As he was ringing up the sale on his old cash register, Gino Marchetti said, 'I still have the picture you painted of me hanging on this wall. People come in all the time and say, "That looks just like you" and I say, "Of course, it is me". I tell them that the girl who painted it has come to my store since she was a little thing and that you painted it from memory and gave it to me on the anniversary of my twenty-fifth year in business. Everyone thinks it is a very fine gift to have.'

'I'm glad you like it, Gino,' Sabrina smiled wanly.

She remembered vividly how proud he had been that day she had presented the portrait to him nearly two years ago. It was that ever-present aura of pride that she had tried to capture in his likeness. It was a loving, generous pride and she had been relatively satisfied with the result. Now she would never know that sense of creative accomplishment again.

'Sabrina, I didn't mean——'

She heard the hint of regret and self-reproach in the elderly Italian's voice and guessed that some of her sadness had tugged down the corners of her mouth. She determinedly curved it upward again and interrupted him.

'It was really a very small gift, Gino,' deliberately misinterpreting the statement of apology he had been about to make. 'The painting was just a small way of saying thank you for all those peppermint sticks you gave me.'

The sensation of being watched tingled down her

neck. Sabrina wasn't surprised when Bay Cameron spoke. Her sensitive radar seemed to be tuned to his presence.

'You did this painting?' he asked quietly.

'Yes.' She snipped off the end of the affirmation.

'It is very good, isn't it?' Gino prompted. 'I sold Sabrina her very first crayons. Then it was water-colours, then coloured chalk. In my small way I helped her to become an artist, and she gave me this portrait as a present. She always comes to my store once, sometimes twice a week. That is, until her accident,' his voice became sad. 'Now she doesn't come as often.' Sabrina moved uneasily and Gino's mood immediately changed to a gayer note. 'Last week I saw her walk by my store and I wonder to myself where she is going. Then I see her walk into the barbershop next door and I say to myself "Oh no, she is going to have that beautiful crown of hair on top of her head cut off", but she had only walked into the wrong store. She was coming to see me.'

'Do you know the very first time I saw her and that little knot of silky brown hair on top of her head, it reminded me of a crown, too.' There was a caressive quality to Bay Cameron's softly musing voice. Sabrina felt the rise of pink in her cheeks.

'I've taken up enough of your time, Gino,' she said hastily. 'I know you have work to do and other customers waiting. I'll see you next week.'

'Be sure it is next week, Sabrina.'

'I will. *Ciao*, Gino.' She turned quickly, aware of Bay Cameron stepping out of her way and following, although there was no guiding hand at her elbow.

'*Addio*, Sabrina,' Gino responded, not showing

31

the least surprise that the stranger was with her.

'The café is to the left,' Bay instructed her as they walked out of the store. 'It's around the corner and down a short flight of stairs.'

'I think I know which one you mean. I haven't been there in several years,' Sabrina said stiffly.

They walked side by side down the sidewalk to the corner. He made no attempt to guide her, letting her make her own way without any assistance.

'That was a very good painting,' Bay ended the silence. 'Did you have training as a child?'

'I took lessons nearly all my life.' She swallowed the lump in her throat and replied calmly. 'It was my career. I was relatively successful.'

'I can believe it,' he agreed. 'You were good.'

' "Were" being the operative word,' she inserted with faint bitterness. Then she took a shaky breath. 'I'm sorry.'

'Don't apologise,' he seemed to shrug. 'It must have been a doubly cruel blow as an artist to lose your sight. There's bound to be a feeling of injustice, otherwise you wouldn't be human.' There was a light touch on her arm to attract her attention. 'The iron banister of the stairs is on your left. You can follow it to the stairwell,' he instructed.

When her left hand encountered the railing, his own hand returned to his side. He had accepted the pain she felt at the loss of her career as a natural thing, hardly needing an explanation. There had been no empty words as others had offered that some day she would get over it. That Sabrina had never been able to believe.

At the base of the stairs, Bay reached past her to

open the café door. A hand rested firmly on the side of her waist and remained there as a hostess showed them to a small booth.

'Let me take your cane,' he offered. 'I'll hang it on the post beside your seat so it will be out of the way.'

Sabrina handed it to him and slid into the booth, her fingers resting nervously on the table top. In the past she had avoided public eating establishments, too self-conscious to be at ease. She touched the edge of a menu and pushed it aside.

Their waitress had evidently appeared at the table because she heard Bay ask for two coffees before he addressed a question to her. 'They make their own pastries here. They're very good. Would you like any, Sabrina?'

'No.' In her nervousness she was too abrupt and she quickly added, 'No, thank you.'

'Would you like a cigarette?' he offered.

'Please,' she accepted almost with a sigh of relief.

The waitress arrived with their coffee just as Bay placed a lit cigarette between her fingers and slid the ashtray in front of her discreetly searching hand. Sabrina drew deeply on the filter tip of the cigarette, slightly amazed that she could feel the warmth of his mouth on the cigarette.

'Do you take anything in your coffee?' Bay asked.

'Nothing, thank you.' Sabrina exhaled the smoke from her mouth, blowing away some of her tension at the same time.

The heat from the coffee made the cup easy to find. The fingers of one hand closed around its warmth. A silence followed, one that Sabrina was pleasantly surprised to discover as comfortable. Her first meeting with Bay Cameron had been tainted by his apparent arrogance. It still existed, proved by the very fact that he had manoeuvred her into this café, but it had somehow been tempered by his understanding.

In spite of that disturbing argument about the white cane, he seemed to approve of her desire for independence. The assistance he had given her had been unobtrusive. That coupled with his matter-of-fact comment about her loss of career made Sabrina wonder if she shouldn't re-assess her opinion of him. Bay Cameron seemed to be an unusual man. Sabrina wished she had met him before she lost her sight. He might have made an interesting portrait study. Then she sighed.

'What was that for?' he chided mockingly.

'Wishing,' Sabrina shrugged.

'A common pastime?'

'Only when I have nothing to distract me. Sometimes,' she ran a finger around the rim of her cup, 'I wonder when I'm alone if I wasn't given the gift of seeing people, places and things in minute detail early in life so I could store up a treasure of beautiful scenes to remember.'

'Do you believe in fate, then?' Bay asked quietly.

'Sometimes it seems the only explanation. Do you?' Sabrina countered.

'I believe we were given certain talents and abilities. What we do with them is the mark of our own character. I can't accept that I might not be the master of my own destiny.' His reply was laced with self-directed humour.

'I doubt there's very little you've wanted that you

'haven't obtained,' she agreed with a faint smile.

'Perhaps. And perhaps I've just been careful about what I wanted.' The smile faded from his voice. 'Tell me, Sabrina, how long has it been since you lost your sight?'

She was beginning to learn that Bay Cameron had a habit of coming straight to the point. Most of the people she knew or had met took special care to avoid any reference to her blindness and took pains that the conversation didn't contain words that referred to sight.

'Almost eight months.' She inhaled the smoke from the cigarette, wondering why his frankness didn't disconcert her. Maybe it was because he didn't seem embarrassed or self-conscious about her blindness.

'No days or hours?' There was the impression of a brow raised mockingly in her direction.

'I stopped trying to keep an exact count after the fourth specialist told my father and me that I would never see again.' Sabrina tried to sound nonchalant, but there was a faint catch to her voice.

'What happened?'

'A car crash. It was late at night. I was driving home from Sacramento and fell asleep at the wheel. I don't know what happened.' Her fingers fluttered uncertainly in the air, then returned to grip the coffee cup. 'I came to in a hospital. There weren't any witnesses. A passing motorist saw my wrecked car in the ditch, the authorities estimate several hours after the accident.'

Sabrina waited for the supposedly bolstering comments that usually followed when she related the

35

details of the accident, the it-could-have-been-worse and the you're-lucky-you-weren't-paralysed-or-maimed sentences. But none of those trite words were spoken.

'What are you going to do now?'

'I don't know.' She didn't have the answer to that problem. She took a sip of her coffee. 'I've just been taking one day at a time, learning over again how to do all the things I used to take for granted. I was so positive that I was going to have a career in art that I never studied anything else but reading, writing and arithmetic. I'm going to have to make a decision about my future pretty soon, though,' she sighed. 'I can't keep being a burden for my father.'

'I doubt if he thinks of you that way.'

'I know *he* doesn't.' Unconsciously she put qualifying emphasis on the masculine pronoun.

Bay Cameron was much too observant to miss it. 'But someone else does, is that it?' he questioned. 'Is it your father's fiancée?'

Sabrina opened her mouth to deny it, then nodded reluctantly that he was right. 'I don't blame Deborah. She wants Dad to herself——' She hesitated. 'I don't want you to misunderstand me. I do like her. As a matter of fact, I'm the one who introduced her to him. She has a small antique shop here in San Francisco. It's just that we both know it would never work for the two of us to live in the same house. She wants me to go to some school she heard about where blind people are taught new skills, not basket-weaving or anything as humbling as that, but legitimate skills. They have a job placement programme, too, when you've completed the term.'

'What does your father think of the idea?'

'I don't believe she's mentioned it to him yet.' A wry smile pulled her mouth into a crooked line. 'I think she wants to weigh me down with guilt so I'll be in favour of it when Dad brings up the subject.'

'Do you feel guilty?' Bay asked as she carefully stubbed out her cigarette in the ashtray.

'I suppose so. It's only natural, isn't it?' Sabrina spread out the fingers of her hands on the table top, looking at them as if she could see them. 'Everyone wants to think of himself as useful.'

'And you don't do anything that you consider useful?'

'I take care of the house and do most of the cooking. I could hardly keep doing that after Dad and Deborah are married. After all, it would be her house then.' She continued staring sightlessly at her long fingers. 'I know I could learn something.' She shook her head wearily, closing her hands around the coffee cup again. 'I'm still filled with too much pride, too much self-importance. My hands have always held an artist's brush. I guess it's just a case of not wanting to let go of that. Which is probably why I keep putting off the day when they'll have to do something else.'

'What does your boy-friend say to all this?'

'Boy-friend? I haven't got any boy-friend. A lot of men who are friends, but no boy-friends,' Sabrina denied firmly.

'You're a very attractive girl. I find it hard to believe that you didn't have a romantic attachment for

37

someone,' Bay commented in a doubting voice.

'I always had my career,' she shrugged. 'I dated, quite often, as a matter of fact. I simply steered clear of any romantic involvement. Love and marriage were always something that would come somewhere in the future. I'm glad now that I did,' she added frankly. 'How many men would want to be saddled with a blind wife?'

'Isn't that a somewhat cynical view of the male sex?' he chuckled.

'Not really,' she smiled. 'It's not even a cynical view of love. It's just realistic. Being blind tends to make other people awkward and self-conscious. They're always trying to be so careful that they don't hurt your feelings by pointing out that there are some things blind people simply can't participate in, and that makes an uncomfortable relationship.'

'That's funny,' he mused mockingly. 'I don't feel the least bit uncomfortable, awkward or self-conscious, and I'm sitting here with you.'

For a moment, Sabrina was flustered by his observation. Mostly because it was true. There were no undercurrents of tension flowing around her.

'Actually I wasn't thinking about you,' she admitted. 'I was referring to some of my other friends, male and female. They all still keep in touch, the ones that count. They call or stop by to see me or invite me out, but it's not quite the same. With some of them our common link was art, so I understand why they don't like to bring up that subject in front of me. The others—there's just a vague uneasiness on both sides. With you,' Sabrina tilted her head to a curious angle, 'I don't really understand.

I'm talking to you about things you couldn't possibly be interested in and I don't know why. Are you some kind of amateur psychiatrist?' A little frown of bewildered amusement puckered her brows.

'No.' Sabrina sensed his smile. 'And I wasn't at all bored. I imagine all of this has been building up inside you for some time. It's always easier to talk to strangers who don't have preconceived opinions. I happened to be an available stranger.'

'In that case, what wise advice do you have to offer me?' she asked with a pertly challenging smile.

'Strangers don't give advice. They only listen.' The laughter was obvious in his low voice as he dodged her question expertly.

Hurried footsteps approached their booth. 'Would you like some more coffee?' the waitress enquired.

'No more for me, thank you,' Sabrina refused. Her fingers touched the braille face of her watch. 'I have to be getting home.'

'Our check, please,' Bay requested.

By the time Sabrina had slid out of the booth seat, Bay was at her side, handing her the oak cane. His hand again rested lightly on the back of her waist, guiding her discreetly past the row of booths and tables to the café door. She waited there while he paid the check.

Once outside and up the stairs to the sidewalk, Bay asked, 'Did you say you only lived a few blocks from here?'

'Yes.' Sabrina turned her head towards him, the smile coming more easily and more often to her mouth. 'And it's uphill all the way.'

39

'Well, there's one consolation about the hills in San Francisco. When you get tired of walking up them, you can always lean against them.' Sabrina laughed at his amusingly accurate description. 'That's a nice sound,' Bay said lowly. 'I was beginning to think you'd lost the ability to laugh along with your sight. I'm glad you didn't.'

Her heart seemed to skip a beat for a few seconds. Sabrina discovered that she wanted to believe that was a personal comment and not a casual observation. That put her on dangerous ground, so she kept silent.

'My car is just around the corner,' Bay said as if he hadn't expected her to reply. 'Let me give you a ride home.'

It was past the hour Sabrina had told Peggy Collins she would be gone. That was why she agreed to his offer, giving him the address of the narrow Victorian house in the Pacific Heights section. The rush hour traffic had begun, so there was very little conversation between them in the car. Using the traffic at the intersections as a guide, Sabrina was able to judge when Bay turned on to the block where she lived.

'Our house is the dark gold one with the brown and white trim,' she told him. 'The number is difficult to see sometimes.'

A few seconds later, he was turning the wheels into the kerb, setting the emergency brake and shutting off the motor. He had just walked around the car and opened her door when Sabrina heard her neighbour call out.

'Sabrina, are you all right?' The question was

followed immediately by the sound of the redwood gate opening and Peggy Collins' footsteps hurrying towards them. 'I was just coming to see if you'd come home and forgotten to let me know.'

'I was longer than I expected to be,' Sabrina said, explaining the obvious.

'So I see.' The curious tone of voice also said that her neighbour saw the man Sabrina was with and was waiting to be introduced.

'Peggy, this is Bay Cameron. Peggy Collins is my neighbour,' she submitted to the invisible arm-twisting.

There was a polite exchange of greetings before Bay turned to Sabrina. 'It's my turn to say I'll have to be going, Sabrina.'

'Thank you for the coffee and the ride home.' She offered her hand to him in goodbye.

'My pleasure.' His grasp was warm and sure and all too brief. 'I'll see you again some time.'

The last sounded very much like a promise. Sabrina hoped that it was. His arrogance of their first meeting was completely erased. It was really strange how readily she had confided in him, she thought as she heard the car door open and close and the motor start. Not even to her father, who was very close to her, had Sabrina been able to talk that freely.

'Where did you meet him?' Peggy asked with more than idle curiosity.

'The other day at the Yacht Harbour when Deborah and I went to pick up Dad,' she explained, forgetting for an instant that her neighbour was standing beside her. 'I just bumped into him this

41

afternoon—well, not literally,' Sabrina qualified. Her head followed the sound of the departing car until she could no longer hear it. She turned to the older woman. 'Peggy, what does he look like?'

The woman paused, collecting her thoughts. 'He's tall, in his thirties I would say. He has reddish-brown hair and brown eyes, not dark brown but they are brown. I wouldn't call him handsome exactly. Good-looking isn't the right description either, although in a way they both fit.' There was another hesitation. 'He looks like a man. Do you know what I mean?'

'Yes,' Sabrina replied softly. 'Yes, I think I do,' guessing that his features were too strong and forceful to be classified in any other way.

'Good heavens!' Peggy exclaimed suddenly. 'I forgot to put the potatoes in the oven! I'll talk to you later, Sabrina.'

'Yes, all right, Peggy.' Her neighbour was already fast retreating to her door by the time Sabrina absently acknowledged her words.

CHAPTER THREE

'ARE you positive you want to walk out on the docks, Sabrina?' Deborah asked sharply.

'I would like to, yes,' she admitted. Unconsciously she raised her chin to a challenging angle. 'That is, of course, unless you want some time alone with Father.'

'It's not that,' the redhead sighed in frustration. 'Grant—worries about you so and there aren't any railings on the piers. He's naturally going to be concerned about your safety.'

'All parents worry, Deborah,' Sabrina said quietly. 'Father just feels he has more cause to worry than most, with justification, I suppose. I can't spend the rest of my life not doing things that might cause him to worry.'

'Believe me, if I could find a way to make him stop worrying about you, I would do it,' was Deborah's taut response as she stepped out of the car.

Sabrina followed, but more slowly, walking around the car parked in the lot of Yacht Harbour to the side of her father's fiancée.

'Has Dad said any more about setting the date?' Sabrina asked as they started towards the fence gates.

'No, and I haven't brought up the subject.' There was a pause before Deborah continued. 'A long time ago I recognised the fact that I'm a jealous and possessive woman, Sabrina. If I married your father while you were still living at home, it would create friction among all of us. You would be hurt; your father would be hurt; and I would be hurt. I'm quite aware that you're a very independent person and have no desire to be a burden to your father for the rest of your life.'

'Which is why you're pushing the idea of this school,' Sabrina breathed in deeply, knowing the vast amount of truth in the redhead's words.

'It may not be the answer, Sabrina, but it is a start,' Deborah suggested earnestly.

'I need more time.' Sabrina lifted her chin into the wind, letting the light ocean breeze play over her face. 'I keep hoping there'll be some other alternative. I don't know what, but something.'

'You are considering the school, though?'

'I have to consider it,' she sighed, 'whether I like the idea or not.'

'Thank you.' Deborah's voice trembled slightly before it steadied with determination. 'I like you, Sabrina, but I love your father. I've waited a long time to meet a man like him. So please, understand why I'm pushing so hard to get you out of the house.'

'I do.' The wooden floor of the dock was beneath her feet, the harbour gate closed behind them. 'If I loved a man, I would be just as anxious as you to have him to myself. But I won't be rushed into a decision, not unless I'm sure there isn't anything else.'

Deborah's guiding hand claimed her elbow. 'Turn left here,' she instructed.

The titian-haired woman was aware of Sabrina's stubborn streak. This was the time to let the subject drop when she had achieved a minor capitulation that Sabrina would consider her suggestion.

Sabrina guessed her tactics and willingly changed the topic. 'Is Dad in?'

'Yes, he's tying everything down now,' was the reply. A few minutes later, Deborah called out, 'Hello, darling, did you have a good time?'

'Of course.' There was contented happiness in her father's voice that brought a smile to Sabrina's lips. 'Sabrina? I didn't expect to see you with Deborah.' A faint anxiety crept in.

'It was too nice a day to wait by the car.' She smiled away his concern. 'Don't worry, I'll be a good girl and not stray from the centre of the dock.'

'I'll only be a few more minutes,' he promised.

'I'll get your thermos and things from the cabin, if you like, Grant,' Deborah offered.

There was hesitation before the suggestion was accepted. Sabrina knew her father was reluctant to leave her alone on the dock. His agreement was probably an indication that Deborah had given him a look that said he was being overly protective.

The creak of the boat was accompanied by the quiet lapping of the water against its hull. There was the flapping of wings near where Sabrina stood, followed by the cry of a gull. The ocean scent of salt and fish was in the breeze lifting the short hair on her forehead.

A tickling sensation teased the back of her neck. Instantly Sabrina was alert to the sounds of footsteps approaching, more than one set. Intuition said it was Bay Cameron and she knew all along that she had been hoping he would be there. But he was with someone, more than one, perhaps three others. The light tread of one pair of feet warned her that they belonged to a female.

'Are you calling it a day, Mr Lane?' Bay Cameron's voice called out in greeting.

'Mr Cameron, how are you?' her father returned with startled pleasure. 'Yes, this is all for me today until next week. Are you coming in or going out?'

'Out. We thought we'd take in an ocean sunset,' he replied, confirming that the other footsteps she had heard were with him. He had stopped beside her. Sabrina's radar told her he was only inches from her left side. 'How are you today, Sabrina?'

'Fine.' Her head bobbed self-consciously. She sensed the eagerness of the others to be on their way.

'I see you made it all the way on to the dock this time without mishap. Did you do it by yourself?' The words were spoken so soft and low that the light breeze couldn't carry them to anyone's ears but Sabrina's.

'No,' she murmured, barely moving her lips.

'Bay, are you coming?' an impatient female voice asked.

'Yes, Roni,' he answered. 'I'll see you again.' The ambiguous promise was offered as a goodbye. The raised pitch of his voice directed it to everyone and not Sabrina alone.

'Good sailing!' her father called out, but Sabrina said nothing.

A faint depression had settled in, intensified when the wind carried the woman's haughty inquiry as to who they were, but her acute hearing couldn't catch Bay's response.

Her fingers tightened around the curve of her oak

cane. She was glad her cane was not white, identifying herself immediately to his friends as a blind girl. She could not have endured the sensation of their pitying looks. It was bad enough imagining the explanation Bay was giving them now. She wished she had not allowed him to bully her into having coffee with him the other day, never poured out her troubles to him with such a complete lack of discretion.

'Are you ready yet, Dad?' she asked sharply, suddenly anxious to be gone, finding no more enjoyment in the scent and the sounds of the sea.

'Be right there,' he answered. 'Have you got everything, Deborah?'

'Yes.'

Seconds later the two of them were at Sabrina's side, her father's arm curving around her shoulders and guiding her back the way she had come. For once she didn't try to shrug away his assistance. She wanted the protective comfort of his arm.

She had tried to block out the memory of that Sunday, but it remained a shadow lurking near the edges of her already dark world. The melancholy violin strains on the stereo were not easing her depression. The position of the furniture in their house had long been memorised, and she walked unerringly to the stereo and switched off the music.

The front door bell buzzed loudly into the ensuing silence. With an impatient sigh at the unwanted intrusion, Sabrina continued to the intercom that linked the street level entrance next to the garage with the living area of the house.

'Yes. Who is it?' she enquired briskly after her

searching fingers had found the switch.

'Bay Cameron.'

A surprised stillness kept her silent for ticking seconds. There was no warmth in her voice when she asked, 'What is it you wanted, Mr Cameron?'

'I'm not selling brushes, insurance or bibles,' his amused voice answered. 'The only reason I can think of why I might be standing in front of your door is to see you.'

'Why?'

'I never did like talking to boxes. Will you come down?'

Sabrina sighed in irritation at the challenging tone. 'I'll be there in a minute,' she said, and flicked off the switch.

She opened the door to the stairwell that led from the second floor to the street entrance. There were two doors at the base of the stairs, one leading to the garage that occupied the ground floor and the second to the street sidewalk.

Opening the second door, Sabrina walked four paces and stopped. There was an iron grillework gate less than a foot in front of her, preventing direct access to the house from people on the street. Bay was on the other side of that gate.

'Now, what was it you wanted, Mr Cameron?' she asked coolly.

'May I come in?' he asked in a mocking voice.

Her common sense lost its silent war. Angry fingers unfastened the lock, swinging the gate open to allow him admittance into the small detached foyer. Sabrina stepped back, clasping her hands in front of her in a prim pose.

'Why did you want to see me?' There was a vaguely haughty arch in her long neck.

'It's what a native would consider a most unusual day. There's not a cloud in the sky. The sun is shining. The breeze is light and warm. It's the perfect day for a walk,' Bay concluded. 'I stopped to see if you'd come with me.'

Sabrina doubted the sincerity of his words. She couldn't believe that his motive for asking was a genuine desire for her company. He was feeling sorry for her.

'I'm sorry, it isn't possible,' she refused with honest cause.

'It isn't possible?' he questioned. Sabrina could visualise the arrogant lift of his brow. 'Why?'

'I'm fixing a pot roast for dinner this evening. I have to put it in the oven in'—she touched the braille face of her watch—'forty-five minutes. So you see, if I went for a walk with you, we would barely be gone and we'd have to come back. An hour after that I'll have to be here to add the potatoes, carrots and onions.'

'Is that the only excuse you have?'

'It's a very legitimate one,' Sabrina returned firmly.

'If that's your only reason, we can soon take care of that,' Bay said complacently. 'Your oven has a timer. While you're getting the roast ready, I'll set the timer to turn the oven on in forty-five minutes. We can put it in now and have nearly two hours for our walk before you have to be back to add the rest of the items.'

49

'But——' She tried to protest, but her mind was blank.

'But what? Don't you want to go for a walk? It's too beautiful a day to stay indoors.'

'Oh, all right,' she sighed in exasperation, turning towards the door.

His throaty chuckle mocked her obviously reluctant agreement. 'I'm amazed at how graciously you always accept my invitations,' Bay taunted.

'Maybe it's because I can't help wondering why you make them,' Sabrina responded with faint acidity in her tone.

'I have the impression,' he reached around and opened the door for her before her searching hands found the knob, 'that if you ever stopped being defensive over the fact that you're blind, you just might be pleasant company.'

Again Sabrina bridled silently at his implication that she spent too much time feeling sorry for herself. When her entire life and future had been based on the ability of her eyes to see the things her hands would paint, it was natural that she should feel bitterness at the injustice of her fate. Even Bay had acknowledged that. If he agreed, then what right did he have to condemn her?

Bay Cameron seemed to make his own laws, Sabrina decided. She ushered him silently up the stairs, through the dining room into the kitchen. By the time she had the meat seasoned and in the roasting pan, he had the oven ready.

'Are we ready to leave now?' Bay asked.

'I have to call my father.' She ran her palms nervously over the rounded curve of her hip bones.

'When Peggy Collins, our neighbour, is gone, he likes me to let him know where I'm going and when I'll be back.'

'In case some unsuspecting motorist runs you down?' he mocked.

Her mouth tightened into a mutinous line as she pivoted sharply away. 'You certainly have a thing about white canes, don't you?' she murmured sarcastically.

'I suppose so,' he agreed lazily. 'Go ahead and phone your father.'

'Thank you, I will, now that I have your permission,' Sabrina snapped.

The switchboard girl at her father's attorney firm put the call through to him immediately. She explained quickly that Peggy wasn't home and that she had called to let him know she was going to be out for a while, not mentioning with whom.

'How long will you be?' Grant Lane asked.

'A couple of hours. I'll call as soon as I'm back,' Sabrina assured him.

'I know the weather is nice, but do you have to be gone that long? I don't like the idea of you wandering about the streets on your own,' he said.

'I'll be all right.' She was strangely reluctant to tell him she was being accompanied by Bay Cameron. 'Don't start worrying,' she laughed nervously.

A muscled arm reached around her and took the receiver from her hand. She tried to take it back, but her hand encountered the rock wall of his chest. Her fingers drew back quickly as if burned.

'Mr Lane, this is Bay Cameron. Sabrina will be

51

with me. I'll see that she's back in plenty of time so that your dinner won't be ruined.' Her father made some affirmative reply then Bay said goodbye and hung up the telephone. 'He asked me to tell you to have a good time.'

'Thanks,' she murmured caustically, and walked to the closet to remove her lightweight coat.

Retrieving her cane from the umbrella stand, she heard Bay open the stair door. She walked quickly through the opening, listening to him lock the door behind him before following her down the stairs to the outer street.

'I thought we'd take the Hyde Street cable car down to Ghirardelli Square. Is that all right?' There was an underlying tone of amusement in his voice, suggesting that he found her sulking display of temper humorous.

'Whatever you like.' She shrugged her shoulders stiffly.

There was no mocking rejoinder at her less than courteous acceptance of his plan. In fact, he said not another word. If it hadn't been for the hand that took her elbow at the traffic intersections, Sabrina might have been walking the blocks to the cable car street alone. Except for a curt thank you when he helped her on to and off the cable car, she didn't address any remarks to him either.

'Are you finished pouting yet?' His question was heavy with concealed laughter as his hand firmly attached itself to her waist to manoeuvre them through the stream of summer tourists.

'I wasn't pouting,' Sabrina asserted coldly.

'You weren't?' Bay mocked.

'Maybe a little,' she acknowledged reluctantly, a trace of anger remaining. 'But you can be insufferably bossy at times.'

'I think you've just got your way too often lately. The people who care about you don't like to say "no",' he observed.

'The same could be said for you.'

'I'm sure it's true.' Again there was a lazy acceptance of her criticism. 'But we weren't talking about me. You were the one who was pouting.'

'Only because you were taking over and running things without being asked,' Sabrina retorted.

'So what now? Do you maintain a state of war or take our walk as friends?' She could feel his eyes on her face. 'We didn't get along too badly the other day.'

Sabrina breathed in deeply, feeling herself surrendering to the invisible charm of his low voice. 'Friends,' she agreed against her better judgment.

Once she had succumbed it was easy to let herself be warmed by his persuasion as he gently steered the conversation to less argumentative topics. They wandered around the fountain in the centre plaza of the old Ghirardelli Chocolate factory renovated into a shopping mall. They stopped at one of the outdoor cafés and sampled some of the thin delicious crêpes freshly made.

Their strolling pace took them by the windows of the multi-level shops in the buildings that made up the square. Bay laughingly challenged Sabrina to identify the type of store by sound and scent. She did quite well at the flower and leather shops and identifying what native cuisine was served at the various restaurants, but the jewellery gift and import stores she missed entirely.

When Bay stopped in front of another shop window, she emitted a defeated sigh, 'I'm really out of guesses. Please, no more.'

'No, no more,' he agreed absently. 'It's a dress-maker's shop, more specifically labelled as Original Fashions by Jacobina. There's a dress in the window, and I'd swear it was made for you. Come on.' His arm tightened suddenly around her waist. 'We'll go in so you can see it.'

Instantly Sabrina strained against his arm. 'You're overlooking one pertinent detail. I'm blind. I cannot "see" the dress,' she reminded him sharply.

'I've overlooked nothing, my blind queen,' he replied patiently. 'So you can wipe that look of indignation from your face. Where's all that crea-tive imagination you were bragging about the other day? I'm taking you into the shop and you're going to see this dress with your hands.'

Feeling roundly chastised, Sabrina mutely al-lowed herself to be escorted into the shop. A tiny bell sounded above their heads as they walked in. Immediately footsteps approached from the rear of the store.

'May I help you?' a woman's voice enquired.

'Yes,' Bay answered. 'We'd like to look at the dress in the window.'

'We don't sell ready-made dresses here, sir,' the woman replied politely. 'It's a model from which we make another using the precise measurements of our customer.'

'Let me explain what I meant.' The velvet charm

54

was very pronounced in his voice. 'Miss Lane is blind. I admired the dress in the window and wanted her to see it. In order for her to do that, she must touch it. Would that be possible?'

'Of course, I'm sorry. It will take me only a few minutes to remove it from the model,' the woman offered quickly and warmly.

Her words were followed by a rustle of motion and material. Sabrina shifted uncomfortably and felt the pressure of Bay's hand on her waist increase in reassurance. Short minutes later there was a silky swish of material in front of her.

'Here you are, Miss Lane,' the clerk said.

'Would you describe it for her?' Bay requested

'Of course,' the woman agreed. 'Miss Jacobina calls this dress "Flame". Its ever-changing colours of red, gold, orange and yellow in irregular layered vees of chiffon, curled at the ends like curling flames.' Sabrina's sensitive fingers lightly traced the edges of the many layers. 'The neckline is vee-shaped but not plunging by any means. The illusion of sleeves is created by the cutaway vees of chiffon from the neckline, draping over the shoulders and the bodice.'

As the exploring tips of her fingers went over more of the dress Sabrina's mind began to form a picture with the help of the clerk's description.

'It's beautiful,' Sabrina murmured finally.

'What size is the model?' Bay asked. The woman told him. 'Would that fit you, Sabrina?'

'I think so,' she nodded.

'Can you stretch the rules to allow her to try it on?' he asked the clerk, again in that persuasive tone that Sabrina was certain no one could resist.

The woman took a deep breath, then laughed. 'I don't know why not. We have a changing room in the back, Miss Lane, if you'd like to come with me.'

Sabrina hesitated and Bay gave her a little push forward. 'Go on. Let's see what it looks like on,' he prompted.

'Why do I let you talk me into these situations?' she sighed.

'Because deep down, you enjoy it,' he teased. 'Besides, I bet you haven't bought any new clothes since the accident.'

'I haven't needed anything,' Sabrina protested weakly.

'When has that ever been a valid excuse for a woman?' Bay mocked. 'Now, go try that dress on. That's an order!'

'Yes, sir.' She didn't really have to have her arm twisted. The vision in her mind and the touch of the expensive material already had her excited about wearing it even if she couldn't see the end result.

Changing swiftly out of her sports clothes into the dress, she only required the assistance of the clerk with the zipper. With her hand resting lightly on the clerk's arm, she moved nervously to the front of the store where Bay waited.

'Well?' Sabrina asked breathlessly when the silence stretched to an unbearable length. Her head was tilted to one side in a listening attitude.

'You look beautiful, Sabrina,' Bay said simply.

'That's an understatement,' the clerk inserted. 'You're stunning, and I'm not saying that because

56

I work here. The dress might have been made for you. The style, the colour suits you perfectly. It's amazing, but you must have the same measurements as the girl who models it.'

Her fingers ran down the neckline of the dress, trailing off with a draping fold of the filmy chiffon. 'Could you—would you sell this one?' Sabrina asked.

'It's not customary,' the woman hesitated, then added with a resigned smile in her voice. 'Let me check.'

When the woman had left, Sabrina turned again to Bay. 'Are you very sure it looks right?' she questioned anxiously.

There was a click, then cigarette smoke wafted through the air to her nose. 'Are you seeking more compliments?' he asked.

'No,' she denied, nervously running her hand along the waist and glancing sightlessly at the floating vees of material cascading over her arm. 'It's just that I can't be positive——'

'Be positive.' With cat-soft footsteps he was at her side, lifting her chin with his finger. 'I told you the truth. You look beautiful in the dress.'

She wished she could see his expression. The sincerity in his voice she didn't doubt, but there was an illusive sensation that he was aloof, withdrawn. The fringe of dark hair hid the tiny frown that knitted her forehead.

'Now what's troubling you?' Bay mocked.

'I——' Her chin was released as he stepped away. 'I was just wondering when I would ever wear this,' Sabrina hedged at the truth.

'Sometime there'll be an occasion when the dress will be just right for it. Then you'll be glad you bought it,' he replied in an indulgent tone.

'I never asked how much it is,' she murmured. Then an accompanying thought drooped her shoulders. 'I have hardly any money with me. Do you suppose I could give them some money to hold it and Daddy and I could come down later with the rest?'

'I could pay for it,' Bay suggested guardedly.

Sabrina bit into her lower lip, eager to possess the dress she wore but unwilling to obligate herself to a man who was neither friend nor stranger.

'If it wouldn't be too much trouble,' her acceptance was hesitant, 'you could write down your address and the amount. I'll have Dad mail you a cheque tonight.'

'You wouldn't consider accepting the dress as a gift?'

Sabrina drew back. 'No.' She shook her head firmly, ready to argue the point further if he should attempt to bully her into accepting it.

'I didn't think you would.' A rush of smoke was exhaled in her direction. He sounded vaguely angry. 'All right, I'll *loan* you the money for the dress.'

'Thank you,' breathed Sabrina, relieved the episode was not going to end on a quarrelsome note.

'Instead of your father mailing me a cheque, why don't I stop by your house Friday afternoon?' he suggested.

'If you like,' she frowned.

'I would like.' The smile was back in his voice and she gave him an answering one.

58

The sales clerk returned with the information that they would sell the dress model to Sabrina. The price of the garment was not as high as she had expected. While she changed into her denim slacks and top, Bay took care of the purchase.

Outside the store he gave her the unwelcome news that they had used up the two hours and it was time for him to take her back to the house. He suggested that instead of taking the cable car, then walking the several blocks to her house, that they take a taxi. At this point, Sabrina would have preferred to prolong the outing, but there had been a subtle change in his attitude, so she agreed to his suggestion.

'I'll see you Friday afternoon around two,' Bay repeated, stopping inside the iron gate but not following her into the stairwell.

'Would y-you like to come in for coffee?' she offered.

'I'll take a raincheck on that for Friday,' he refused.

'All right. Till Friday, then,' Sabrina agreed with a faint smile of regret.

CHAPTER FOUR

Sabrina touched the face of her watch. Two o'clock. She reached to be certain the cheque was still on the coffee table where her father had put it this morning. It was. She leaned against the cushion of the couch, rubbing the back of her neck to try to relax the tense muscles. It was crazy to be so on edge because Bay Cameron was coming over, she told herself.

The front buzzer sounded and she hurried to the intercom answering it with an eager 'Yes?'

'Bay Cameron.'

'I'll be right down.'

Recklessly Sabrina nearly flew down the stairs. A smile wreathed her face as she opened the door and walked to the gate.

'You're right on time,' she said.

'I try to be punctual.' The warm huskiness of his voice swept over her as she unlocked the gate, swinging the iron grille open to admit him.

'I have the coffee all ready if you have time to stay,' she offered.

'I have time,' Bay answered.

Leading the way up the stairs to the second floor living area, Sabrina motioned towards the living room. 'Have a seat while I get the coffee tray. The cheque for the dress is on the table in front of the sofa.'

Bay made no offer to help pour the coffee when she returned, letting her take the time to do it herself. He took the cup she held out to him, the almost silent swish of the cushions indicating that he had leaned back against the chair next to the sofa.

'You have a very nice home. The paintings on the wall, are they yours?' he asked.

'Yes,' she acknowledged carefully balancing a cup in her lap. 'My father likes landscapes, so he chose those for the house. Because of his love for the sea, they are actually ocean scenes.'

'Are these the only paintings of your own that you have left?'

Sabrina bent her head. 'No.' Her jaw tightened.

'May I see them later?' Bay requested with watchful softness.

'I'd really rather not show them to you.' She swallowed, lifting her chin defiantly.

'If you'd rather not, I won't insist,' he shrugged. 'But I won't pretend that I'm not curious why. I've already seen several examples of your work. Why wouldn't you want to show me the rest?'

Sabrina fidgeted nervously with the handle of her cup. Trying to adopt an uncaring attitude, she set the cup on the table.

'I'll show them to you.' Not certain whether her change of mind had been prompted by the patiently humorous tone of his voice or an application of common sense. 'They're in the studio upstairs.' She rose to her feet, pausing to turn her head in the direction of his chair.

'Lead the way,' Bay agreed, now on his feet, too.

Climbing the stairs to the upper floor, Sabrina trailed her hand along the wall until she came to the second door. The knob was cold beneath her fingers as she swung the door open. The lingering scent of oil paints whirled around her.

'The room isn't used—any more, so it might be a bit stuffy,' Sabrina explained self-consciously, halting against the wall just inside the door.

Bay didn't comment. It wasn't really necessary. She listened to the quiet sounds as he wandered about the room, pausing sometimes to take a closer look at something that had caught his eye. Other times she could hear him moving canvases to see the paintings behind them. A tightness gripped her chest with a painful hold.

'They're very good, Sabrina,' he said at last. Her head turned in the direction of his voice only a few feet from where she was standing near the door. 'It's a pity to keep them hidden in this room.'

'Dad and I have talked about selling them. We will some day.' Sabrina swallowed to ease the constriction in her throat.

'Did you ever do any modelling?'

'Modelling? No,' she replied, striving for a lightness even though she knew neither of them would be fooled by it. 'I was always the one painting the person who was posing.'

'I meant modelling in clay,' Bay explained. Quiet, unhurried footsteps brought him to her side. A hand lightly touched her arm to turn her towards the open door.

'Yes, when I was studying the different mediums of art,' Sabrina acknowledged with a slight frown. 'Why?'

'Have you ever considered taking it up now that you're blind?'

'No.' She shook her head.

Unconsciously she had allowed him to lead her into the hallway. His enquiry had been unexpected and it set off a chain of thoughts. The closing of the studio door brought her back to their surroundings.

The subject was not explored further as Bay let her descend the stairs ahead of him, deliberately allowing her to mull the idea over in her own mind without any attempt to influence her. In spite of an ego-born desire to reject the idea to do anything but her chosen field of painting, the seed had been planted in fertile ground.

The coffee Sabrina poured had grown cold. While she emptied the cups, there was more time to contemplate his indirect suggestion. She marvelled that none of her art friends had mentioned it before. Perhaps the objectivity of a relative stranger had been needed.

'I meant to ask,' Bay said as Sabrina handed him his cup refilled with hot coffee, 'whether you and your father had any plans for tomorrow evening.'

Her own cup was half-filled, the coffee pot poised above it for a startled, split second. 'No,' Sabrina answered in a curious tone. 'Saturday afternoon and evening Dad spends with Deborah. Why?'

'I thought we could have dinner somewhere. It would give you an excuse to wear your new dress,' Bay answered smoothly.

'No, thank you,' she refused with cutting abruptness.

'Do you have other plans?'

'No.'

'Then may I ask why you don't want to have

dinner with me?' he asked, completely unruffled by her cold rejection.

'You may.' With a proud set to her head, Sabrina replaced the coffeepot on the tray and leaned against the sofa, protectively cradling the cup in her hands. 'I simply don't eat at public restaurants. I have a habit of knocking over glasses and dropping food on the floor. It's embarrassing,' she concluded self-consciously.

'I'm willing to take the risk,' Bay returned.

'Well, I'm not.' Impatiently she took a sip of the hot liquid, nearly scalding her tongue in the process.

'If this is not a refusal of my company,' there was a hint of amusement in his voice, 'then would you consider a less formal suggestion? For instance, we could buy some shrimp and crab at the Wharf, sourdough bread and a salad of sorts, then have an impromptu picnic somewhere along the shore line of the Golden Gate Promenade.'

Sabrina hesitated. It sounded like fun, but she wasn't certain she should accept his invitation. In between the moments when she was angered by his arrogance, she had discovered she liked him. Yet she doubted if any enduring friendship would ever develop between them.

'Is it such a difficult invitation to accept?' Bay taunted.

His gentle mockery made her feel foolish. She was magnifying the importance of the invitation out of all proportion. A faint pink tinted her prominent cheekbones.

'It isn't difficult,' she murmured, bending her

64

head towards the cup in her lap to hide the flush of embarrassment. 'I do accept.'

'Would six o'clock be all right, or would you rather have me come earlier?'

'Six is fine.' There was a thump from something falling to the floor. Her head jerked up with a start. 'What was that?'

'It's a little something I bought for you as a present,' Bay replied with studied casualness. 'I meant to give it to you earlier, but I got sidetracked. I had it propped against my chair and I accidentally knocked it over. Here you are.'

A long, narrow box was placed on her lap after Sabrina had set her coffee cup on the table. Her hands rested motionless on the cardboard lid.

'Why did you buy me a present?' she asked warily.

'Because I wanted to—and please don't ask me to take it back, because I wouldn't have any use for it and neither would anyone else I know. I doubt if I can have it returned either,' he stated.

'What is it?' Sabrina tilted her head curiously to the side.

'You'll have to open it and find out for yourself,' Bay answered noncommittally.

With a trace of nervous excitement hampering her movements, Sabrina eased the lid off the box and set it on the sofa. She could feel his alert gaze watching her. Her pulse accelerated slightly. Hesitantly exploring fingertips encountered tissue paper. It rustled softly as she pushed it aside to find what it protected.

The object in the box was round and hard. Initially the cylindrical object was unidentifiable until

Sabrina felt along its length. Her hand had barely curled around it to lift it out of the box and she replaced it, folding her hands tightly in her lap. A sickening sensation curled her stomach.

'It's a white cane, isn't it?' she accused tightly, a bad taste bitterly coating her tongue as she uttered the words.

'Yes,' Bay admitted without any trace of remorse. 'But I like to think it isn't an ordinary white cane.'

The box was removed from her lap. The action was followed almost instantly by the rustling of tissue paper, then the sound of the box being set aside. Her lips were compressed tightly shut in an uncompromising line while her hands maintained their death grip on each other. Bay's fingers closed over her wrist and firmly pulled her hands apart, ignoring the resistance she offered.

One hand he released. The second he held with little effort. The curving handle of the cane was pressed into her palm and Bay forced her fingers to curl around it.

Sabrina's first impression was of a smooth glassy surface, then her sensitive touch felt the carving. Almost unwillingly her fingertips explored the design. It was several seconds before she followed the intricate serpentine lines flanking the sides of the cane to the end of the handle. There she was able to identify the design of reptilian heads as those of a dragon.

'It's a cane carved out of ivory,' Bay explained. 'I saw it in a shop window in Chinatown the other day.'

'It's very beautiful,' Sabrina admitted reluctantly.

66

The hand covering hers relaxed its grip, no longer forcing her to hold on to the cane. She held on to it for a few more exploring moments. 'It must be valuable,' she commented, and extended it towards him. 'I couldn't possibly accept it.'

'It's artistic in design but hardly an art object.' He ignored the outstretched hand with the cane. 'What you really mean is it's still white.'

Sabrina didn't deny his charge. 'I can't accept it.'

'I can't return it,' Bay replied evenly.

'I'm sorry.' She pushed the cane into his hands and released it. He had no choice but to hold on to it or let it fall to the floor.

'I know you were trying to be thoughtful, but you knew my views on the subject of canes before you bought it, Bay. The cane is unique and beautiful, but I won't accept it. I get along very well with the one I have.'

'Is that your final answer?'

'Yes, it is,' Sabrina answered firmly, resolved not to be bullied or made to feel guilty because she had refused.

'I suppose if I try to persuade you to change your mind, you'll go back on your agreement to go out with me tomorrow night,' he sighed with almost resigned acceptance.

'Probably,' she shrugged, hoping he wouldn't put her in such a position.

'Then I'll save my arguments for another time.' There was the rustle of tissue paper and the lid being placed on the box. 'Mind you, I'm not giving up,' Bay warned mockingly, 'just postponing the battle.'

'I won't change my mind,' Sabrina replied stubbornly but with a trace of a smile curling her wide mouth.

'I accept the challenge.' She could hear the answering smile in his voice. 'While we're still on speaking terms, may I have another cup of coffee?'

'Of course.' She held out her hand for his cup and saucer.

The subject of the ivory cane was not re-introduced into the conversation, but when Bay Cameron left a half an hour later, Sabrina made certain he had the box with him and did not 'accidentally' forget it.

It was not until that evening when Deborah came that Sabrina discovered the way Bay had tricked her.

'When did you get this, Sabrina?' Deborah asked in a voice that was as one in the same time curious and surprised.

Her fingers stopped their braille reading in mid-sentence as she turned her head in the direction of Deborah's voice 'What is it?'

'An ivory cane. The handle has a dragon design carved on the sides. I found it on the floor beside the chair. Were you hiding it?' the red-haired woman laughed shortly.

'No, *I* wasn't.' Sabrina's mouth thinned grimly.

'It's very elegant. Where did you find it?' Deborah murmured.

'Yes, where?' Her father joined in. 'I haven't seen it before. Is this something else you found the other day when you were with Bay Cameron?'

'You should know by now, Father, that I would

68

never buy a white cane, much less an ivory one,' she retorted. 'It was a present from Bay. I refused it, of course. I thought he had taken it with him.'

'Refused it?' Deborah questioned in amazement. 'Why would you refuse something as lovely as this?'

'Because I don't want it,' Sabrina answered tautly.

The sofa cushion beside her sank as it took her father's weight. His hand gently covered the rigid fingers resting on the now closed cover of her book.

'Aren't you being a little foolish, honey?' The chiding question was spoken softly. 'We both know you didn't refuse it because you thought it was too expensive or because you didn't think it was beautiful. It's because it's white. And a white cane means that you're blind. You can't escape the fact that you're blind simply by not using a white cane.'

'I don't wish to advertise the fact,' was her curt reply.

'People are bound to notice, no matter what kind or colour of cane you have. There's no shame in being blind, for heaven's sake,' Grant Lane argued.

'I'm not ashamed!' Sabrina snapped.

'Sometimes you act as if you are,' he sighed.

'I suppose you think I should use it,' she challenged with a defiant toss of her head.

'I'm your father, Sabrina. Take the chip off your shoulder.' The mildly reproving tone of his voice lessened the jutting angle of her chin. 'You're too old for me to tell you what to do. You know what the right and wise thing to do is. Whether you do it or not is your decision.'

'Excuse me, I think I'll go to my room.' Sabrina set the book on the table and rose stiffly to her feet.

It was impossible to argue when her father wouldn't argue back. She hated it when he appealed to her logic. She invariably lost.

'What should I do with the cane?' Deborah enquired hesitantly.

'Put it in the umbrella stand for now,' her father answered. 'Sabrina can decide what she wants to do before Bay Cameron comes over tomorrow night.'

As Sabrina put her foot on the first step of the stairs leading to the upper floor and her bedroom, she heard Deborah ask, 'Bay Cameron is coming tomorrow night. Why?'

'He's taking Sabrina to the Wharf,' her father replied.

'You mean a date?' his fiancée asked with amazed disbelief.

'I suppose you could call it that. He called me yesterday afternoon at the office after he'd seen Sabrina to ask if I had any objection. I couldn't bring myself to ask him what his intentions were. It would have been too presumptuous when he's been kind to her.'

'Did he mention the cane?'

'No, it was a complete surprise to me,' he answered.

Well, Sabrina sighed in relief, at least her father hadn't been a part of any conspiracy with Bay Cameron. For a moment, she had been worried. She should have realised her father wouldn't do anything underhanded to trick her into making the decision he wanted. It was a pity the same couldn't be said for Bay Cameron.

Still, she had to concede that Bay had not forced

her to accept the ivory cane. He had simply left it. And its presence had produced another dilemma, thanks to her father.

A few minutes before six o'clock, Sabrina sat on the sofa, nibbling on the tip of one fingernail. She absently reached out for the second time to be certain the hooded blue windbreaker was lying on the arm of the sofa. Then her pensive mood was broken by the front door buzzer.

Quickly she pulled on the windbreaker, stuffing the small clutch purse in its oversize pocket. A smoothing hand ran up the back of her neck, tucking any stray strands of hair into the knot atop her head. Her enquiry via the intercom was answered as she had expected by Bay.

'I'll be right down,' she murmured.

Her hand closed over the doorknob, but she hesitated. Her sightless eyes stared at the umbrella stand. Her other hand was poised on the smooth oak cane. For several more seconds she remained immobile, then with a resigned sigh, she removed her hand from the oak cane and tentatively searched for the carved dragon heads of the ivory cane.

Slowly she descended the stairs, opening the outside door and locking it behind her. Squaring her shoulders, she turned towards the iron gates and Bay.

'You took your time,' he commented. 'I was beginning to wonder what was keeping you.'

'I had to put on my jacket,' Sabrina lied, waiting for him to comment on the ivory cane in her hand.

'My car is parked at the kerb,' Bay said as she

swung open the gates and joined him on the sidewalk.

The hand on her elbow firmly guided her to the car. The suspense of waiting for his expression of triumph began to build as he helped her into the car. When Bay had still said nothing after the car was started and turned into the street, Sabrina knew she could not continue waiting for a moment of his choosing.

'Well?' she challenged finally, turning her head towards him in a slightly defiant angle.

'Well what?' Bay countered evenly.

'Aren't you going to say anything about the cane?'

'What do you expect me to say?' The low, calm voice remained controlled and unruffled.

'I should think you'd be feeling pretty smug. After all, you did leave the cane behind deliberately,' Sabrina accused.

'I gave it to you. It was a present, and I don't take back presents. It was entirely up to you what you did with it. I never insisted that you use it. I wouldn't have stopped you if you'd thrown it in the garbage,' responded Bay.

'Well, I have decided to use it,' she stated, facing straight ahead.

'I'm glad.' The car turned and went steeply down a hill. 'May we leave the subject of the cane behind now?'

Sabrina sighed, 'Yes.'

It seemed as if every time she thought she knew how he would react, Bay did not do the expected. He should have been triumphant or a little righteous. Instead he was so calm and matter-of-fact that it was impossible for Sabrina to feel resentment. She had made the decision to use the ivory cane, not Bay, and he knew it.

At the bottom of the inclining street, Bay turned the car again. 'I thought I'd park at the Yacht Harbour. We can follow the sea-wall by Fort Mason to Aquatic Park and on to Fisherman's Wharf. All right?'

'Fine,' Sabrina agreed.

Once the car was parked and locked, they started out at a strolling pace with Bay hooking Sabrina's left arm under his right. Gulls screeched overhead. As they passed Fort Mason and neared the docks of the fishing fleet, the heavier flapping wings of pelicans accompanied the soaring seagulls. The damp salt odour of the air was altered by a fishy smell.

Although the seafood stalls were their ultimate destination, they mutually decided to walk further and come back. The sidewalks were filled with tourists exploring the sights and sounds of the colourful area. A few were jostling and in a hurry, but most took their time absorbing the atmosphere as Sabrina and Bay were doing.

The churning propellers of a tour boat indicated the start of another harbour cruise. The highlights would be a close look at the famed Golden Gate Bridge, the Oakland Bay Bridge and the former maximum security prison of Alcatraz. Now the island was a national park, only a mile out in the bay from the wharf.

At the end of the piers, they crossed the street to the rows of shops and started slowly back towards the seafood stalls.

73

Sabrina lifted her face to the breeze, salty and damp. 'Is the fog coming in?'

'Starting,' Bay agreed. 'It's just beginning to obscure the top spans of the Golden Gate and the Marin hills north of the Bay. It might get thick tonight.'

'In that case, I'll have to lead you back to the car,' she grinned impishly, and Bay chuckled. Sabrina tipped her head curiously towards him. 'Where did you get the name Bay?'

'My parents gave it to me—or didn't you think I had any?' he teased.

'Of course I did. Are they still living?' she asked, sidetracked momentarily from her original question.

'Last I heard they were. They're in Europe taking a second honeymoon.' His arm tightened fractionally in warning. 'You have to step down here.'

'Is Bay a family name?' Sabrina questioned again after negotiating the intersection kerb.

'I wish it were. No, I was named after the obvious, the San Francisco Bay that my mother saw from the hospital window. She was born and raised here, so she'd seen it thousands of times,' he explained. 'What about Sabrina?'

'My mother liked the sound of it. She was very romantic.'

'And you're not?' he mocked.

'Maybe a little bit,' she smiled faintly.

'We've been walking for over an hour. Are you getting hungry?' Bay enquired with an easy change of the subject.

'Very close to starving.'

'You should have said something sooner.'

Sabrina shrugged that it didn't matter and breathed in the tantalising aroma carried by the light breeze. 'It's just across the street, isn't it?' Then she laughed. 'All I have to do is follow my nose.'

'Are you certain you wouldn't rather eat in one of the restaurants here?' Bay checked her movement into the street and a car drove slowly by.

'Positive,' bobbing her head firmly.

At the long row of seafood stalls, Bay selected the cooked crab, including a round loaf of sourdough bread, a salad and cocktail shrimp to the order. Sabrina pressed a hand against her rumbling stomach. The delicious smells were making her all the more hungry. With the purchase completed, Bay handed her the bag and asked her to wait outside while he bought a bottle of chilled white wine to go with it.

Tingles ran down the back of her neck an instant before his hand touched her arm signalling his return. She decided that she must have telepathic powers that told her when Bay approached.

'Are you ready for our picnic?' he asked. At that moment her stomach growled the answer and they both laughed.

Taking the bag of food from her grasp, Bay added it to the one he already had in his arms. The hand she linked in his arm was not for guidance but companionship as they set out for the Yacht Harbour and the shoreline beyond.

They were on the edge of the harbour when Sabrina noticed the fine mist on her face had intensified. 'It's drizzling rain,' she moaned angrily.

'I was afraid it was an overcast more than fog,' Bay sighed.

'I suppose we could always take the food to the house,' Sabrina suggested.

'I have a better idea. My ketch is tied up here. We can eat aboard her. What do you say?'

'I say,' she smiled, 'that it sounds much more pleasant than my house.'

'Let's go!'

Bay had Sabrina wait on the dock while he stowed the food below. Topside again, his strong hands spanned her waist and lifted her aboard. He maintained the hold for steadying minutes, her own hands resting on the rippling muscles of his forearms. The dampness of the drizzling rain increased the spicy aroma emanating from his shaven cheeks and the heady male that enfolded her. The deck beneath her feet moved rhythmically with the lapping waters of the bay.

'It's been so long since I've been on the water,' Sabrina said with an odd catch in her voice, 'that my sea-legs are a bit shaky.' It seemed a reasonable explanation for the weakness in her limbs.

With an arm firmly circling her waist in support, Bay led her below deck. Making certain she had something to hold on to, he went down the steps ahead of her. Sabrina knew it was to catch her in case she fell. Once below he told her where the seats were and let her make her own way to them.

'Do you like sailing?' he asked. The rustling of bags indicated he was getting the food out to eat.

'Love it.' A wry grimace pulled down the corners

of her mouth in a rueful expression. 'I used to go out every weekend with Dad.'

'You haven't been out since your accident? Why?' His low voice was honed sharp with curiosity.

'Oh, a couple of times, but I had to stay below. Dad can't swim. He was afraid I would fall overboard and he wouldn't be able to save me. I like to be on deck where the salt wind stings your face and the waves breaking over the bow sprays you. So I don't go out any more,' she concluded.

'And you aren't afraid of falling in?'

'Not really,' Sabrina shrugged.

A shrimp cocktail was set before her as Bay took a seat opposite her. For a time the conversation centred around sailing, then shifted smoothly to other topics of interest, mainly leisure activities, as they slowly ate their picnic meal.

'I used to really enjoy watching people, studying their faces.' She sipped lightly at the wine. 'Of course, I did it often in connection with my work. Most of my better character came from the faces of people I saw on the streets. A great deal of a person's attitude towards life is written on his face. The grumpy look of a pessimist, the hardness of a cynic, the authority of a leader, the harried worn look of a man driven to succeed, an eagerness for life, the contentment of family and home. There are so many things,' Sabrina exhaled slowly. 'It's not so easy to do it with just voices, but I'm learning. It's difficult, though, to visualise a person's looks from their voices.'

'What have you learned about me?' Bay challenged mockingly.

'Well,' a hint of mischief tickled the corners of her mouth, 'you're self-confident to the point of arrogance. You're well-educated, accustomed to having authority over others. You obviously enjoy the outdoors and especially the sea. You have a quick temper, but you can be thoughtful when it suits you.'

'Have you put a face with my voice yet?'

Sabrina ducked her head from his gaze self-consciously. 'Only a blurred image of strong features.' She pushed her plate away. 'That was good.'

'Why haven't you asked to look at me?' Bay asked quietly, ignoring her attempt to switch the subject to food.

'W-What?' she stammered.

'As you did with the dress,' he explained patiently.

Humour hovered on the edge of his voice after she had shifted uncomfortably in her seat. The thought of exploring his face with her hands was disturbing.

'I could fill in the blank spots for you. I have green hair and purple eyes, a long ugly scar down the side of my face. I keep it hidden with a bushy green beard. I have a tattoo of a skull and crossbones on my forehead—and I won't tell you what the picture is on my chest.' The spreading smile on Sabrina's face broke into laughter at his absurd description. 'Don't you believe me?'

'Hardly. Besides, my neighbour's already told me you have reddish-brown hair and eyes,' Sabrina laughed, her tension fading.

'Cinnamon, according to my mother,' Bay corrected. 'At least you were curious enough about me to ask.'

'Naturally.' She worked to make her reply sound casual and offhand.

'What else did she tell you about me?' he prodded.

'Peggy isn't very good at describing,' Sabrina hedged, unwilling to pass on the comment concerning his masculinity.

'All the more reason for you to see for yourself,' he challenged.

There was the clatter of plates being stacked, then movement as the dishes were carried away. Bay's actions gave her time to think of an excuse to avoid the exploration of his features that he had invited. Try as she could, Sabrina was unable to come up with one that did not reveal her inner apprehension at such intimacy.

When Bay returned, he did not take his former seat across from her but one that placed him beside her. Before she could voice her half-formed protest, he had taken her wrists in a light yet firm grip and carried her hands to his face.

'There's no need to feel shy and self-conscious,' he scolded gently as she tried to pull away. 'It doesn't embarrass me.'

The hard outline of his powerful jaw was beneath her hands, pressed by his on either side of his face. As her resistance faded, he released his hold. The initial contact had been made and the warmth of his body heat eased the cold stiffness of her fingers. Tentatively Sabrina began to explore his face.

From the jawline, her fingertips searched over his

cheeks to the hard angles of his cheekbones. Fluttering over the curling lashes of his eyes, she reached thick brows and the wide forehead. Thick, slightly waving hair grew naturally away from his face, maintaining a suggestion of dampness from the fog and the drizzle. There was an arrogant curve to his Roman nose and a gentle firmness to his male lips. After inspecting the almost forceful angle of his chin, her hands fell away.

It was a masculine face, Sabrina thought in satisfaction. There was no doubt about that. No one would ever refer to him as conventionally handsome, but he was certainly striking. Heads would turn when he walked into a room.

'What's the verdict?' Bay asked in a husky caressing voice like deep velvet.

She guessed her approval was mirrored in her expression. She averted her head slightly from the warm gaze she felt on her face.

'The verdict is,' she answered with false lightness, 'that I like your face.'

A finger tucked itself under her chin and turned her head back towards him. 'I like your face, too,' he murmured softly.

The warm moistness of his breath caressed her cheek a warning instant before his lips touched hers. Initial surprise held Sabrina rigid under his kiss, but the gently firm pressure of his mouth transmitted a warmness that seeped into her veins. Her heart seemed to start skipping beats. With expert persuasion, his mouth moved mobilely against hers until he evoked the pliant response he wanted.

Then slowly, almost regretfully, he drew away from her.

Sabrina could still feel the imprint of his mouth throbbing on hers. She had to resist the impulse to carry a hand to her lips. A wondrously satisfying warmth filled her, leaving her bemused to its cause.

'Why the pensive look, Sabrina?' Bay's husky voice enquired gently.

'I've . . . never been kissed before,' she murmured, uncertain if that was the cause.

'Liar,' he mocked softly. 'That was no inexperienced maiden who kissed me back just now.'

'I—I meant,' crimson flames stained her cheeks, 'since I lost my sight.'

'That I will believe.' Bay took hold of her hand in a casual, not intimate grip. 'Let's go get ourselves a cup of coffee at a restaurant somewhere.'

Sabrina willingly agreed to leave his ketch. For some reason the floor beneath her feet didn't feel very steady. She wanted the security of solid ground beneath her.

It was a few minutes past ten o'clock when Bay parked the car in front of her house and walked her to the grillework gates. He didn't follow her inside the small enclosure and Sabrina turned to him hesitantly.

'I've had a wonderful time. Thank you,' she offered.

'So did I, therefore no thanks are necessary,' Bay said with a smile in his voice. 'I'll be in L.A. all of next week. I'll give you a call when I get back.'

'It isn't necessary.' Sabrina didn't want him to

81

think that he was under any obligation to see her again.

'I know that,' he chided gently. 'Goodnight, Sabrina. I'll wait in the car until I see the light on upstairs, so be sure to turn it on, will you?'

'Goodnight, Bay,' she nodded.

He swung the iron gate closed and Sabrina locked it. She felt his gaze follow her to the door. Cinnamon brown eyes they were, to go with his cinnamon hair.

CHAPTER FIVE

THE switch on the stereo was snapped abruptly to the 'off' position. There was nothing soothing to the music as far as Sabrina was concerned.

What was there to do? She wondered tiredly. She did not feel like cooking or cleaning even if it was needed, which it wasn't. She was tired of reading. Besides, her fingers were still slow to read the raised braille letters, so the task required her total concentration. In this restless mood, she knew her thoughts would wander.

An inner voice unfairly blamed the mood on Bay Cameron. Although why his business trip to Los Angeles should affect her this way, Sabrina didn't know. These restless moods had been with her before anyway, even before her accident. Then she had channelled the surging energy into her paintings. Now there was no outlet.

'Have you ever done any modelling—in clay, I mean?'

Bay's voice spoke clearly in her mind as if he was standing beside her. The seed that had been planted several days ago began to germinate.

Walking to the telephone, Sabrina felt for the receiver, picked it up, then hesitated. Before she changed her mind, she dialled the number. Excitement pulsated through her veins at the sound of the first ring.

'Art Supplies,' a voice answered on the second ring.

'Sam Carlysle, please,' Sabrina requested. Her fingers nervously twined around the corkscrew curl of the telephone cord. A few minutes later a familiar male voice came on the line. 'Hello, Sam. This is Sabrina.'

'Sabrina, how are you?' he exclaimed in glad surprise. Then his tone changed immediately to contriteness. 'Listen, I'm sorry I haven't phoned or stopped by for so long, but what with one thing or another——'

'That's all right,' she interrupted quickly. 'Actually I was calling to see if you could do me a favour.'

'Name it and it's yours, Sabrina.'

'I wondered if you could send someone over today with some artist's modelling clay and an inexpensive set of tools?'

'Are you taking up modelling?' he asked in a stunned voice.

'I'm going to give it a try,' Sabrina acknowledged. 'That's why I only want the bare necessities to see if I'm going to like it or be any good at it.'

'I think it's a tremendous idea!' Sam enthused. 'A stroke of genius!'

'Can you send someone over?'

'I'd come myself if I could, but I'll have a delivery boy leave here in about ten minutes and I'll make sure your place is his first stop.'

'Thanks, Sam.' A contented glow spread over her face.

'Hey, listen, I'm just sorry I didn't suggest something like this to you before,' he replied, shrugging aside her thanks. 'I'll get this stuff out to you right away. We'll get together soon, okay?'

'Yes, Sam, soon,' Sabrina agreed.

Barely a half an hour had elapsed when the delivery was made. She had already cleared a small area in the studio where she could work, realising that her father would have to give her a hand this evening with the heavier items. The delivery man had thoughtfully offered to carry the packages wherever Sabrina wanted them so she hadn't had to carry them to the studio.

After he had left and she had returned to the studio, a thrill of excitement danced down her spine. Her old smock was behind the door, smelling of oil paints and cleaning fluid. Soon, the odour of clay would wipe out that smell, she told herself gaily as she donned the protective smock and felt her way to the work table.

All conception of time vanished. She started out with simple shapes, using fruit she had taken from the kitchen for her hands to use as a guideline. Her name was called for the third time before it penetrated her concentration. It was another full second before she recognised her father's voice.

'I'm upstairs in the studio!' she answered.

She stepped back, wiping her hands on a rag as she listened to his hurrying steps up the stairs. A look of apprehension and excitement was in the expression Sabrina turned to the open doorway.

'I was getting frantic,' Grant Lane declared with an exasperated sigh. 'Why didn't you answer me? What are you doing up here anyway?'

'Working,' Sabrina replied softly, but she could tell by the tense silence that her explanation wasn't necessary. Her father had already looked beyond her and seen for himself. She waited interminable seconds for his comment. 'What do you think?' she asked breathlessly.

'I ... I'm speechless,' he told her. 'How——— When———' Then he laughed at his inability to get his questions out and came the rest of the way into the room, throwing an arm about her shoulders and giving her a fierce hug. 'You are one fantastic little gal. I'm proud of you.' His voice was choked with emotion.

'Yes, but what do you think?' she repeated anxiously.

'If you're asking whether I can tell the apple from the pear, the answer is a definite "yes". I can even see that's a cluster of grapes you're working on now,' her father smiled. 'And I didn't need that assortment of real fruit spotted with clay to make the identification either!'

'Do you mean it?'

'I mean it,' he assured her firmly. 'Now how about an explanation? When did you decide to do all this? You never mentioned a word about it to me. Where did you get all this?'

'Last week Bay asked if I'd ever worked in clay. I guess that's when I started thinking about it, subconsciously at least. This morning I decided to try it and called Sam at the art supply store. He had this delivered for me,' Sabrina explained.

'This morning? And you've been working ever since? You must be exhausted!'

'Exhausted?' She turned her face to him, her wide mouth smiling broadly. 'No, Daddy, I'm alive. For the first time in a very long while.'

There was a moment of silence. Then her father took a deep breath. 'Just the same, you'd better call it a day. No sense in overdoing it. You clean up here and I'll see about the dinner you forgot,' he teased.

'All right,' she submitted.

For the rest of the week, Sabrina spent every waking minute she possibly could in the studio room. The end results were more often failures than successes. It didn't do any good for her father to insist that she couldn't expect to be perfect as a beginner. But Sabrina demanded perfection of herself. Nothing less would satisfy her.

On Sunday morning, Grant Lane ordered her out of the studio. 'For heaven's sake, Sabrina,' he declared, 'even God rested on the seventh day!'

The mutinous set of her chin dipped as she sighed her reluctant surrender to his logic. Her fingers ached to feel the moulding clay beneath her hands, but she knew her father was right.

'I've got some work to do on the boat. Why don't you come with me this morning?' he suggested. 'Deborah is going to be busy in the kitchen. If you have nothing to do, I know you're going to sneak back up here the minute I leave.'

'I wouldn't do that,' Sabrina laughed softly.

'Oh, wouldn't you?' he mocked. 'You're coming with me.'

'I think it's awful that you don't trust me, your own daughter!' She clicked her tongue in reproval. 'But if that's the way you're going to be, I guess I'll have to go with you.'

'There's a pretty stiff breeze blowing in from the

87

Pacific, so dress accordingly. But make sure it's something you won't mind getting dirty,' her father added. 'I thought I'd put you to work cleaning below deck.'

'That's why you want me to come along,' Sabrina nodded sagely.

'You don't think it was your company I was wanting, did you?' he teased, and walked to the stairs.

The wind was chilly, Sabrina discovered. It had not yet blown away the morning fog, so the sun had not warmed the air. Below deck, she didn't feel the cool breeze. Wiping the perspiration from her forehead that had separated her dark silky bangs into damp strands, she wished she could feel it.

She pushed up the sleeves on her navy blue pullover and set to work scrubbing the galley sink. The perspiration was making the wool blend of the turtleneck collar tickle the sensitive skin of her neck, but she couldn't very well scratch it with her soapy hands. As soon as she finished this Sabrina decided she would call her father down for a cup of coffee. From the sound of voices overhead, he was doing more chatting with fellow sailing enthusiasts than work.

Maybe she should take the pot of coffee and some cups on deck and offer it around. There was a waterproof tin of cookies in the cupboard. Then she smiled to herself. That would really make certain nothing was accomplished today!

The quiet step of rubber-soled shoes approached the steps leading below. Sabrina was rinsing the soap from the sink when they began their descent.

She stopped, turning slightly in the direction of the footsteps.

'I thought I would bring some coffee up as soon as I finish here, Dad. I'll bring some extra cups if you think the others would like to join you.'

'That sounds fine.'

'Bay! You're back!' The exclamation of delight sprang unchecked from her lips.

'I got in late yesterday afternoon,' he acknowledged. 'I thought I might see you here today with your father. I never guessed he would make you a galley-slave.'

Sabrina smiled at the teasing voice. 'Did you have a good trip?'

'Yes. I had some investment property to check on and inspected some other land I've been interested in acquiring. I even ran into an old friend I went to university with. He's topside talking to your father. Why don't you come and meet him?'

She had half expected it to be a woman, and she wondered if her relief was reflected in her expression. She hoped not. She didn't want Bay to think she was jealous. They were only friends.

'I'll be through here in a minute,' she said. 'If you'd like, you can take the coffeepot on up. There are some mugs in the cupboard. I can bring the sugar and powdered cream.'

'All right,' Bay agreed.

A few minutes later, Sabrina joined the others on deck. The wind lifted her bangs and she turned her face into the cooling flow of air.

'Here, Sabrina, let me take those.' Her father took

89

the tins of sugar and powdered cream from her hands and helped her on deck.

'This is Grant's daughter, Sabrina Lane,' Bay said. 'This is my old fraternity brother, Doctor Joe Browning.'

'You'd better watch who you call old,' said a gruff male voice in a mock serious tone. Then Sabrina's hand was taken in greeting. 'I'm more commonly known as Joe or Doctor Joe to my patients.'

Cold fingers raced icily down her spine. 'How do you do.' Her greeting was stiff. Since her accident and the string of doctors she had been to, Sabrina had developed an aversion to those in the medical profession.

'Joe, the name is Joe,' he said. 'Your father tells me you've been blind for only a year. You seem to be getting along rather well.'

'There really isn't much choice, is there?' she retorted.

'Of course there is. You could always get along badly.'

His nonsensical reply unwillingly brought a faint smile to her mouth. She had always expected that even at home doctors were somewhat staid and unemotional, spouting platitudes and doing charitable deeds. This one seemed to be different.

'I ran into my share of furniture and buildings in the beginning,' she admitted.

'Do you use a cane or do you have a seeing eye dog?' He didn't give her a chance to reply. 'I hear they're using standard poodles as well as shepherds and other breeds as seeing eye dogs. Can you imagine a poodle prancing down the street with its

90

fluffy pompadour and that ball of fluff on his tail leading some blind man? It always seemed like the height of absurdity to me. Not that I have anything against the intelligence of poodles.'

Sabrina laughed at the image he had created in her mind. She liked his irreverent attitude and her wariness disappeared. The relaxed sound of her laughter began a natural flow of conversation among all of them. Doctor Joe Browning dominated most of the topics with his dry wit.

Some time, Sabrina was not certain when, the subject became centred on her blindness, the accident, and the damage to her optic nerves that had resulted from the head injury. She was suddenly aware that the enquiries were not casual but had a professional undertone.

'Wait a minute,' she interrupted the doctor in mid-sentence. 'Exactly what kind of a doctor are you?'

'A very good one,' he quipped. 'A surgeon, to be specific.'

'What kind?' Then she raised her hand in a halting gesture, and accused angrily. 'No, let me guess. You're an eye surgeon.'

'You're right with the very first guess. Now that's the mark of a girl who pays attention,' Joe Browning replied without the least embarrassment.

'What have all these questions been? A subtle examination?'

'Yes,' he admitted simply.

Seething with indignation, Sabrina turned in the direction she knew Bay to be sitting. 'You put him up to this, didn't you, Bay Cameron? And you must have been in on it, too, Father.'

'It was my idea for you not to know the real reason why Doctor Joe was seeing you,' her father replied in a contrite tone. 'Bay did contact him originally, but the rest was my idea so you wouldn't have to go through the whole rigmarole again, maybe unnecessarily.'

'That's why you pretended,' Sabrina said tautly, 'that he was an old school chum of yours, isn't it, Bay?'

'No, that's the truth,' the doctor replied, 'and it's also the truth that we bumped into each other in Los Angeles. He had no idea I was there since I've been on the East Coast for the last few years. He mentioned you to me and professional curiosity took over.'

'I'm sorry, Sabrina,' Bay offered quietly. 'I knew you'd be upset when you found out.'

'Then why did you try to trick me?'

'I felt I should respect your father's wishes. And there was the likelihood that you wouldn't find out, not if Joe didn't think there was any hope that your vision could be restored,' he answered.

'And do you?' Her chin tipped proudly towards the doctor. The aura of pride was a defence mechanism to conceal any reaction to his verdict.

'I'd like to run some more tests in a hospital before I give you a definite answer, Sabrina,' he said honestly. 'I would guess you have no more than a ten per cent chance, if that much, that there's a surgical cure.'

'Four specialists told my father and me that I

would never see again. What makes you think you can help me?' Sabrina challenged.

'I don't know that I can,' Doctor Joe answered, 'but I don't know that I can't either. On occasions, the body's natural healing processes repair some of the damage, making a condition that was inoperable shortly after the injury operable a period of months later. It has happened.'

'I see,' she said tautly. 'And that's what you think has happened to me.'

'I don't know, but I don't think we should overlook the possibility,' he replied. 'To be certain, I'd have to admit you to a hospital and run some tests. I don't want to raise any false hopes, Sabrina. You have a very slim chance of having your vision restored, right next to none at all. The decision is yours.'

Not even the scent of roses that her father had brought could overcome the strong medicinal and antiseptic odour of the hospital. In the corridor, there were the hushed voices of a pair of nurses walking swiftly by her door. Sabrina listened to the even breathing of the female patient who shared her room.

Visiting hours were over. The lights were out. She knew that because she had heard the flick of the switch when the nurse left the room a few minutes ago.

Her dark world seemed blacker this night. She felt so very much alone and vulnerable. She was afraid to hope that the tests tomorrow would be encouraging. Yet it was impossible to be indifferent to the reason she was here.

A hand doubled into a fist at her side. Damn Bay for running into his doctor friend, Sabrina thought dejectedly. She had accepted her blindness, stopped fighting the injustice of it and had started living with it.

Since Bay was partially responsible for her presence in the hospital, the least he could have done was come to visit her. But no, he had sent a message of good luck with Doctor Joe, passed on when Sabrina had been admitted.

A trembling shivered over her body and wouldn't stop. She hadn't realised she was so scared. Her chin quivered. She wanted to break down and cry. The brave front she had worn was crumbling and she didn't care.

A swirl of air blew over her face. She had come to recognize that as the silent opening of the door to her hospital room. Someone was approaching her bed, and she had the sensation that it wasn't the nurse. A spicy scent of aftershave lotion drifting to her nose confirmed it.

'Are you awake?' Bay asked softly.

'Yes,' Sabrina whispered, pushing herself into a more upright position while trying to keep the flimsy hospital gown securely around her. 'Visiting hours are over. You're not supposed to be here.'

'If they catch me, they can ask me to leave, right?' he smiled with his voice. 'How are you doing?'

'Fine,' she lied. The edge of the bed took his weight. 'I thought Doctor Joe said you had to go to a party or something.'

'I did go,' Bay acknowledged, 'but I slipped away to see you. Is that all right?'

'It's all right with me as long as it was all right with the lady you were with,' Sabrina returned.

'What makes you think I was with anyone?'

'I certainly hope you were, because otherwise you're wearing some very expensive French perfume!' Her fingers clutched the bedcovers tightly. It was important that she maintain this air of light-hearted teasing so Bay would not guess her inner apprehension.

'Aha, the blind detectīve,' he mocked.

'Elementary,' she shrugged. 'After all, you were at a party. That makes it only logical to assume that you would turn your charm towards some attractive woman there.'

'Now that's where you're wrong.'

'Why?' Sabrina tilted her head to the side in mock challenge.

'Because I've been directing all my charms to a certain blind lady that I know, a very attractive one,' Bay responded lightly.

Her throat constricted. 'I find that difficult to believe.'

A hand warmly covered the hands clinging to the sheets. Gently he prised them free. 'Your hands are like ice, Sabrina. What's the matter?'

His frowning accusation sent an uncontrollable shiver quaking over her shoulders. Emitting a shaky sigh, Sabrina admitted, 'I'm frightened, Bay—of tomorrow.'

He said nothing for a minute. She felt him shift his weight on the bed. Then his arm circled her shoulders and he drew her against his chest, the back of his hand cradling her head near his chin.

'Let's think about this,' he murmured calmly. 'It's not the thought of the tests Joe is going to do that frightens you. That only leaves two alternatives. One is that you're afraid to have your sight restored and the second is that you won't, right?'

Numbly Sabrina nodded her affirmation. The steady beat of his heart beneath her head and the protective circle of his strong arms was blissfully comforting.

'I know you can't be afraid of seeing again,' he continued. 'That result would have everyone rejoicing. That only leaves the second.'

'I——' she began hesitantly. 'I had accepted the fact that I was blind. I've started working in clay, did I tell you that? I'm an awful coward,' she sighed. 'I wish I'd never agreed to these tests. I wish I'd never met Doctor Joe. I don't want to go through the agony of accepting all over again that I'm permanently blind.'

'Where is that gutsy girl who was always trying to thumb her nose at convention?' Bay mocked softly. 'You aren't a coward, Sabrina. A coward wouldn't be here in the hospital taking the slim gamble that Joe offered. If the tests prove negative, you aren't going to wail and pound your chest. The gutsy blind girl I know is going to shrug her shoulders and say, "Well, I gave it a go".' She felt him smile against her hair. 'To borrow an old cliché, Sabrina, you have everything to gain and nothing to lose.'

'That's what I keep trying to tell myself,' she sighed.

, 'The secret is to stop saying and start admitting that it's true.' He didn't require a reply as he held her for more long minutes. The strength seemed to flow from the muscles in his arms into her, chasing away her unreasonable fears. 'Are you all right now?' he asked finally.

'Yes,' she nodded against his chin, and smiled faintly.

'Then I'd better be going before the nurse comes in and gets the wrong idea about what we're doing,' Bay teased softly.

Very gently he shifted her on to the pillow, tucking the sheet around her chest. As he started to straighten, Sabrina reached out for his arm.

'Thank you for coming, Bay,' she whispered tightly.

'Don't thank me for something I wanted to do.' Then he bent over her and there was a tantalising brush of his mouth on hers. 'Goodnight, Sabrina. I'll be seeing you.'

'Yes. Goodnight, Bay.'

There were soft footsteps, then the swish of air as the door opened and closed.

The hospital bed felt like a pincushion. Sabrina knew it was the waiting. Two days of tests were over, and Doctor Joe would be relaying the results any minute. The grimness that had been in his voice the last day had convinced Sabrina that the results thus far hadn't been encouraging.

Her father walked again to the window in her room. She knew he had no interest in the parking lot below, his patience giving way to restless pacing.

She wished she could join him. In almost mid-stride, he stopped and turned abruptly. A second later air from the corridor fanned her cheek and she turned towards the door.

'Goodmorning, Sabrina, Mr Lane,' Doctor Joe Browning greeted each of them. His voice was professionally bright. 'It's really a lousy morning, but I suppose you San Franciscans are used to the fog.'

'Goodmorning, Doctor Joe,' Sabrina returned.

But her father skipped the pleasantries. 'Are all the results in?'

'Yes.'

The back of Sabrina's neck prickled. Unconsciously she called out hesitantly, 'Bay?'

'Hello, Sabrina,' he answered quietly.

'Don't tell me my patient has mental telepathy?' the doctor laughed shortly in surprise.

'A keen sense of smell,' Bay corrected in a smiling voice. 'She probably recognised my aftershave lotion.'

Sabrina didn't correct him. She wasn't certain herself how she had known he was there and she couldn't be positive that she hadn't unconsciously caught a whiff of the spicy fragrance.

'Well, to get back to the business at hand,' Doctor Joe breathed in deeply, 'I've analysed the test results twice.'

He paused and Grant Lane prompted, 'And?'

'We knew when we rolled the dice, Mr Lane, that it was a long shot, not even house odds.' The grimness of his voice was all the warning Sabrina needed to brace herself for the rest of his answer. 'The dice came up snake eyes. There isn't anything that can be done. I'm deeply sorry that I put both of you through this.'

The silence from her father told Sabrina how much he had been praying for a miracle. So had she, for that matter, but she wasn't as crushed as she had been the other times that the verdict was pronounced.

She summoned a weak smile. 'We had to take the chance, Doctor Joe.' Her smile deepened as she remembered Bay's words that first night in the hospital. 'We had to give it a go.'

The doctor walked to the bed and clasped one of her hands warmly between his. 'Thank you, Sabrina.'

As Doctor Joe took his leave of her father, apologising again, she heard Bay approach the bed. He stopped somewhere near the side. She felt his penetrating gaze run over her face.

'Are you all right?' he asked quietly.

'Yes,' she whispered, and she knew suddenly that it was the truth and not simply brave words.

'I knew that gutsy blind queen would resurface,' he told her.

'With your help, she did,' Sabrina answered.

'I can't take credit for the strength you already possessed,' Bay denied, 'but we'll argue the point another time. How about Saturday night?'

'Saturday night?' she repeated.

'Yes, we can have dinner together. I'll pick you up around seven.'

There was a breathless catch in her throat. 'Is that an order or an invitation?' she asked unevenly.

'Both, depending on your answer.'

'I'd be proud to have dinner with you, Mr Cameron.' Sabrina accepted with a demure inclination of her head.

More than proud, she added silently to herself. She found she was looking forward to Saturday night with uncommon eagerness.

CHAPTER SIX

SABRINA slowly descended the steps to the second floor, fingering the soft knit of her top uncertainly. A tiny frown of indecision pulled the arch of her brows together. In the living room, she could hear her father's and Deborah's voices. She walked to the open doorway and paused.

'Deborah, may I see you a minute?' Sabrina requested, a hint of anxiety in her voice.

'Of course.' Footsteps muffled by the carpet quickly approached the doorway where she waited. 'What is it?'

'This pants suit, is it too dressy?'

'I shouldn't think so,' Deborah frowned in confusion. 'Bay is taking you out to dinner, isn't he?'

'Not to dinner exactly,' Sabrina explained. 'We'll pick up something to eat at the Wharf like we did the last time and have a makeshift picnic somewhere. He's not taking me out to a public restaurant.' Her hand touched the camel tan slacks stitched in dark brown and the matching boat-necked top in the same brown. Over her arm, she carried a matching jacket and around her neck was progressively longer strands of gold chain. 'Maybe I should wear something simpler?'

'I don't think so,' Deborah decided after several seconds of consideration to the question. 'You may not be going out to a fancy restaurant to dine, but that isn't any reason why you have to look like an urchin. That pants suit is versatile enough to fit any occasion except the most formal one.'

'Good,' Sabrina sighed in relief. It was so difficult sometimes trying to judge by memory the clothes she wore. The front door bell rang. 'That must be Bay now.'

'Your purse is on the table,' Deborah stated. 'I'll tell Bay you're on your way down.'

Retrieving her purse, Sabrina slipped the ivory cane from the umbrella stand, hooked it over her arm and opened the stairwell door, calling a goodbye to her father before closing it. She darted eagerly down the stairs and through the street door to the gates.

'I'm ready,' she declared unnecessarily, unlocking the gates and walking through.

Bay's hand touched her arm in light possession as he directed her to his parked car. 'I was hoping you might wear that new dress tonight.'

Sabrina laughed softly. 'I'd look pretty silly wearing that to a picnic!'

'A picnic?' he repeated. 'We aren't going to a picnic. I'm taking you out to dinner, remember?'

'But——' she stopped short.

'But what?' he paused patiently beside her.

'You know very well that I don't eat in public places,' she stated, punctuating the sentence with an emphatic tap of her cane.

'Yes, I remember what you said.' His arm crossed her back and he forcibly moved her towards the car. The door was opened and Sabrina was helped and shoved inside. She fumbled for the door handle, only to find the door was locked. Before she could find the lock, Bay was in the car, his hand tightly closing over her wrist.

'You're not paying attention to me,' Sabrina accused.

'I can't give you all of my attention and drive, too,' Bay countered logically, starting the car and turning it away from the curb with one hand. 'We're going to a nice little Italian restaurant. It doesn't look much from the outside, but the food is excellent.'

'I'm not going,' she declared.

'Sabrina, you can't keep avoiding things on the offchance that you'll do something embarrassing.' The firm tone of his voice said his patience was thinning.

'You're going to look pretty silly yourself dragging me into that restaurant,' she commented smugly.

'I hope you aren't counting on the fact that I won't, because if that's the only way I can get you in the door, I'll do it,' Bay stated.

In that flashing second, Sabrina realised that he meant it. No stubbornness or anger on her part would change his mind. He actually meant to get her in the restaurant one way or the other.

'You're a brute and a bully!' she hissed angrily. 'I don't know why I ever agreed to come with you tonight. I should have guessed you would do something like this.'

'You'd better be careful,' he warned mockingly. 'I could change my mind and take you to a Chinese restaurant and put a pair of chopsticks in your hand. I don't think you'd fare too successfully with those.'

The pouting line of her mouth twitched as her innate sense of humour surfaced. She covered her mouth with her hand to try to hide the smile that was breaking through. She had never mastered the use of chopsticks when she could see. Any attempt now that she was blind would be absurd.

'I see that smile,' Bay laughed softly. 'It's a decided improvement on that stubborn blind monkey that was sitting beside me a minute ago. You just keep wearing it. And don't be embarrassed if you spill something. Sighted people do that all the time.'

'Why can't I ever win an argument with you?' Sabrina sighed, but with humour.

'Because, my little blind queen,' he drawled, 'you always know that I'm right.'

Surprisingly, as far as Sabrina was concerned, the dinner was without mishap. The other times she had eaten out shortly after the accident, she had invariably tipped over a glass or dropped food on the table, but not this time. Bay had laughingly threatened to order her spaghetti, but it was a very excellent lasagne that she had received instead.

She leaned back in her chair, a hand securely touching the coffee cup so she wouldn't forget where it was. A tiny sigh of contentment broke from her lips.

'What was that for?' Bay inquired softly.

'For a very enjoyable meal,' she responded. 'Thank you for making me come.'

'I prefer the word "persuaded".' Amusement danced in his voice.

' "Persuaded" me to come, then,' she acknowledged with a dimpling smile.

'No depression because of the negative test results?' Despite the teasing tone, there was an underlying hint of seriousness.

'I wish it had been otherwise, of course,' Sabrina shrugged, 'but I don't mind as much as I might have. Partly because of the advice you gave me and partly because I'd already started working again, in a creative sense. My life as a blind woman was not without purpose when I went into the hospital this time. Before when the specialists gave me their verdict, I had nothing to look forward to but emptiness. Now I have a goal.'

'You're referring to the modelling you've started in clay. When are you going to show me what you've done so far?'

'When I'm willing to stand some criticism,' Sabrina smiled ruefully.

'And you think my judgment would be critical?' Bay prompted.

'I don't think you're going to let me get by with mediocrity simply because I'm blind,' she acknowledged.

'I don't think you would learn on that crutch and lower your standards either,' he returned.

'I couldn't,' admitted Sabrina with a nod of her head. A fervent note crept into her voice. 'I want to be more than just good. I want to be great. It's the only way I'll be able to support myself with art as my career.'

'And that's very important to you, isn't it?'

'Yes. Not just for pride's sake or to be independent,' she went on earnestly, 'but because I don't want to keep being a burden to my father. I know he doesn't think of me that way, but I know that because of me he hasn't married Deborah. Only by having an independent income could I prove to him that I'm capable of living on my own.'

'You could always get married. That's a very excellent reason for leaving home,' Bay suggested.

'There happen to be two obstacles to that solution,' Sabrina laughed shortly, not taking his suggestion seriously.

'What are they?'

'First, there isn't anyone I happen to be in love with, and it would be pretty shallow to marry a man simply to get out of the house.'

'And the second?'

'The second is a very crucial one. There would have to be someone around willing to marry me.' There was a dubious shake of her head as if such a contingency would never occur.

'Is that so unlikely?' Bay asked with curious mockery.

'If they're sane, it would be.' She laughed quietly again.

'I've always considered myself to be sane. I guess that puts me out of the running, doesn't it?'

Sabrina felt his gaze searching her face, alert to her reaction. She was suddenly self-conscious about the subject they were discussing.

'It certainly would,' she answered firmly.

'I guess that settles that,' Bay stated. The nonchalance in his voice didn't match the sensation Sabrina had that he had been interested in her answer. Maybe he thought she wanted to take advantage of his apparent wealth. 'Would you like some more coffee, Sabrina, or shall we leave?'

'No more, thank you. I'm ready if you are.' Her hand found the ivory cane hooked over the arm of her chair.

After that first successful dinner, Bay took Sabrina out several times during the following three weeks. The restaurants he chose were seldom crowded but served excellent food.

The only twinges of self-consciousness she experienced came when friends of Bay's stopped at their table to say hello. She had sensed their surprise upon learning she was blind and guessed that they wondered why Bay was with her.

At odd times, she wondered why herself, but the answer had ceased to be important. It was enough to enjoy his company without constantly questioning his motives for being with her. In a way she didn't want to find out. She was afraid his reason might be a charitable one. Although she had come a great distance out of her shell, she was still averse to pity from any quarter and most especially from Bay.

Carefully she smoothed the arm of the clay figure, letting her fingers transfer the image to her mind's eye. A faint shiver of subdued elation trembled over her at the completed picture of a ballet dancer captured in the middle of a pirouette that her mind saw. With each passing week her hands had become more sure and more adept. The successes had begun to outnumber the failures.

Footsteps echoed into the studio from the stairway. Quelling her excitement, Sabrina stepped back from the work stand, a faint smile of triumph tickling the corners of her mouth. Wiping her hands on the towel, she turned slightly towards the door as the footsteps approached. An eagerness she couldn't conceal was in her stance.

'Come in, Dad,' she called when the footsteps paused at the door. 'I've finished the third. Come and see it.'

The instant the door opened, her head tipped sideways in a listening attitude. The person entering the room was not her father but Bay. She knew it instinctively.

'What are you doing here?' she breathed in surprise. 'You said you wouldn't come until seven. It can't be that late.' She had removed her watch so she couldn't check the time.

'It isn't. It's the middle of the afternoon,' Bay returned with faint amusement. 'Since you haven't extended an invitation for me to see your work, I persuaded your father to send me up here rather than have you come down.'

In an instinctive, protective movement, Sabrina moved a few steps to try to block his line of sight. Only her father and Deborah had seen the result of her many hours of labour in the studio. She was not yet ready for someone outside her family to see what she had done.

'That doesn't explain what you're doing here in the middle of the afternoon,' she murmured defensively.

'Doesn't it? I thought it did.' She could hear the smile in his tone. 'Actually you're right,' Bay conceded. 'I had another purpose for coming other than sneaking into your studio. I'm afraid I have to cancel our dinner date tonight—I'm sorry, Sabrina.'

'That's all right,' she shrugged.

It wasn't all right, but she didn't want him to realise how much she looked forward to an evening with him. She didn't like to admit it to herself. There was no future in it. The future was here in this studio with her work.

'I don't know whether I should be pleased or insulted that you've taken the news so calmly.' Sabrina sensed the arching of a thick brow in her direction, faintly mocking and faintly curious. 'You might show a little regret.'

'I would have enjoyed the evening.' Pride inserted a slightly indifferent tone in her voice. 'Obviously whatever it is that's forced you to cancel our dinner together must be important or I don't think you would have cancelled.' The intense scrutiny of his gaze was disturbing. Striving for lightness, Sabrina added with a taut smile, 'I certainly hope you've warned your jealous girl-friend that she doesn't need to scratch my eyes out. I'm already quite blind and disfigurement I don't need.' It was a facetious remark, not an expression of self-pity.

'What makes you think it's a jealous girl-friend who's changing our plans?' The inflection in his voice was mockingly amused, but Sabrina was still conscious of his penetrating look.

'I don't know that it is,' she answered with a teasing smile. 'But I certainly hope you don't expect me to believe that you're a celibate.'

'What makes you think I'm not?' Bay countered.

The virilely masculine face her hands had seen was immediately before her inner eye. The image made a mockery of his question. In too many little ways, Bay's actions in the past had answered his own question.

'A girl has ways of knowing these things,' Sabrina smiled complacently. 'A kind of female intuition, I suppose.'

'If you believe that about me, then what conclusion have you reached to explain why I haven't brought our relationship to a more intimate level?' he asked lazily.

'Really, Bay!' Sabrina laughed as if the question was ridiculous under the circumstances. 'We're friends, nothing more.'

'Strictly platonic, is that it?'

'Of course.' A tiny frown puckered her forehead at the faint harshness in his remark.

'In that case, when are you going to step aside to let a "friend" see your work? My view is somewhat limited with you standing in front of it,' he mocked.

Sabrina decided that she had imagined the sharpness in his previous question. She had only been stating the obvious and he had agreed in an indirect way.

For a hesitant moment, she remained where she was, wanting to know his reaction to her work but unsure yet of the extent of her own skill in this field of art. Almost reluctantly she stepped to one side, apprehension edging the corners of her bland expression as Bay walked forward for a closer look.

'S-some of my first attempts are on the side table,' she explained nervously. 'As you can see, they aren't very good, but I've slowly been improving. Right now I'm working on a series of ballet figures. I thought I'd do a small "corps de ballet" with the central model being a dancing couple. I'm only a third done with the secondary figures, though.'

The silence stretched seemingly without end. Sabrina thought she would burst with the suspense of waiting. Her hands were unconsciously clasped in a praying position.

'Have any of your friends seen your work?' Bay asked absently. 'Your art friends, I mean.'

Her throat worked convulsively as she shook her head in a negative answer before she could speak. 'Only Dad and Deborah.'

'I'm no critic, Sabrina,' he murmured. 'I only know what I like, and I'm impressed by what I see here. You've never done any extensive work in this medium before?'

'Never,' she breathed. 'Do you really think it's good? You're not saying it because I'm blind, are you?' She needed to hear his approval again.

'I haven't treated you with kid gloves since the first time I met you, and I'm not going to put them on now,' he answered seriously. 'You know that what you've done is more than good. I can see that it is. A professional is the only person who can tell you how good you are. If you want my suggestion, I think you should get hold of someone who can give you that answer.'

'Not—not yet,' Sabrina refused. Confidence in her own ability was not to the point where she could endure the scrutiny of her work by an art critic. 'I'm not ready for that. I need more time.'

'No one is ever ready to have anything judged by others, but you can't postpone it for ever.' His observance was gently understanding while reminding her of the practical need if she intended to make this her career.

'Not yet,' she repeated, running her palms nervously over the sides of her clay-stained smock.

'Cigarette?' Bay offered.

'Yes, please.' Sabrina accepted with a quaking sigh.

As the scent of burning tobacco reached her nose, she extended her hand for the cigarette, but Bay placed the filter tip against her lips, his fingers touching her mouth and sending a shiver of awareness down her spine. Invariably when she came in contact with him, she was intensely conscious of his maleness, the memory of that one fleeting first kiss haunting her again with its tender mastery and checked fire.

'There's coffee and cake downstairs,' she offered hesitantly. 'If you'd——'

'No, I'm sorry, I can't stay any longer,' Bay refused before she could complete the invitation. 'I won't be able to see you this coming week either. I do have a couple of tickets for the Light Opera's performance next Saturday if you're willing to accept that as a raincheck for tonight.'

'I would enjoy that,' Sabrina smiled.

'I promise I'll make certain I don't have to cancel that one,' he smiled. 'Oh, by the way, there's something I meant to give you as an apology for tonight.'

'Give me?' she frowned as she listened to him reach into his pocket and heard the faint rustle of paper. He placed a small, wrapped box in her hand, long and thin, similar in shape to a jeweller's box.

'Open it,' he ordered laughing at her hesitation.

'It's nothing expensive, if that's what's concerning you. In fact, you might decide to throw it in my face when you find out what it is.'

Curious and apprehensive, Sabrina began unwrapping the package. Removing the cardboard top of the small thin box, her exploring fingers touched a pair of tapering sticks. She turned a bewildered expression to Bay.

'Sticks?' she questioned in disbelief.

Bay clicked his tongue in mock reproval. 'Not just sticks,' he chuckled. 'They're chopsticks. I'm giving you a couple of weeks to practise before I take you to a Cantonese restaurant in Chinatown.'

Laughter bubbled in her throat and she bit into her lower lip to hold it back. With mock seriousness she replied, 'I suppose I should be grateful that you've given me advance warning.'

'Yes, you should,' he agreed in a tone of pseudo-arrogance.

'Even with practice,' Sabrina couldn't hold back the laughter, 'the only thing I'll probably eat is egg rolls, soup and fortune cookies. All the rest will end up on the floor or the table cloth.'

'I'll take the chance,' Bay smiled. 'As for next Saturday, I think the occasion will warrant the sophistication of that flame-coloured dress.'

'Is that an order, too?' she laughed.

'If it is, will you obey it?' he countered.

'Yes,' she nodded, a wide smile spreading across her cheeks, softening her square jawline.

After Bay's approval of her work, Sabrina strove even harder for the perfection she demanded. This renewed vigour made the week pass swiftly. The

113

performance of the Light Opera Company the following Saturday seemed a reward for her efforts.

The faint initial nervousness she had felt at the prospect of going to such a very public place vanished under the genuine praise from Bay at her appearance. She had taken extra pains, enlisting Deborah's aid with her hair and make-up. The two of them had got along much better since Sabrina had started working in the studio again.

No further mention had been made by Deborah of the special school she had thought Sabrina should attend. It was as if they were both counting on the efforts in the studio for the future happiness of each.

Sabrina had not intended to take her ivory cane, vanity not wanting her to be easily identified by the crowd attending the opera as being blind. However, Bay handed her the cane from the umbrella stand as they walked out the door of the house. She had known he would chide her reason for not wanting to carry it, so she had said nothing.

Now the cane was hooked over her arm as they stood in the foyer of the theatre. It was the intermission between acts. Had Sabrina been with anyone else she would probably have remained in her seat, but Bay had ushered her into the outer lobby.

Bay Cameron was not a man to be overlooked by those around him. His very stature would draw attention to him even if his male magnetism didn't. Thus Sabrina knew she was the object of many people's interest and curiosity, especially once they saw the cane on her arm, because she was in his company.

Several people acquainted with Bay stopped,

politely including her in their greeting. Bay did not encourage conversation with anyone and they gradually drifted away after the initial exchange. Sabrina wasn't certain whether it was because he was aware of her uneasiness with strangers or because he was self-conscious that she was blind. The last didn't seem to fit with his nature and she dismissed it.

'Bay Cameron!' an older woman greeted him effusively. Unconsciously Sabrina edged closer to be nearer his protection. 'I haven't seen you in ages!' the woman exclaimed. 'Where have you been keeping yourself? Is this the little lady I have to blame for your absence?'

His hand moved to rest on the back of Sabrina's shoulders, drawing her slightly forward as he introduced her. 'Pamela, I'd like you to meet Sabrina Lane. Sabrina, this is a very dear friend of mine, Pamela Thyssen. She tends to be a bit overpowering and nosy, but she has a gentle heart.'

'Don't you believe him!' the woman commanded gruffly, a raspy edge to her otherwise cultured voice. 'My bite is every bit as bad as my bark, so beware, Miss Lane. It is "Miss" Lane, isn't it?'

'Do you see what I mean, Sabrina?' Bay chuckled. 'She's a nosy busybody.'

'Yes, it is Miss Lane,' Sabrina confirmed with a faint smile.

She was beginning to agree that Bay's description of Pamela Thyssen was correct. Although curious and forceful, underneath the woman seemed to be kind.

'We single women must stick together,' Pamela Thyssen averred. 'Not that I intend to remain single. I've outlived two husbands, and they always say the third time is a charm. And you, my dear, are you setting your cap for our Bay?'

Sabrina flushed deeply. 'Hardly, Mrs Thyssen,' she denied vigorously.

'I guess that puts you in your place, Bay!' the woman laughed loudly.

'She's a very independent young lady,' he agreed with faint amusement, yet she sensed an inner displeasure in his tone.

'I must get to know Sabrina better. Bring her to my party after the performance.' It was a command, not a request, and the older woman bade them goodbye before Sabrina could prompt Bay into a refusal.

'You aren't actually intending to go, are you?' she said in a half-demand when they were alone.

'Why not?' he countered smoothly. 'Pamela's parties are quiet ones and friendly.'

'I'm uncomfortable with a lot of strangers,' Sabrina answered defensively.

'It's about time you got over that,' Bay responded, the hand on her back prodding her into movement. 'Now we only have a few minutes to find our seats before the curtain goes up.'

CHAPTER SEVEN

Sabrina curled her fingers into the soft rabbit fur of her black evening jacket, pushing the collar around her neck. The corners of her mouth drooped downward in frustration as she nibbled at her sensitive lower lip. The closed window of the car did not completely block out the sound of other cars exiting the theatre lot.

'Why can't you take me home and go to the party by yourself?' The suggestion she made had a vaguely desperate ring to it.

'The invitation was for both of us,' Bay reminded her.

'Mrs Thyssen doesn't know me. She wouldn't even miss me if I wasn't there,' Sabrina reasoned.

'Yes, she will.' A smile lightened the firmness of his tone. 'Especially since you were the one who prompted her to extend the invitation.'

'I did no such thing!'

'Let me rephrase it,' he said patiently. 'It was after meeting you and having her curiosity aroused that she invited us to her party.'

'She never gave us a chance to say whether we could come or not. We could have made other plans for all she knows,' Sabrina argued.

'But we don't have other plans, do we? There isn't any reason why we can't go to her party for a short while.'

'I don't want to go. That's a good enough reason for me.' Her chin jutted out defiantly.

'No, it isn't,' Bay replied in a voice that said he would not be swayed by any more arguments.

'You're a bully, Bay Cameron!' Sabrina accused lowly, slumping in her seat.

'A gentle one, I hope,' he chuckled softly.

'A bully,' she repeated with no qualifying adjectives.

Bridling at the way Bay had manoeuvred her again into a situation not of her choosing, Sabrina couldn't concentrate on the direction they were taking. She lost track of the turns and eventually stopped guessing what streets they were on. The absence of any heavy traffic indicated a residential area, but she had no idea what section of the city they were in.

The car slowed down and turned into the kerb. 'Here we are,' Bay announced, switching off the motor and opening his door.

Sabrina said nothing, sitting in mutinous silence as the door opened and closed on his side. In her mind, she watched him walk around the car to her door, judging almost to the second when he opened her door. Stubbornly she didn't move.

'Are you coming in with me or are you going to sit in the car and sulk like a little child?' Bay mocked softly.

'If I have a choice, I'll stay in the car,' she declared coldly.

'Sabrina.' His sighing voice held indulgent patience in its gentle tone. 'Are you really going to let some strangers intimidate you into staying in the car?'

'They don't intimidate me.'

118

'You're afraid to go in. What other word fits?'

'I'm not afraid,' Sabrina asserted forcefully.

'Of course not,' Bay agreed in a deliberately disbelieving voice.

'I'm not!' she repeated angrily.

'Whatever you say,' he agreed again with the same inflection. 'If you're going to stay in the car, I suggest you lock all the doors. I'll be gone about an hour.'

'You're not really leaving me here?' Sabrina frowned, tipping her head back, not certain any more if he was teasing or serious.

'You said you'd rather stay in the car,' Bay reminded her complacently. 'I'll put in my appearance and explain why you couldn't come.'

'You wouldn't dare tell Mrs Thyssen that I'm sitting out here in the car?' she breathed. But her question was only met with silence, a silence that held an affirmative answer. 'You're completely without scruples,' she grumbled, turning to slide her feet out of the car, his hand reaching out for her arm to guide her safely to the sidewalk.

A maid admitted them into the house. The sound of warm, friendly voices filled the foyer entrance. It seemed to come from several directions, indicating that the party was larger than the small gathering that had been Sabrina's impression.

With her evening jacket in the maid's possession, Bay took her arm and led her in the direction where the majority of voices seemed to be coming from. Her mouth tightened into a grim line.

'Smile.' Bay's order was whispered near her ear.

119

'No.' But the severe displeasure of her expression lessened.

Sabrina was unaware of the faintly regal tilt of her head, accenting the swanlike column of her neck as they entered the room. Her queenly posture and the softly moulding flame-coloured gown drew as much attention to her as was given to Bay. Since he was acquainted with most of the people there, the expressions of greeting were offered to him.

Stubbornly Sabrina didn't acknowledge any of them. Only the white knuckles of the hand clutching the ivory cane revealed the inner tremblings she felt at being in a roomful of strangers.

From their right, the instantly recognisable voice of Mrs Pamela Thyssen called out to them. 'Bay— Sabrina! I'm so glad you could come.'

Sabrina's greeting when the woman was beside them consisted of only a polite 'hello'. She did not intend to lie by saying that she was glad to be there.

Bracelets jangled from the older woman's wrist. The hand that grasped Sabrina's free hand was heavy with rings, small and large. Her perfume was a comfortable, old-fashioned scent of violets.

'Bay, be a dear,' Pamela Thyssen commanded. 'Go and fetch Sabrina and me a drink. I'll take my usual and bring Sabrina the same.'

'Really, Mrs Thyssen,' Sabrina started her protest, but Bay had already moved away from her side, 'I don't care for anything to drink.'

'Neither do I. My usual happens to be iced tea,' the woman murmured in a confidential aside. 'That's a little secret between you and me. A hostess is expected to drink at her own parties or the guests

120

don't feel free to imbibe. Iced tea looks sufficiently like drink to make the others feel at ease. So relax, my dear, I shan't attempt to free your tongue with intoxicating beverages.'

'I doubt if you could,' Sabrina answered almost beneath her breath.

'You have spirit. I like that,' Pamela pronounced. 'I'm Bay's godmother. Did he tell you?'

'No.' Was that the reason for the woman's apparent curiosity about her? Sabrina wondered to herself.

'His parents are in Europe on a second honeymoon. Louise, that's Bay's mother, and I grew up together. We've always been very close friends.'

'He mentioned they were in Europe,' she confirmed, since there seemed little other comment she could offer.

'I've been admiring your cane. It is ivory, isn't it?' There was no pause for a reply. 'It's a beautiful piece of workmanship, and so elegant as well. Where did you ever find it?'

'It was a gift—from a friend,' Sabrina added after a second's hesitation. Bay could tell the woman himself if he wanted her to know it was from him.

'A special friend?' the woman queried in a prompting way.

'A friend,' was the only explanation Sabrina offered.

'How long have you been blind, Sabrina?'

'Almost a year.' Her chin lifted fractionally as if to say she did not want any probing questions into her past.

'And how long have you known Bay?'

'About two months. Mrs Thyssen——' Sabrina began, taking a deep breath in the hopes of switching the conversation to some other topic less personal, hopefully without offending the other woman.

'Speak of the devil,' Pamela Thyssen murmured, cutting her off in midsentence. 'That didn't take you very long, Bay. Thank you.'

The clink of rings against a glass accompanied the words. In the next instant, Bay's voice said, 'Here you are, Sabrina,' and a cold glass was placed in her outstretched hand. 'How have you two been getting along while I've been gone? I see by the queenly tilt of Sabrina's nose that you must have been prying already, Pamela.'

'Not prying, Bay,' Pamela corrected with a laugh. 'I was merely trying to find out more about her.' In absent musing, she added, 'She does have a queenly air about her, doesn't she?'

'Please, I——' Sabrina started another protest, but it wasn't allowed to be completed either.

'——don't like to be talked about as if you weren't here,' Pamela Thyssen finished the sentence. 'I know very well what you mean and despise it myself. But it was meant as a compliment. Sabrina and I don't need a referee, Bay. Why don't you go and circulate or something? Let me have her for an hour. I'll take care of her.'

Sabrina turned in Bay's direction, her lips parting in a silent plea for him not to desert her. For a fleeting second she thought he was going to debate the other woman's request.

'You're in good hands, Sabrina,' he said quietly. 'Pamela won't let you fall. I'll see you later on.'

The line of her mouth thinned angrily as he moved away. First he manoeuvred her into coming to this party attended by strangers, then he deserted her! Irritation seethed beneath the surface at her inability to escape from the situation on her own. Independence could only be attained to a certain point, after that she was at the mercy of those around her.

'Come, my dear,' Pamela Thyssen hooked her arm in Sabrina's, 'I want to introduce you around. I try to choose my friends carefully, so with luck we'll avoid meeting any snobs.'

Gritting her teeth silently, Sabrina was practically forced to accompany her hostess. The following flurry of introductions and new voices were difficult to assimilate and put the correct name to the appropriate voice.

There was not one condescending remark or patronising comment regarding her blindness. The main topic of conversation was the performance that evening. Several of the people she met had seen her at the theatre and enquired about her opinion. Everyone's interest in her seemed to be friendly without pitying overtones. Gradually Sabrina's defensive attitude relaxed.

'Tommy, why don't you let Sabrina sit in that love-seat with Mrs Phillips?' Pamela Thyssen suggested in the firmly ordering tone. 'The armrest is just to your left, dear.'

The glass of tea, empty now, was taken from her hand as the searching tip of her cane found the front edge of the small sofa. Willingly Sabrina sat down. The obstacle course of strange names and voices was

123

beginning to tire her and she guessed that the astute Pamela Thyssen had sensed it. She conceded, but only to herself, that Bay had been right when he said he was leaving her in good hands.

'That's an absolutely stunning dress you're wearing, Miss Lane,' the woman at her side stated, obviously the Mrs Phillips that Pamela had mentioned. 'I noticed it in the theatre.'

The compliment was followed by the woman's lengthy dissertation on the difficulty she had finding clothes to fit her properly and how uncomplimentary the present styles were to her figure. Sabrina listened, inserting a monosyllablic answer when she thought one was required but letting the other woman carry the conversation.

The sensitive area on the back of her neck began to tingle. Sabrina instantly guessed the cause. Bay Cameron had to be somewhere near. Her radar was seldom wrong where he was concerned. Pretending a concentration on the woman speaking to her, she strained her hearing to catch any sound that might pinpoint his location.

Then came the husky caressing sound of a feminine voice, vaguely familiar although Sabrina couldn't place it. 'Bay darling, I didn't expect to see you here.'

'It's a surprise running into you, too,' she heard Bay answer calmly. 'I thought you didn't care for Pamela's parties. They were much too tame for you.'

'A girl can change her mind, can't she, darling?' the voice purred.

'And a man can always wonder why?' Bay countered.

'Actually a little bird saw you at the theatre to-night and passed the word on to me. I took a guess that you might bring your little sparrow to Pamela's party.'

'Did you?' was his noncommittal reply.

'I don't think I'll ever understand that streak of charity you possess, Bay,' the silky feminine voice said. 'I mean, why do you have to take such a personal interest in the poor girl? Why can't you simply give her a bunch of money and be done with her? You certainly can afford it.'

Sabrina stiffened. She couldn't help it. The only saving grace in the whole situation was that she doubted anyone possessed the acute hearing that blindness had given her and Bay's conversation with the woman wasn't being overheard by anyone but herself.

'Would that be your solution, Roni?' he murmured in a low voice. 'Sometimes I think when they were handing out compassion, you went back to the line marked "passion".'

Roni. That was the name of the girl who had been with him that one day at the Yacht Harbour. Sabrina also remembered that Bay had said they were going to take in an ocean sunset, a romantic offer if she had ever heard one.

'Is it so bad,' the woman named Roni was speaking again, 'to be passionate, Bay?' Her voice was a caressing whisper that Sabrina could barely understand.

'Not in certain situations.' He sounded amused as if he was remembering times when he had not felt the need to criticise Roni's passion. Sabrina's blood started to boil, temper bubbling hotly to her nerve ends.

'Tell me, darling,' Sabrina had the impression that the girl moved closer to Bay in an intimately confiding manner, 'you aren't trying to use that blind girl to make me jealous. Isn't that just a little ridiculous?'

'Why? She's a very attractive girl,' Bay stated, without denying the charge.

'But she's blind,' Roni reminded him. 'I know you must feel sorry for her. We all feel pity for those less fortunate than ourselves, but how cruel it must be for the girl when she eventually discovers that all the attention you've been giving her is because of pity. I don't think she'll thank you.'

'Knowing Sabrina, she would probably slap my face if——' Bay drawled.

But Sabrina didn't listen to the rest of his statement. She had heard enough. Her stomach was twisted into knots of tortuous pain. A black nausea attacked her head, swirling in sickening circles as she rose to her feet, unmindful of Mrs Phillips' continuing voice.

'Excuse me,' she interrupted sharply. 'Mrs Thyssen?' Her questing voice searched for the location of her hostess somewhere nearby.

'Yes, Sabrina.' Pamela Thyssen was instantly at her side, a curious note in the voice that answered her summons.

Sabrina swallowed, trying to calm her screeching nerves and make her voice sound as natural as possible. 'Would you please direct me to your powder room?'

126

'Of course. It's this way. Come with me.' A ringed hand guided her from the small group. 'Are you all right, Sabrina?' Pamela Thyssen asked in a concerned tone. 'You look pale. Are you quite sure you're feeling all right?' her hostess repeated.

'Quite sure,' Sabrina forced a smile of assurance.

Free of much of the party, they turned into what Sabrina guessed was a hallway. Her nerves were raw. The voices in the other rooms seemed to take on a higher pitch. Although she tried desperately, she couldn't block her hearing.

'Here we are,' Pamela stated. 'The door is directly to your left.'

Sabrina stopped, letting her cane determine the distance to the door before she turned to her hostess. 'Thank you, Mrs Thyssen.'

'Would you like me to go in with you?' the woman offered hesitantly.

'No, that's not necessary.' Sabrina wanted solitude and quiet to get her chaotic senses back in order.

'I'll wait out here for you then.'

'No,' Sabrina refused swiftly, then drew a breath and made her voice sound calm. 'I can make it back on my own. I can't keep you from your guests. Just give me an idea of where I am and I'll find my way back. I'm really quite good at following directions.'

The older woman hesitated, then gave Sabrina a simple set of directions to follow back to the main party area. After thanking her, and assuring her again that she was all right, Sabrina walked unerringly to the door, aware that her hostess watched. Fortunately no one else was in the room and Sabrina had it to herself. The closed door reduced the voices to a low hum.

The exploring tip of her cane touched a chair leg. Sighing heavily, Sabrina sank on to the velvet cushion. A vanity table was in front of her and she rested her arms on its smooth top. But the silence didn't stop the racing of her mind.

She had always wondered—she had always questioned Bay's motive for seeing her. Secretly she had stopped believing it was because of pity. Bay had used the word compassion, but not even that less offensive word eased the stabbing hurt of the conversation she had overheard. And he was letting pity for her serve a twofold purpose. While he was charitably spending a night or two a week with Sabrina, he was trying to make this Roni jealous.

Her fingers balled into tight fists. Damn this acute hearing! She moaned silently. No, another voice inside remonstrated her, she should be glad she had discovered his real motive. She was lucky she had regarded him as nothing more than a friend and had found out the truth before she had begun to misinterpret his attention. How awful it would have been if she had started to care for him as a man!

The problem was—what was the next step? Should she confront him with what she had learned? That was what she wanted to do. She wanted to throw his charitable, pitying words in his face. But what good would that do? He would simply deny it as he had all the other times.

Bay Cameron was smooth and cannily intelligent —that was something Sabrina mustn't overlook. Look at the way he had manoeuvred her first into accepting the ivory cane she used, then going out to dinner at a public restaurant and finally coming here tonight to this party of strangers. Well, the last had backfired. Now Sabrina knew his true colours.

The door opened and a woman walked in. Her voice as she greeted Sabrina was familiar, but she couldn't recall the woman's name. Self-consciously Sabrina smoothed the back of her hair, pretending that she was in front of the vanity table checking her appearance. With fingers crossed, she hoped the woman wouldn't tarry long. Unfortunately she did, and each passing second ticked loudly in Sabrina's head.

At last Sabrina knew she couldn't stay any longer without arousing suspicion. She had already been in the room a considerable time. She didn't want Mrs Thyssen sending a search party for her. If only she could slip away from the house she wished as she rose to her feet. She didn't want to go back to the party. It was taking on the overtones of a nightmare.

But where would she go? she asked herself, pushing open the door to the hall. Even if she could sneak away unseen, there was little likelihood there would be a taxi cab cruising in this residential neighbourhood. She doubted very much if she could hold her tongue during the long ride home with Bay.

Not concentrating on where she was going, she bumped into a small table sitting against the wall of the hallway. Instinctively her hand reached out to prevent whatever was on the table from falling to the floor. A vase had started to tip, but she set it upright again. As she started to withdraw her hand, her fingers encountered a familiarly smooth object —the receiver of a telephone.

There was the answer! Not caring who might be observing her action, Sabrina picked up the receiver, her fingers quickly dialling Information and requesting the number of a taxi company. Without allowing any time for second thoughts, she dialled the number given her.

When the phone was answered on the other end, Sabrina said quietly, 'Would you please send a cab to——' She stopped. She didn't know where she was. Footsteps were approaching. 'Just a moment,' she requested the man on the other end of the line to wait. Taking a deep breath, she turned to the person coming nearer. She had to take a chance. 'Excuse me, please, but would you tell me what the address is here?'

'Yes, ma'am,' a courteous female voice replied, and gave her the address.

The studied politeness of the woman's voice prompted Sabrina to ask, 'Are—are you the maid?'

'Yes, ma'am,' the woman answered in a voice that said she had noticed the white cane in Sabrina's hand.

'Would you bring me my jacket? It's a black rabbit fur,' Sabrina requested.

'Right away, ma'am.'

At the departing footsteps, Sabrina removed her hand from the mouthpiece and gave the address to the man patiently waiting on the other end. He promised only a few minutes' wait. With the receiver safely in its cradle, Sabrina turned away from the table. The smell of success was intoxicatingly near.

Footsteps approached again from the direction the maid had taken. Sabrina could not tell if it was the maid and she held her breath, fearful that at any second she would be discovered by Bay or Mrs Thyssen.

'Here you are, ma'am,' the maid spoke. 'Shall I help you on with it?'

'Please,' Sabrina agreed nervously.

The maid deftly helped her into the fur jacket. 'Shall I let Mrs Thyssen know you're leaving?'

'No, that won't be necessary. I've already spoken to her,' she lied hurriedly. 'The cab will be here any minute. I'll wait outside. The front door, is it straight ahead down this hall?'

'Yes, ma'am,' the maid acknowledged. 'But the fog is rather thick tonight. It would be best to wait inside.'

'I'd prefer the fresh air. The smoke has got a bit thick in here.' She didn't want to risk being discovered when she was so near her goal.

'Very well, ma'am,' the maid submitted, and silently withdrew.

As quickly as her searching cane would permit, Sabrina travelled the length of the hallway to the front door. Her palms were perspiring with excitement as she opened the front door and stepped into the night.

The cool air was a soothing balm to her taut nerve ends. She moved away from the door, seeking the shadows she knew would be at the side of the entrance. The damp fog was heavy against her face.

The thick walls of the house shut out the noise within. The sleeping night was profoundly still.

A smile turned up the corners of her wide mouth as she imagined Bay's confusion when he discovered she was gone. His overworked sense of pity would have him concerned for her safety, but she knew it wouldn't be long before the maid would be questioned. She would tell him that Sabrina had taken a taxi. He would be angry, but at this point Sabrina didn't care. Whatever debt she might have thought she owed him for his assistance and supposed friendship had been paid in full tonight.

Time went by slowly, but it always seemed to double its length when she was waiting anxiously for something. Sabrina remained in the shadows, hopefully concealed from anyone who might decide to leave the party early. Finally the steady growl of a car motor sounded down the street. She waited to see if it stopped at this house or continued past. It halted at the kerb and a car door slammed.

As she stepped from the shadows, a man's voice asked curtly, 'Did you call for a cab, lady?'

'Yes, I did.' She walked as swiftly as she could towards him, victory lightening her step. A car door opened. She used the sound to judge the distance. The man's hand took her elbow to help her into the rear of the cab. 'I want you to take me to——'

Sabrina never got the address of her home out. The front door of the house opened and the hairs on the back of her neck stood out, freezing her muscles into immobility. She had nearly made it.

Maybe she still could. There wasn't much time.

Bay's long strides were already eating up the distance from the front door to the taxi.

As she tried to slip into the rear seat, an arm circled her waist, a hand spreading across the flat of her stomach and drawing her back to the sidewalk.

'Let me go!' She struggled against the steel band that held her mercilessly.

'Be still, Sabrina,' Bay ordered, only tightening his hold. There was the crisp sound of money being removed from his pocket. 'I'm sorry you were called out unnecessarily,' he was talking to the cab driver. 'I'll see her home.'

'I don't want to go with you,' she protested vigorously. The driver had not moved, and there was a chance he could be an ally. 'Please, tell this man to leave me alone.'

'Will you stop involving others in our quarrels?' Bay demanded curtly. The implication of his demand was that they were having a little spat, a ruse on Bay's part to assure the driver that his assistance was not really needed.

There was a crisp exchange of money before the man wished Bay good luck and Sabrina knew her means of escape was lost. For a deflated moment she stopped struggling to free herself from Bay's pinning grip while the cab driver closed the rear door and walked around to the other side.

Turning her at right angles, his hand shifted to the side of her waist as he forced her to walk away from the departing taxi. Bay did not lead her back to the house but towards his car parked at the kerb some distance down the street.

'Would you like to explain to me what's going

133

on?' he requested grimly in a voice that was not at all amused.

'Surely it's obvious. I was going home,' Sabrina retorted.

'If you wanted to leave, why didn't you look for me? I never said we had to stay at the party until the last minute.' His fingers were biting into the soft flesh of her waist.

'I didn't want *you* to take me home, that's why!' she snapped.

'Then you should have left your cane behind. Maybe no one would have noticed you leaving if it hadn't been for that little white stick!' He was angry. It vibrated through his tautly controlled voice.

'If I'd given it a thought, I would have.' She refused to be intimidated by his tightly held temper.

'And why, after all this time, would you suddenly not want me to take you home?' Bay demanded.

'I don't need a reason,' Sabrina answered haughtily.

'Yes, you do, and before this night is out, I'm going to hear it,' he informed her with unrelenting arrogance.

Sabrina stopped shortly and Bay did likewise. 'Maybe I'm tired of your pity and your patronising attitude!' she challenged boldly, tilting her head so he could see the dislike in her expression. 'I don't need you or anybody else to feel sorry for me!'

'What?' She could sense his frowning alertness.

'Go and join the Boy Scouts!' Her voice grew shrill. 'I'm tired of your good deeds!' There was a traitorous quiver of her chin.

'Pity! Is that what you think I feel?' The accusation exploded around her.

Sabrina opened her mouth to retaliate, and in the next instant she was jerked against him. The violence of his action sent her cane clattering on to the sidewalk. An arm curved punishingly between her shoulder blades. His hand gripped the back of her neck, forcing her head back while he drew her on to tiptoes.

Her startled cry was smothered by his hard mouth. Roughly, almost savagely he kissed her, not allowing her to draw a breath as he ground her lips against her teeth.

An elemental tension crackled in the air when he raised his head. His hands moved, closing over the slender bones of her shoulders, keeping Sabrina in front of him.

'You're a brute and a bully, Bay Cameron!' The hissing accusation was offered between gasps for air.

'Then I might as well be hanged for a sinner as a saint!' The harsh words carried the steel edge of sarcasm.

Again he gathered her to his chest, pinning her against the rock wall while the muscles in his arms rippled around her. Sabrina had not recovered from the brutal pressure of his first kiss when she was punished by the second. She strained against him weakly, her strength ebbing from the riptide of his embrace.

As her resistance faded, an angry passion was transmitted to her by his demanding lips. A feverish warmth enveloped her and unwillingly her flesh began to respond to the hard, commanding mouth that possessed hers.

Mindlessly her hands stopped pushing against him and her fingers curled into the lapels of his jacket. Through the rainbow explosion of her senses, Sabrina realised she was falling victim to the very virility she had warned herself against.

As suddenly as it all began, it ended with Bay firmly holding her an arm's length away. Her equilibrium was completely gone. Up was down and down was up. It was a topsy-turvy world, this midnight velvet blackness she lived in. And it was because of Bay and his punishing embrace.

'Get in the car!' The harsh command was like a physical slap in the face.

But even the abrupt jolt to reality couldn't prod Sabrina into movement. Finally Bay dragged, carried, and shoved her into the passenger seat. Her voice didn't return until he was behind the wheel and driving the car away from the kerb.

'Bay——' Her weak voice was barely above a whisper.

'Shut up, Sabrina.' The terse, grating tone of his voice indicated that the words were drawn through clenched jaw. 'Maybe when I can think clearly, I'll be able to offer an apology. Right now all I want to do is wring your bloody neck!'

CHAPTER EIGHT

OBEYING his command, Sabrina had not spoken during that tense ride to her home. She had been too frightened to speak—not because she had thought he would carry out his threat or that he would subject her again to the punishment of his kisses. Sabrina had been frightened by herself. For a few fleeting moments in his arms, she had not been a blind woman, only a woman.

Her bruised mouth had retained the burning fire of his hard, demanding kiss. The racing of her heart had kept pounding in her ears as if she were on a runaway locomotive that she couldn't jump off. The impression of those muscled arms that had locked her in his embrace had still been felt.

Her breast and hips had remembered the solid rock pressure of his chest and thighs, implanting the hard male outline of his body so firmly in her mind that Sabrina thought she would never be able to up-root it. The scent of his maleness and spicy cologne had clung to her skin. Nothing had seemed to remove it.

What was worse, she didn't want to erase any-thing. That was why she was still frightened two days after the fact. Over and over again she had asked herself why he had kissed her that way.

Had the brutally volatile embrace been prompted by anger that she had found out his true motive? Could he have used her as an outlet for frustration because his plan to make the girl Roni jealous had failed? In view of the conversation she had over-heard, that was the most likely explanation. Probably it was a combination of several things.

Sabrina would not consider the possibility that Bay had been prompted by any physical desire for her. Not that she believed that there would not be a time when she would meet some man who truly loved and wanted her. But visualising Bay Cameron as that man was something she could not do. He had position, wealth, charm, and looks. There were too many other women he could have at his side in an intimate sense.

Her blindness had touched him. It didn't matter which noun was used to identify the emotion he felt —pity, compassion, sympathy. They were all one in the same thing.

Pain gnawed at her heart. Pride said that she couldn't regard Bay as a friend any longer. A true friend might commiserate, but he would never seek her company because he felt sorry for her. But Sabrina's heart honestly acknowledged the main reason why she must reject him. She was the one who had stopped regarding him as a friend and had started thinking of him as a man. For her, that was dangerously foolish.

A sob rasped her throat, choking her with its futility. Sabrina buried her face in her hands, letting the misery wash over her. For a little time in the solitude of this afternoon, she would feel sorry for herself and not regret it. She had earned the right.

Before the first tear slipped from her brown eyes,

the telephone rang. 'No!' Sabrina denied its call softly. But it persisted.

The urge was there to ignore it, to let it ring until the person on the other end gave up. Grimacing at the possibility that it was her father, she knew she had no right to cause him unnecessary concern. Reluctantly she rose to her feet and walked to the telephone.

'Lane residence,' she answered in a pseudo-calm voice.

'Sabrina.'

The sound of Bay's low husky voice nearly made her drop the telephone. It was as if a bolt of lightning had struck her. A weakness quaked her knees and she quickly sought the support of a chair.

'Are you there, Sabrina?' his frowning voice asked when she failed to reply immediately.

'Yes, hello, Bay.' Her reply was strained and unnatural, but it didn't matter any more.

'How are you?' It was not a casual question. There was too much guarded alertness in his tone.

'Fine. And you?' She was purposely distant and polite.

Bay ignored her aloof enquiry. 'You know why I've called, don't you?'

'How could I possibly know that?' Sabrina asked with cutting disinterest.

'Would you have dinner with me Saturday night?' A grimness changed the invitation into a challenge.

But Sabrina had guessed that if Bay did make any conciliatory gesture as he had indicated he might, it would be wrapped in a suggestion for a Saturday night date. She realised now that he always chose Saturday night because that was the evening her father devoted exclusively to Deborah and Sabrina spent it alone—at least, she had for the most part before she met Bay. Yesterday she had invited an old girl-friend, Sally Goodwin, over on Saturday night.

'I've already made other plans,' she answered truthfully and a shade triumphantly.

'You have?' The mocking inflection doubted her statement.

'I do know other people besides you, Bay,' she retorted.

A tired yet angry sigh came over the wire. 'May I take a guess that you *arranged* to be busy on Saturday night?'

'You may guess if you want,' she shrugged, neither affirming nor denying.

'May I also guess that because of my—indiscretion the other night, you've decided not to see me again?' He didn't let her reply. 'You didn't make any allowances for the possibility that I might have had the right to lose my temper because you walked out without even having the courtesy to leave a message that you were leaving? I probably should have turned you over my knee, but the other seemed more appropriate at the time.'

There was some validity to his argument, but Sabrina was not going to allow herself to be swayed. 'It's done. There isn't any point in discussing it.'

'Then that's your decision. You aren't going to see me again,' Bay stated with almost arrogant blandness. 'Those few moments of my anger wiped out all the memories of the hours, enjoyable hours I thought, that we spent together before, is that right? They mean nothing to you?'

His challenge had to be answered. 'Yes, they did,' Sabrina admitted coldly, 'until they were tarnished by the discovery that you felt sorry for me. I told you once I don't need anyone's pity.'

'Who in their right mind would feel sorry for a pigheaded, spoiled brat like you?' he snapped. He drew a deep, calming breath. 'There are times, Sabrina, when you test a man's patience. How many times do I have to tell you that I don't feel sorry for you before you'll believe me?'

'Then explain to me why you see me,' she demanded defiantly.

'There has to be an ulterior motive, is that it?' Bay answered grimly. 'It can't be because I might' —he paused an instant, choosing his words—'admire you, your courage when you aren't being unreasonable stubborn. Let me put the question to you. Why do you go out with me? Am I a convenient means to get out of the house? Do you simply tolerate me because I take you places you want to go? What's your ulterior motive, Sabrina?'

'I ... I have none,' she answered, taken aback by his counter-attack.

'Come now. Surely you must,' he mocked derisively. 'You had to have a reason for going out with me.'

'No, I don't,' Sabrina insisted in helpless confusion. 'I simply enjoyed it. I had——'

Bay interrupted. 'Yet it's inconceivable that I might have simply enjoyed your company, too?'

'How could you?' she protested, seeking to regain the offensive. 'I'm pigheaded and spoiled. You said so yourself.'

'So? I'm arrogant and a bully. You said so yourself.' He deflected her argument with mocking humour. 'That makes us equal with two flaws a piece.'

The corners of her mouth twitched in reluctant amusement. Her stand against him was weakening. She could feel the firm resolve crumbling under his persuasive charm and logic.

'You're smiling, aren't you, Sabrina?' he accused softly. 'Don't bother to answer,' Bay chuckled. 'I know you'll deny it. I won't ask you to cancel your well-laid plans for Saturday night but come sailing with me Sunday.'

'Sailing?' she echoed weakly. Of all the invitations Bay could have extended, her own love of the sport made this one she wanted least to refuse.

'Yes, sailing,' he repeated with amused patience.

'I——' Sabrina couldn't get the words of refusal to come out.

'I'll pick you up bright and early Sunday morning around seven. We'll spend the day.'

'I ... I'll be ready.' Her words of acceptance stumbled over each other in their rush to get out before better judgment decreed that she changed her mind.

'At seven Sunday a.m.,' Bay agreed, and hung up as if he had the same thought.

Sabrina didn't change her mind. She had a multitude of second thoughts, but none of them had lasted long enough to bring her to the point of cancelling. Any thought that her father might take the decision out of her hands had ended the same day Bay had called.

When she had told her father of Bay's invitation that evening, his reply had been: 'Yes, Bay called me this afternoon to be certain I had no objections. I don't, and I promise you I won't worry. You'll be in good hands. Besides, Bay can swim.'

Sunday morning, therefore, found Sabrina aboard his trim ketch *Dame Fortune*. Fog and dormant wind had delayed their departure for nearly an hour.

Now they were under sail, the stiff breeze ruffling the scarf tied around Sabrina's head, the salty taste of ocean spray on her lips. Passing under the rust-orange span of the Golden Gate Bridge, Bay had turned southward into the open sea, past Cliff House and Seal Rocks. He continued beyond the ocean beaches, the treacherous undertow in the area restricting their use to sunbathing and walking.

As always, Sabrina champed at the constricting life-vest tied around her even while she accepted the wisdom of the precaution whether for sighted or unsighted boaters. The deck was slanted sharply beneath her, heaving with each ocean swell, as Bay expertly took advantage of all the wind he could and still remain on course.

The billowing wind in the canvas, the ocean waves slapping the sleek hull, and the comfortable groans of a sailing ketch at sea were the only sounds around her. She had hardly exchanged five words with Bay since they had left the Yacht Harbour. Conversation wasn't necessary and would have been superfluous to the serene beauty of the moment.

Each seemed to sense the other's deep pleasure and nothing needed to be said.

It was some time before Sabrina noticed there had been a change in their course. The sun was not in the place it normally would have been in their initial heading. Blocking out the song of sea and sail, she listened intently, trying to gauge by memory and sound their location and failing.

She turned to Bay. 'Where are we?'

'In the waters of Monterey Bay near Santa Cruz. Were you daydreaming?' he smiled with his voice.

Instantly she visualised his ruggedly forceful features, tanned by the sun and the wind, cinnamon brown hair dampened by the salt spray and tousled by the breeze. The sun was directly overhead. His light brown eyes would be narrowed against its brilliance, crinkled at the corners because of that flashing smile she had detected in his voice. It was disturbing how vividly clear her picture of him was, so vitally alive and masculine.

Her heart beat a rapid tattoo against her ribs. 'Daydreaming or sea-dreaming, I don't know which,' she murmured.

Again there was a change in the motion of the ketch. The wind was catching less canvas and their speed had decreased. The deck beneath her had begun to right itself.

'What are you doing now?' Sabrina asked.

'Taking her in close to shore. We just passed the natural bridges north of Santa Cruz. I thought we'd anchor south of Santa Cruz for lunch. There's a small quiet cove I know about that I hope no one else has discovered.'

Once anchored, with Sabrina giving what assistance she could, the only sound was the gentle lapping of the almost calm surf against the hull. She turned her head enquiringly towards Bay and felt his gaze moving over her face. A fiery warmth started in her midsection. She was suddenly and intensely aware that they were alone, the two of them, a man and a woman. She put brakes to that thought sharply.

'I'll go below and fix lunch.' She pivoted abruptly away. 'What are we having?'

'Sandwiches, salad and the like. It's all fixed,' Bay answered. 'What about a swim before we eat? The water is warmer here than up the coast and there aren't any dangerous undercurrents.'

'Sorry,' Sabrina shrugged away his suggestion nervously. 'You didn't warn me to bring a swimming suit and I didn't.'

'That doesn't matter.' Bay dismissed her excuse. 'I always keep a few swimming clothes on board in case there's a spur-of-the-moment decision by one of my guests to take a dip in the ocean. I'm sure one of them will fit you.'

'But——' She hadn't been in any water other than her bathtub since before the accident.

'But what?' he prompted. 'You can swim, can't you?'

'Yes, I can swim,' she swallowed tightly.

'I'll point you in the right direction so you won't head out to sea if you're worrying about losing your reference points. Go and change.'

He told her which locker he kept the spare swimming suits and Sabrina went below. It was better to go swimming with the wide limits of the ocean and shore than remain on the small deck alone with him.

Most of the swimsuits were two-piece outfits, some bare triangles of cloth. Sabrina chose the close-fitting knit of a one-piece with diamond cut-outs at the waist crisscrossed with ties. At least in it she felt less naked when she walked up on deck. Her long hair was let down and curling around her shoulders. The water would have pulled it free of its knot eventually, so she had done it first.

'I'm ready,' she said nervously.

Bay didn't comment on her appearance. 'I've put a rope ladder over the side.' He took her hand and led her to the rail. 'I'll go in the water first.'

When he released her hand after her silent nod of agreement, Sabrina tightened the hand into a fist to retain the warmth of his touch a while longer. It was a stupid thing to do. This was not a romantic outing but a friendly one—which was why the sensations she was feeling were troubling her.

The deck rocked slightly, followed by the sound of something slicing into the water, and Sabrina knew that Bay had not used the ladder but had dived into the water. A second later she heard him surface, turning her head in the direction of the sound. A few clean strokes brought him to the bottom of the ladder.

'Come on in. The water's fine,' he called to her.

While Bay held the ladder steady, Sabrina started down, her toes feeling for the rope rungs. In the water which was neither warm nor cold, Sabrina clung to the security of the ladder for a few minutes, adjusting to the eerie sensation of having nothing

146

solid beneath her feet. The chattering of her teeth was from nerves and not the tepidly cool water.

'Are you ready?' Bay was still beside the ladder.

'I think so,' Sabrina answered, clenching her jaw so he wouldn't hear the clatter of her teeth.

He moved a few strokes from the ladder, then said, 'Swim towards my voice.'

Forcing her hand to release its death-grip on the rope, Sabrina took a deep breath and struck out towards him. At first she was hampered by nervousness and unco-ordination, but they soon faded as she became accustomed to watery environment. She could hear Bay's firm cleaving strokes keeping pace beside her and drew strength and assurance from his presence.

It seemed as if they had been swimming a long time. Sabrina had begun to get tired. Her reaching arms were beginning to feel heavy. She stopped to tread water and catch her breath, and Bay did the same.

'How much farther?' she asked as she swallowed down gulps of air.

'About another fifteen feet before we can touch bottom.' He sounded not at all out of breath. 'Can you make it?'

She didn't answer but started out again, maintaining a slow steady rhythm that would not wear her out too quickly. Surprisingly it didn't seem as if she had travelled any distance at all before a kicking foot scraped the sandy bottom. Sabrina righted herself quickly, wiping the salt water from her face and tucking her long wet hair behind her ears.

'You made it,' Bay spoke from somewhere near her left side. 'How do you feel?'

She smiled faintly. 'Exhausted, but good otherwise.'

'Let's go ashore and take a breather.'

Her hands were lightly resting on top of the almost chest-high water, letting the gentle swells roll over them. The waves would have told her which way the shore was if she had been in doubt, but Bay took her hand anyway and led her to the beach.

'This beach comes equipped with its own sunning rock,' he said as they waded on to the sandy ground, smooth and firm beneath her feet. 'It's a little hard, but it's better than the sand when you don't have a towel.' The pressure of his hand stopped her after they had gone a few yards. 'Here it is.'

Before Sabrina could protest, his hands were around her waist and he was lifting her on to the hard, warm surface of the stone. Her own fingers had automatically gripped the sinewy wetness of his arms for balance. Her flesh burned where his hands had covered the open diamond patches of the swimsuit waistline. It was several seconds before her racing heart settled to a more respectable pace. By then he was on the rock, too.

'Did you have a good time last night?' he asked after he had moved into a comfortable position. He was sitting. Sabrina could tell by the direction of his voice.

'Last night?' she frowned, and shifted more fully on to the rock. Then she remembered. 'Yes, I did.' Actually it had been a quiet evening. She and Sally

148

had sat around and talked, listening to records part of the time.

'Where did you go?'

'Nowhere. Sally and I stayed at the house,' she shrugged, turning her face to the warmth of the sun, letting it chase away the shivers on her damp skin.

'An evening of gossipy girl-talk, is that it?' There was a mocking smile in his tone.

Sabrina wasn't certain whether he was laughing at her uneventful evening or that she had chosen it over one with him. From what she knew of Bay, the first seemed more likely.

'Men gossip as much as if not more than women,' she replied.

He didn't argue the point. 'I suppose it's true of an equal number in each sex.'

An awkward silence followed. At least it was awkward for Sabrina. She was too aware of Bay, physically aware of him. She leaned back on her hands.

'The sun feels good,' she suggested.

'I think I'll stretch out and enjoy it,' Bay stated.

At the same time that he spoke, his movements were carrying out his words. And the silence that Sabrina had not wanted reigned, broken only by the slow rush of the ocean on to shore. There was little for her to do except to follow suit.

Her searching hands found a small, elevated hump in the rock behind her, a natural headrest, and Sabrina lay down on her back. For a long time she listened to the sound of Bay's even breathing. Her own was shallow, her chest muscles constricted with tension. Finally the heat of the sun and the rock coaxed her into relaxing.

Sabrina didn't fall asleep, but she did drift into that strange state of half-sleep. She was aware of her surroundings and the man beside her, yet deaf to them at the same time. Then something brought all of her senses alert. Her eyes blinked uselessly as she tried to determine what had disturbed her. She turned her head slightly in Bay's direction and accidentally brushed his hand with her cheek. Then her sensitive nerve ends transmitted the message that he was holding a lock of her silky brown hair.

'Do you know this is the first time I've ever seen you wear your hair down?' he mused softly.

'I—I don't like to wear it down. It gets in the way.' There was an odd tremor in her voice as she guessed how close he was to her. She could almost feel the heat of his body stretched beside hers. His voice had come from a position slightly above her, indicating that he was possibly lying on his side, an elbow propping him up.

Bay didn't seem to pay any attention to her explanation.

'When you wear your hair up in that little topknot, you look poised and sophisticated, a well-bred young queen. With your hair down like this,' he twined the strand around his finger, 'there's a gamin vulnerability about you.'

A pulse was beating wildly in her temples. It was impossible to roll away from him. The edge of the rock was too near.

'Do you think we should be heading back?' Her throat was taut, making her voice likewise.

'What's the matter?' he mocked. 'Don't you like my comments on your hairstyle?'

'It doesn't matter.' Sabrina shook her head determinedly, loosing the lock of hair from his fingers and feeling it fall against her bare shoulder. 'I'm going to wear it up because it's the easiest to take care of, regardless of how you prefer it.' It was a challenging statement, but she didn't care.

Bay reached back and gave her hair a sharp tug. 'Then you'll probably be sorry to hear that I prefer that silky knot. The way it is now would be appropriate for the privacy of a bedroom.'

The sensual implication of his statement drew a sharp breath from Sabrina. Her heightened awareness of his masculinity made this type of conversation impossible. She wasn't capable of idle flirtation, this suggestive playing with words. She started to push herself back into a half-sitting position to escape his nearness, but Bay was already straightening to his feet.

'We'll head back,' he said as he towered above her.

Sabrina thankfully swung her legs to the edge of the rock. Bay was on the sand, his hands gripping her waist to lift her down before she could slide the short distance to the sand. Straining away from his unwanted assistance, her effort to keep from landing too close to him brought a heel down on a partially buried outcropping of the rock. The unexpected jarring pain sent her against his chest. His hold tightened to steady her.

'Are you all right?'

Her unspoken answer was negative. It couldn't be

otherwise when the nakedness of his muscled torso and thighs pressed against her was playing havoc with her heart. Soft, curling chest hairs sensually tickled her palms. His head was inclined towards her, warm breath stirring a wing of her dark fringe.

The desire was strong to slide her arms around his broad shoulders and nestle her head against his neck. To resist the nearly overpowering impulse, she moistened her lips nervously and tipped her head back.

'I'm all right,' she assured him in a shaking voice. 'I stepped on a rock or something.'

A sudden breath of wind tossed a thin lock of hair across her face. It clung to the gleaming wetness of her lips. Sabrina started to push it away, but her hand was only part way there when Bay's fingers drew it gently away, pushing it back with the rest of her long hair.

His hand remained along the side of her face, his thumb absently caressing her cheekbone. She held her breath, motion suspended under the magic spell of his touch.

The heady warmth of his firm mouth was barely felt against hers before Sabrina sharply twisted her head away. Her defences couldn't endure a casual kiss.

'Don't, Bay, please!' she requested stiffly.

'I wasn't going to hurt you.' Her words brought a rigid stillness to his touch as he misinterpreted the reason for the shudders quivering through her.

'I simply don't want you to kiss me,' Sabrina stated, pulling free of his unresisting arms and taking several quick steps away until common sense warned her that she couldn't see where she was going.

She wrapped her arms tightly around her, trying to fight off the chill that shivered over her where the warmth of his body had been.

Bay walked over to stand beside her. She could feel his eyes boring into her. Her lashes fluttered downward in case her sightless eyes mirrored the heady sensations swimming in her mind. For an electric moment, she hardly dared to breathe.

'We'd better head back to the boat.' The savage bite of his words betrayed a tightly leashed anger. Sabrina couldn't tell if it was directed at himself or at her.

The hand that gripped hers and led her towards the water was cold and impersonal. Sabrina was glad when the water became deep enough to swim and he had to release her. She hadn't thought it possible that his touch, which usually started a fire, could chill her to the bone.

It was not a leisurely swim back. Sabrina set herself a pace that took every ounce of her strength to maintain. It was a form of self-punishment for being so foolish as to let Bay persuade her to come on this outing when wisdom had dictated that she stop seeing him.

She was completely spent when Bay reached out and pulled her to the rope ladder, but she climbed aboard without his assistance. She paused on deck to catch her breath.

'If we'd been anchored another ten feet away, you would never have made it. What were you trying to prove?' Bay snapped.

'Nothing.' Sabrina averted her head and self-consciously felt her way to the steps leading below deck.

'When you're dressed, you can get the lunch ready. I think you can find everything. In the meantime, I'll get us under way,' he ordered tersely.

'Don't you ... Don't you want to eat first?' she faltered.

'I think we're both in a hurry to get back, aren't we?' There was a derisive challenge in his voice that dared her to deny it. When she didn't reply, he added grimly, 'I'll enjoy the food as much as you once we're under sail.'

Actually Sabrina found the food tasteless. Most of it wanted to stick in her throat, but she forced as much of it down as she could. There was no atmosphere of friendliness on the return trip. Their mutual silence was brittle with tension.

Bay's acceptance of her polite words of thanks at the conclusion of the day was as cool and aloof as her offer had been. When the iron gate closed behind him, Sabrina knew why she was so totally miserable. She had had plenty of time to ponder the reason on the way back. She had fallen in love with Bay Cameron. She was literally a blind fool.

CHAPTER NINE

BAY's last parting remark to her had been 'I'll call you'. In Sabrina's experience, those particular words had always signalled the end of a relationship. It was Friday night and he had not phoned.

Another tear slipped down her cheek. She wiped it away with her fingertips, leaving a streak of dark clay to smudge her face. Why couldn't her tearducts have been damaged as well as her eyesight? she wondered forlornly, then sighed. Perhaps it was better to have a way to release the pain.

There was a knock on the studio door. She had kept it closed this last week, not wanting anyone to pop in without at least the warning click of the doorknob. She had told her father it was because she wanted to block out any distractions. The truth was she could work in the middle of rush hour traffic. Lately, however, she had discovered herself simply standing and crying. It was this she didn't want her father or anyone else to see.

Sabrina took the hem of her smock and wiped her face carefully just in case there was a betraying tear she had missed. 'Come in,' she called in answer to the knock.

A cloud of perfume swirled into the room, a scent her mind labelled as Deborah's. The lightly graceful steps confirmed the identification.

'I came to remind you we would be leaving in an hour so you would have plenty of time to clean up here and change clothes,' her future stepmother said brightly.

'I don't think I'll go,' Sabrina murmured, centring her attention on the partially completed clay bust on the work pedestal.

'Grant has been looking forward to the three of us dining out tonight,' Deborah reminded her.

'I know, but I'd rather keep working a while longer. I'm right in the middle of this piece. I want to keep going while the concept is still fresh in my mind,' she lied.

'Are you sure?' came the slightly troubled question.

'I've just really grasped the form, and I don't want to lose it,' Sabrina assured her.

'I didn't mean about the work,' Deborah said hesitantly.

'What did you mean, then?' Her hand was poised along the half-formed ear of the bust. Was Deborah's womanly intuition at work?

'I ... I wanted to be sure you weren't refusing because of me. I don't want you to think you would be the superfluous third tonight,' the attractive redhead explained self-consciously.

'No, Deborah, it wasn't because of you.' Sabrina expelled a silent sigh of relief. 'We'll go out another night. I probably shouldn't have started this so late, but now that I have, I must work a little longer.'

'I understand. I know how important this is to you. And don't worry, Sabrina.' There was the warmth of a smile in her voice. 'I'll explain to Grant.'

'What were you going to explain to me?'

'Grant!' Deborah exclaimed in a startled voice. 'You shouldn't sneak up on a person like that.'

'I didn't sneak. You simply didn't hear me.' There was the faint sound of a kiss exchanged. 'Now, I repeat, what are you going to explain to me?'

Sabrina answered for Deborah. 'I've decided to stay and work tonight instead of going out to dinner with you two.'

'The two of us were going out to dinner with you, not the other way round,' her father frowned.

'Then we'll go out another night,' she shrugged, determined not to let him change her mind.

'No, we'll go out tonight.'

'Grant!' Deborah interjected a silent plea into his name.

'Dammit, she's working too hard, Deborah,' he declared forcefully. 'Look at the dark circles under her eyes and the hollows in her cheeks. She doesn't sleep. She doesn't eat. All she does is work from dawn to dusk, or more aptly midnight.'

'Dad, you're exaggerating,' Sabrina sighed. 'Besides, my work is important to me.' It was the only thing that kept her sanity. Without it, the emptiness of a life without Bay would be more than she could stand. 'I promise as soon as I can leave this piece I'm doing I'll fix myself something to eat and go straight to bed. How's that?'

'I think that's a fair bargain, don't you, Grant?' Deborah murmured.

'I——' He took a deep, angry breath, but arguing with the two women he loved was not something he enjoyed. He sighed heavily. 'All right,' he surrendered. 'You can stay home this time. But next week we're all going out together, with no excuses. Now, why don't you let me have a peep at this work of art that is too important to leave?'

Sabrina stepped to the side as he walked closer. 'I only have it roughed in right now. I'm doing the head and shoulders of Gino Marchetti as he was in his youth. Over a year ago, he showed me a picture taken at his wedding. I had intended to do a painting, but——' She left that unfinished for obvious reasons. 'He looked very Roman, very proud and very strong.'

'Gino, the druggist?' Grant Lane repeated with a hint of disbelief.

'It's only rough,' Sabrina defended.

There was a moment of silence as he studied the partially completed head of the bust. Then he turned suddenly. 'Deborah, who does it look like to you?'

'Well——' Her hesitation was pronounced. 'I don't know Gino very well.'

'I've known him for years. I'm sorry to be the one to tell you, Sabrina, but that doesn't look like him at all, not even when he was younger,' he said emphatically.

'When it's finished——' Sabrina began.

'It will look exactly like Bay Cameron,' her father finished the sentence for her.

'You must be mistaken,' she responded evenly, but she clenched her hands tightly together until they hurt, punishing them for having betrayed her. 'It doesn't look at all like Bay, does it, Deborah?'

'It does bear a slight resemblance to him,' the

other woman admitted reluctantly, 'but as you said, it isn't finished.'

'The man has an interesting face. If you could see it, Sabrina, I know you would have had the urge to put it on canvas. But nevertheless, I'm not going to argue with you. You're the artist not me. If you say it's Gino, it's Gino. I suppose there's Roman characteristics in both of them.' He put his arm around her shoulders and gave her a reassuring hug. 'Now if you two ladies will excuse me, I came up here to shower and change.'

After bestowing a light kiss on Sabrina's cheek, he left the room. Sabrina stared sightlessly at the mound of clay on work pedestal, her heart crying with pain. For a moment she had forgotten Deborah was still in the room, until the faint click of a heel reminded her.

'Sabrina, about Bay——' The gentle voice paused.

'What about Bay?' Sabrina challenged, her tone cold and aloof.

'You aren't becoming ... too involved with him, are you?' Deborah faltered as if sensing she was trespassing on private territory. 'I mean, I admire him very much, but I don't think you should——'

'——take his attentions too seriously,' Sabrina finished for her. 'I'm well aware that he only sees me to be kind.' She couldn't bring herself to use the word pity.

'I'm glad.' There was a faint sigh of relief in the redhead's statement. 'I'm sure he likes you, Sabrina. I just don't think it would be wise if you became too

159

fond of him. After all you've been through, it wouldn't be fair.'

'I am fond of him,' she asserted. 'He helped me a great deal. Bay was even the one to suggest that I try working in clay.' Silently she admitted that it wasn't a fair trade to give away her heart for a career, but when was anything connected with love classified as fair? 'But don't worry, Deborah. I haven't misinterpreted his motives.'

'You always seem to have your feet on the ground,' was the faintly envious response.

Only this time my head was in the clouds, Sabrina thought to herself. She mumbled an absent reply when Deborah said she would leave Sabrina to her work.

As the studio door closed behind her father's red-haired fiancée, Sabrina's hands reached tentatively towards the bust, lightly exploring the roughed-in features, confirming for herself that indeed it was Bay. A cold anger pervaded her body.

Destroy it! Smash it! her mind ordered. Turn it back into an ordinary lump of clay!

Her hands rested on either side of the face, but they couldn't carry out the order. One tear fell, then another. Finally silent sobs racked her slender form, her shoulders hunching forward at the excruciating pain in her chest.

But her hands didn't remain immobile. Shakily they began working, painstakingly defining each detail of his face in the moulding clay. It was a labour of love, and what pieces of her heart she hadn't given to Bay went into the soft clay.

Later, Sabrina wasn't conscious of how much

time had passed, her father knocked once on the door and opened it. She didn't have time to wipe the river of tears from her face, so she kept her back to the door.

'We're leaving now,' he told her. 'Don't forget your promise. Eat and straight to bed.'

'Yes, Dad,' she answered tightly. 'Have a good time.'

The interruption checked the onslaught of tears. She suddenly realised how drained she was, emotionally and physically. When the front door leading to the stairwell to the street closed, signalling the departure of her father and Deborah, Sabrina sank on to the work stool. She tiredly buried her face in her hands, not wanting to move or expend the energy to breathe.

A pounding began. For an instant she thought it was coming from inside her head. Then she realised it was coming from the stairwell door downstairs. She grimaced wryly as she rubbed her cheeks dry.

'Dad must have forgotten his key,' she muttered aloud, and slipped off the stool.

Her legs refused to be hurried as she made her way out of the studio and down the stairs to the second floor. The knocking continued, more demanding than before.

'I'm coming!' Irritation raised her voice and the sound stopped.

The muscles at the back of her neck had become knotted with tension and she rubbed them wearily as she turned the automatic lock and opened the door.

'What's the matter? Did you forget your key?' She

161

tried to make her voice sound light and teasing, but it was a hollow attempt. Her greeting was met with silence. Sabrina tilted her head to the side in a listening attitude. 'Dad?'

'Did you know there's a smudge of clay on your cheek?'

Sabrina recoiled instinctively from the sound of Bay's voice. Her hand moved to shut the door, but he blocked it effectively and stepped into the room.

'How did you get up here? What do you want?' she demanded angrily.

'I met your father and Deborah on their way out. He let me in,' he explained calmly.

'Why?' She pivoted away, unable to face him, a hand nervously wiping the clay from her cheek.

'Why did he let me in?' Bay questioned. 'He said something about you working too hard.'

'Well, I'm not!' she said emphatically. 'And I meant why did you come?'

'To ask you to have dinner with me.'

'No.' Sabrina tipped her head back, her lashes fluttering down in a silent prayer to be left alone.

'I won't accept that,' he stated. 'You have to eat, and it might as well be with me as alone.'

'You'll have to accept it, because I'm busy. It doesn't bother me in the least to eat alone.' A solitary meal was something she had better get used to, she told herself.

'Sabrina, stop being stubborn,' Bay admonished calmly. 'There's no need to change clothes. Just take off your smock and go as you are. We'll eat and I'll bring you directly back here to finish your work, if it's essential it be done tonight.'

'I'm not going to be talked into going,' she warned.

With a fluid step, Bay reached out and untied the sash of her smock. Quickly she tried to tie the bow again, but his fingers closed over her wrist to prevent it.

'You are not going to bully me this time, Bay Cameron,' Sabrina muttered, straining to free her wrist from his grasp.

He held it easily. 'It's going to be a long night, because I'm not leaving here until you agree.'

It was not an idle threat. He was just arrogant enough to carry it out. The fire spreading through her arm was a second threat, a threat that she might not be able to hide her feelings or hold her tongue if she tried to outwait him.

Sabrina closed her mouth tightly for a moment. 'If I agree to this blackmail of yours, do I have your word that from now on you will accept my decisions about going with you as final?'

Her request was met by guarded silence for long seconds. 'You have my word, if,' there was an edge of fine steel in his voice, '*if* you will agree that we will discuss the reason for your sudden animosity.'

'I don't know what you're talking about,' she said coolly. Her heart started pounding frantically.

'Your word, Sabrina,' Bay ignored her denial.

The sigh she released was a well disguised checked sob. 'All right, you have it. Now let go of me.' Her wrist was freed. She rubbed the tender area unconsciously. 'But I still don't know what you're talking about,' she lied.

Her attitude towards him had changed, but not

163

for anything did she want him to discover why. Pity because she was blind was one thing, but pity because she loved him was something she refused to tolerate.

'We'll see,' Bay murmured quietly.

How she hated his air of confidence! Sabrina flung her smock in the general direction of a chair and stalked to the umbrella stand to get her cane, the ivory cane that Bay had given her.

'Let's go, so we can get this over with,' she declared.

'Aren't you forgetting your bag?' he mocked. 'You might need your key to get back in unless— you plan to spend the night with me.'

'Perish the thought!' Sabrina spat.

But the thought was pure torture stabbing into her heart as she hurried up the stairs to her room. It hurt that Bay could joke about making love to her, especially when it was something that she wanted so very much.

Downstairs with her purse in hand, she brushed past him through the door, ignoring his mocking, 'Are you ready now?'

Her continued silence in the car was for her own protection, not a desire to be rude. She couldn't begin to guess Bay's reasons for not speaking. He was an enigma. She didn't understand why he did anything he did. For instance, why did he want her company when she had made it obvious that she didn't want his?

Poignantly Sabrina realised that this was probably the last time she would be with Bay, if he kept his word. It was really impossible and impractical to keep going out with him when she knew the truth of her feelings. It would only bring more pain.

She knew he hoped to change her mind and persuade her to continue their relationship. He had succeeded the last time when she hadn't been aware of her love. Naturally he was sure that he could do it again—why, she didn't know. She had to guard against his charm. She mustn't prolong the time when they separated.

Her thoughts were centred on the man behind the wheel. Nothing else around her penetrated her consciousness. She couldn't hear the traffic. Up or down a San Francisco street, it didn't matter. She could not care less where he was taking her, although at some future time she would probably think of the restaurant with pain.

'Sabrina.'

The faint command for her attention drew her out of the sheltering cocoon of her misery. She sat up straighter, realising with a start that they had stopped. The engine had been turned off. Pink heightened her cheekbones, but she knew the dimness of the car concealed it.

'Are we here?' She tipped her head to a haughty angle.

'Yes,' Bay answered.

Her fingers closed tightly around her cane while she waited for Bay to walk around the car to open her door. The serpent heads carved into the ivory handle left an imprint in her fingers. Since she didn't know where she was going, she had to accept the guidance of his hand at her elbow. Several paces further, he opened a door and ushered her into a building.

Footsteps immediately approached them and a woman's voice greeted them in pleasant surprise. 'You're here already, sir. Let me take your coat.'

Bay shrugged out of a light topcoat. 'Yes, it didn't take me as long as I thought, Mrs Gibbs. Mrs Gibbs, I'd like you to meet Sabrina Lane. Sabrina, this is Mrs Gibbs.'

'How do you do, Mrs Gibbs,' Sabrina greeted the woman warily, her ears straining to hear the sounds familiar to a restaurant.

'I'm pleased to meet you, Miss Lane.' Then she footsteps retreated.

'What kind of a restaurant is this?' Sabrina whispered, not certain if anyone could overhear.

'It's not a restaurant.' His hand was at her elbow again, leading her forward.

'But——' Sabrina frowned.

'This is my home, Sabrina,' Bay stated calmly.

She stopped abruptly. 'You said you were taking me out to eat,' she accused.

'But I never said to a restaurant.' He released her elbow and curved his arm around the back of her waist, propelling her forward. 'And you never asked.'

Sabrina twisted away from his arm. 'You've tricked me for the last time, Bay Cameron.' Her voice trembled with emotion. 'You can just turn around and take me home right now.'

'I gave Mrs Gibbs a list of your favourite things. She's gone to a great deal of trouble to cook a meal

166

you'll like. She'll be very disappointed if you don't stay.'

'You were never concerned about my feelings,' she reminded him sharply. 'Why should I worry about hurting hers?'

'Because essentially you're a gentle and sensitive woman and because,' his low voice became ominously soft, 'you gave me your word.'

'And I'm supposed to honour it even when you don't keep yours.' Sabrina swallowed back a helpless sob of frustration.

'I've never lied to you.'

'No, you've only tricked, manoeuvred and bullied me into doing what you want, but after all, you are Bay Cameron. You can make up your own code of ethics, can't you?' she snapped sarcastically.

'Shall we go into the living room?' A fine thread of cold steel ran through his voice and Sabrina knew her barbs had pricked.

Paradoxically she felt remorse and satisfaction at hurting him. She loved him desperately, but she hated him, too, for seeing her only as an unfortunate blind girl and not as a woman with physical and emotional needs. She didn't oppose the arm that firmly guided her forward. They turned at right angles and his steps slowed.

'Why did you bring me here, Bay?' Sabrina challenged coldly.

'We couldn't spend the evening in the hallway,' he answered, deliberately misunderstanding her question.

'You know very well I was referring to your home,' she accused.

'It offered privacy for the talk we're going to have.'

'Privacy could be obtained in your car, or for that matter at my house,' Sabrina reminded him.

'They wouldn't do. In a car, you could lose your temper and possibly jump out the door before I could stop you and be run down by some passing motorist,' Bay explained logically. 'Your home wouldn't work either. You know it better than the back of your hand. As stubborn as you can be sometimes, I would probably have found myself talking to the door of some room you'd locked yourself into. Here, in my home, you don't know which way to move without running the risk of falling over furniture or banging into a wall.'

'And you wonder why I've suddenly begun to dislike you!' Sabrina protested, spinning away, but unable to move with any swiftness.

He had laid the trap too cleverly. The end of her cane raced out to search for any obstacles in front of her and banged against a solid object.

'The sofa is directly in front of you. There's a chair to your right,' he said. 'Take one step backward and turn to your right and you'll avoid the chair.'

'What's in the way after that?' she asked caustically.

'Why don't you see for yourself?'

Slowly Sabrina followed his instructions, putting distance between them as she crossed an empty space with the aid of her cane. Finally the ivory white tip touched what appeared to be a table leg. She carefully sidestepped around it only to find the table had been sitting against a wall. Or at least, it was something solid, maybe a door. Sabrina reached out with her hand to investigate, and sheer filmy curtains met her fingers.

'The window overlooks San Francisco Bay.' His voice came from the centre of the room. 'There's an unobstructed view of the Golden Gate and the Harbour.'

Sabrina didn't know what she had hoped to discover, a way out, possibly. Frustrated, she turned away from the window and partially retraced her steps, stopping before she came too near the area she guessed him to be.

'Bay, take me home, please,' she asked softly.

'Not yet.'

The carpet was soft and thick beneath her feet. She wondered at its colour, the type of furnishing that surrounded her. There was a desire to explore this place where he lived and slept. She shook her head firmly. She mustn't think about that.

'If you don't take me home, I'll just call a cab.' She raised her chin defiantly.

'Where's the telephone, Sabrina? Do you know?' mocked Bay. Averting her face from the watchfulness of his eyes, she released a frantic, sobbing sigh.

'What's troubling you, Sabrina?'

'You're virtually holding me prisoner in this house and you have the nerve to ask why I'm upset!' she cried angrily.

'There's more to it than that and I mean to find out what it is.'

His voice was moving closer, the plushness of the carpet muffling his steps. Sabrina turned to face him, trying to use her sensitive radar to pinpoint his location.

'Maybe I'm tired of being treated like a child,' she suggested icily.

'Then stop acting like one!' Bay snapped.

With a start, she discovered he was closer than she had realised. His hands touched her shoulders, but before his fingers could dig into her flesh, she shied quickly away.

'For God's sake, Sabrina, why are you afraid of me?' he demanded. 'Every time I come near you any more you tremble like a frightened rabbit. You've been like this ever since Pamela's party. Is that what upset you? Why you're afraid to let me near you?'

Her breathing was shallow and uneven. 'It didn't inspire me to trust you,' Sabrina lashed back, unable to explain that it had precipitated the discovery that she was in love with him.

'I was angry. I never meant to frighten you,' Bay said forcefully. This time his hands closed over her shoulders before she could elude them. His touch was firm but not bruising.

'Isn't it a little late to be regretting it now?' She lowered her chin so he couldn't see into her face as she made the sarcastic retort. 'We can't be friends, Bay, not any more.'

'Then I'll undo the damage,' came his low, clipped response.

He pulled her towards him. Her hands automatically pushed against the solidness of his chest. It was the last resistance Sabrina offered as his mouth closed over hers. It took all of her strength and will to keep from responding to the persuasive mastery of his kiss. At all costs she had to prevent him from discovering the effect he had on her. He mustn't know the fiery leap of desire in her loins that nearly made her limp in his arms.

The kiss seemed to go on for ever. Sabrina didn't know how much longer she could hold back the raging fire Bay had started. Before the shuddering sigh of surrender escaped, he dragged his mouth from her throbbing lips.

'Sabrina.' The husky, whispering tautness of his caressing voice was very nearly the final blow.

Her heart had a stranglehold on her throat, but she forced the words of rejection through. 'Now, will you let me go?' she demanded in a strained voice.

'What is it, Sabrina?' he asked guardedly. 'My kiss doesn't frighten you, nor my touch. I don't think you're frightened of anything, but there's something wrong, some explanation why you don't want to continue to see me.'

She stood silently for a minute, realising he was not going to free her immediately. Sabrina took a deep breath and tossed back her head. She was about to make the biggest bluff in her life and the most important.

'Do you want the truth, Bay?' she challenged boldly. 'Well, the truth is that when you first met me I was lost and lonely. I was nothing and my destination was nowhere. You pushed me out of my shell and gave me companionship. More important, you gave me back a chance for a career in a field I love more than anything else in the world.

I'll always be eternally grateful to you for that.'

She paused for an instant, feeling his stillness. 'I wish you hadn't forced me to say this, Bay. I don't mean to be unkind, but I'm not lost or lonely any more. I have my career and a goal, and that's all I ever wanted in life. I've enjoyed the times we spent together. But you tend to dominate and the only thing I want to dominate my life is my work. To sum it all up in one sentence, I simply don't need you any more.'

'I see.' His hands fell away from her shoulders as he stepped away. His voice was cuttingly grim. 'I don't think you could have put it more clearly.'

'It was never my intention, consciously or unconsciously, to use you, I hope you'll believe that,' Sabrina explained. 'About two weeks ago I realised that I wanted to devote all of my time to my work, but I didn't know how to tell you that without sounding ungrateful for all you'd done. All you were asking in return was a casual friendship, and I was too selfish to even want to give you that. So I tried to pick a fight with you, thinking that if you became angry, you might be the one to break it off. I'm sorry, Bay.'

A tear slipped from her lashes at the magnitude of her lie. Nothing was further from the truth, but his silence told her that he believed her.

'Would you mind taking me home, Bay?' she requested, her voice choked with pain.

'I don't think either one of us has much of an appetite,' he agreed bitterly. 'It really isn't very surprising.'

An impersonal hand took her elbow. Not another

172

word was spoken. Bay made no comment on the tears that ran freely down her cheeks. He didn't even tell her goodbye when he saw her to the door, but his sardonic 'good luck' echoed in Sabrina's ears all the way to her room where she sprawled on to the bed and cried.

CHAPTER TEN

'SABRINA! Would you come downstairs a minute?' Grant Lane called from the base of the stairs.

She sighed heavily. 'Can't it wait?'

'No, it's important,' was the answer.

Reluctantly Sabrina covered the lump of clay just beginning to take shape. If she had persisted, she probably could have persuaded her father to postpone whatever it was that was so important, but she was simply too tired to argue. In the last two weeks, she had worked hard and slept little.

'I'll be right down,' she said as she forced her legs to carry out her statement. 'What did you want, Dad?' Halfway down the stairs, she felt a prickling along the back of her neck. For a few steps, she blamed the sensation on strain and tired nerves. She stopped abruptly on the last step, her head jerking towards the stairwell door.

'Hello, Sabrina. I apologise for interrupting your work.' The sardonic derision in Bay's tone cut her to the quick.

Blanching slightly, Sabrina dropped her chin, taking the last step and shoving her trembling hands in her pocket. 'What a surprise, Bay,' her own voice sounded anything but delighted. 'What brings you here?'

'Bay stopped to——' her father began to explain.

'You might call it my last good deed,' Bay interrupted blandly. 'I want you to meet Howell Fletcher, Sabrina.'

'This is the young lady you've been telling me about?' a cultured, masculine voice said, stepping forward to greet her. 'Miss Lane, I hope this is a pleasure, for both of us.'

Bewildered, Sabrina offered her hand. It was gripped lightly by smooth fingers and released. 'I'm sorry, I don't think I understand,' she apologised.

'Howell is here to see your work and give his considered opinion on your talent and potential,' Bay explained. The total lack of warmth in his voice almost made him seem like a stranger. There was none of the gentle mockery or friendliness she was accustomed to hearing.

'I don't think——' Sabrina started to protest stiffly that she didn't believe she was ready to have her work criticised by a professional.

'You might as well find out now whether or not you're wasting your time or building false hopes,' the man identified as Howell Fletcher stated.

'Good deed'—that was what Bay had said his motive was. Sabrina couldn't help wondering if he wasn't wishing she would fall flat on her face.

'I keep all my work in the studio upstairs.' Her chin lifted proudly. 'Are you coming, Bay?'

'No, I won't be staying.' The outcome apparently mattered little to him as he took his leave of her father and Howell Fletcher. Sabrina he ignored.

Robotlike, Sabrina led Howell Fletcher to the studio. The man spoke not one word while he slowly studied each piece, but she didn't mind. Strangely she didn't care what his opinion was. There was only one man who mattered, and Bay had walked in and out before her broken heart could start beating again.

Her work was a way of filling the empty, lonely hours, providing a challenge and a reason to get up each morning. Some day, she hoped her labours would allow her to be independent of her father. She wanted him to marry Deborah and be happy. It was only right that one of them should have the person they loved. She would never have Bay.

'How much of this work have you done since you became blind, Miss Lane?' the man asked thoughtfully.

'In clay? All of it,' she answered absently. 'The paintings were done before my accident.'

'I understood that you've only know Mr Cameron for a few months,' he commented.

'Yes, that's right.' Sabrina wearily rubbed the back of her neck.

'How did you manage to do this bust?'

A wry smile curved her mouth. 'A blind person sees with their hands, Mr Fletcher.'

'You haven't asked what I think yet. Aren't you curious, Miss Lane?'

'It's always been my experience that criticism comes without asking and compliments come without,' she shrugged dryly.

'You have a remarkable amount of wisdom,' he commented.

'Not in all things.' Not in loving wisely.

Then Howell Fletcher began to talk, more correctly to criticise. He didn't temper his words but sliced them into her, uncaring that it was her future he was cutting away. He dissected each piece. Every

176

flaw, no matter how minute, was called to her attention. Each object was pushed into her hands so she could examine it for herself.

On and on the cultured voice droned until Sabrina wanted to cry out for him to stop. The weight of failure began to hunch her shoulders, trying to ward off the final, crushing blow. Her face, already haunted by the torture of unrequited love, became bleaker. Pride kept her chin up as the last piece was disposed of with the same analytical surgery as the others. A heavy silence followed his statement.

'Well,' Sabrina breathed in deeply, 'I never realised I was such an incompetent amateur.'

'My God, child,' the critic laughed, 'you're not incompetent nor an amateur. Some of the pieces are clumsy, the inanimate ones that need work on the flow of their line. But the others are stunning. The pride and power that you've stamped in Bay's face is unbelievable. The pathos of the madonna-like figure is touching in the extreme. Like your paintings, your talent lies in people. You bring them to life, heighten the qualities that attract people.'

'Then,' she couldn't believe she was hearing him correctly, 'you think I should keep working?'

'If you can keep up this pace and this standard, I can promise you a showing within six months,' Howell Fletcher declared.

'You must be joking,' Sabrina breathed.

'My dear, I never joke about money. And if you'll pardon me saying so, your blindness is going to attract a great deal of beautiful publicity. What we will do is combine a display of your very best paintings with the very best clay models and start out with an invitation-only showing for all the "right" people——' The plans continued to spew forth long after the shock of his announcement wore off.

'You aren't saying this because of Bay, are you?' Sabrina interrupted, suddenly afraid that Bay had exerted his influence to arrange this.

'Are you asking me if I was bribed to tell you this?' he demanded, sounding indignantly affronted. She nodded hesitantly. 'Bay Cameron did apply pressure to bring me here today, but I would never risk my reputation for anyone! If you had neither talent nor potential, I would have told you so in no uncertain terms.'

Sabrina believed him. The victory cup of success was within her grasp. She let the man issue forth his plans, knowing that the nectar from the cup did not taste sweet because she couldn't share it with the man she loved. The triumph was as hollow as she was.

A private show within six months, Howell Fletcher had declared. After careful consideration, he had pushed the date ahead to the first week of December, timing it for the holiday season and loosened purse strings. Sabrina had silently realised that his appreciation of art went hand in hand with his appreciation of money.

'I think you've done it, Sabrina,' her father murmured so he couldn't be overheard by the people milling about. 'All I've heard is one compliment after another.'

Sabrina smiled faintly, not at his words of success

but at the deep pride in his voice. She could imagine the beaming smile on his face.

'Words of praise are cheap, Mr Lane,' Howell Fletcher put in from the other side of Sabrina, but there was triumph in his tone. 'You're a success, my dear Sabrina, because our guests are putting their money where their mouth is, to put it crudely.'

'Thanks to you, Howell,' she said softly.

'Always the diplomat,' he chided. 'It took both of our talents, as you very well know. Now, I must circulate. You stay here and look beautiful.'

'Sabrina.' A warm, female voice called her name, followed by the floral scent of violets. 'It's me, Pamela Thyssen. You were at my home some months ago.'

'Of course, Mrs Thyssen, I remember you very well.' Sabrina extended her hand and had it clasped by beringed fingers. 'How are you?'

'A little upset, if you must know,' the woman scolded mockingly. 'It was dreadful of you not to volunteer any information about your remarkable talent. And wait until I get my hands on Bay. I'll teach that godson of mine a lesson for keeping me in the dark.'

'At the time, there wasn't anything to tell.' She swallowed nervously. Every time his name was mentioned her heart started skipping beats and an icy cold hand would close around her throat.

'I should think Bay would be here tonight, helping you to celebrate your success. Surely he could have cut short his sailing trip to Baja for an occasion like this,' Pamela stated.

'Oh, is that where he is?' Sabrina tried to sound

179

unconcerned. 'I haven't seen him lately. I've been so busy getting ready for this show and all.'

Pamela Thyssen obviously wasn't aware that she and Bay had parted company several months ago. Sabrina didn't intend to enlighten her either.

'The bust you did of him is positively stealing the show. Everyone is talking about how remarkable the likeness is,' the woman observed in a faintly curious tone. 'Howell must have realised how successful it would be, judging by the price he put on it.'

'I'm merely the artist,' Sabrina shrugged to indicate that she had nothing to do with the price of the items.

She had not wanted to exhibit the bust at all, but Howell had been adamant in his arguments, insisting that she could not allow sentiment to colour her judgment. When she had finally given in, it was with the proviso that the bust would not be for sale.

That was when she learned that Howell Fletcher's shrewdness was not limited to money and art. He had asked if she wanted to raise speculation as to why it wasn't for sale. It would be better, he suggested, to put an exorbitant price tag on it, too high for anyone to purchase it. Sabrina had finally agreed.

'What was Bay's reaction when he saw the model you did of him?' Pamela enquired.

One of the other guests chose that moment to offer his congratulations and comments and Sabrina was able to ignore the question. A few others stopped after that. Eventually Pamela was sidetracked by someone she knew and Sabrina had escaped the question completely.

'It's stunning, Miss Lane,' a woman gushed. 'Absolutely stunning. The paintings, the statues, they're all so breathtakingly real.'

'Thank you,' Sabrina nodded politely, not knowing how to counter the effusiveness of the woman's praise.

'Excuse me, Mrs Hamilton, but I must steal Sabrina away from you for a moment,' Howell Fletcher broke in, a smooth hand tucking itself under Sabrina's elbow.

Sabrina offered her apologies to the woman and gratefully allowed Howell to guide her away. The ivory cane tapped its way in front of her. She had learned that Howell often forgot she was blind and let her run into things.

'Who are you spiriting me off to see this time?' she asked, wiping a damp palm on the skirt of her black dress.

'I don't know how to tell you this exactly, Sabrina.' Apprehension echoed in his cautious statement. 'We have a buyer for the bust, and he wants to see you.'

'A buyer?' She stiffened. 'You know it's not for sale.'

'I tried to explain that you were very reluctant to part with it, that its real worth was something less than the price. I couldn't very well tell him how much less for fear the information would get around and the other prices would be questioned,' he replied defensively.

'I shouldn't have been persuaded to display it in the first place. You guessed how I felt about it,' she accused.

'Yes, I did,' he agreed quietly. 'Perhaps you can

appeal to his better nature and persuaded him to choose something else. He's waiting in my office. It will afford some privacy for the discussion.'

'I'm not going to sell it,' Sabrina stated emphatically as they left behind most of the guests to enter a back hall. 'I don't care what the repercussions are.'

Howell didn't comment, slowing her down and turning her slightly as he reached around to open the door. She walked into the room with a determined lift of her chin. There was a quietly murmured 'good luck' from Howell and he closed the door. She turned back, startled, expecting to have his support.

Then she heard someone rise to his feet. She had been in the office many times and knew the potential buyer had been sitting on the Victorian sofa against the left wall. Fixing a bright smile on her face, she stepped towards the sound.

'How do you do.' Sabrina extended a hand in greeting. 'I'm Sabrina Lane. Howell told me you were interested in purchasing a particularly favourite piece of mine.'

'That's right, Sabrina.'

The voice went through her like a bolt of lightning. Her hand fell to her side as she fought to remain composed. The floor seemed to roll madly beneath her feet, but it was only her shaking knees.

'Bay—Bay Cameron,' she identified him with a breathless catch in the forced gaiety of her voice. 'What a coincidence! Pamela Thyssen was just telling me a few moments ago that you were on a sailing trip somewhere around Baja California. It must be difficult to be in two places at once.'

Howell, that traitor, why hadn't he warned her that it was Bay who was waiting for her? No wonder he had sneaked away, leaving her alone!

'It was a natural mistake for Pamela to make. I hadn't planned to return for some time,' he replied in that impersonal tone that made her feel cold. 'Tonight you've achieved the success you wanted. How does it feel?'

Miserable, her heart answered. 'Splendid,' her voice lied.

'You're looking very chic and sophisticated in your dress of mourning black. The single strand of pearls around your long neck is a nice simple touch. The two make your complexion pale and hauntingly beautiful as if you've suffered great tragedy and risen above it. The press must be having a field day with your story,' Bay commented cynically.

She longed to tell him that her tragedy had been in losing him and not her sight, but she kept silent, trying not to hear the sarcasm underlining his voice.

'I would have thought by now you would have discarded the cane in favour of another.' The reference to the ivory carved handle in her hands made her grasp it more tightly as if afraid he would try to take it back.

'Why should I? It serves its purpose,' she shrugged nervously.

'I wasn't going to accuse you of attaching any sentimental importance to it,' Bay responded dryly. 'Although when I saw the bust you did of me, I was curious to find out if you look back on our association with fondness.'

'Naturally.' Her voice vibrated with the depth of

her fondness. 'Besides, I told you once before that I liked your face. The features are strong and proud.'

'Howell did tell you that I'm going to buy it, didn't he?'

'Yes, but I never realised you were an egotist, Bay.' Her laughter was brittle. 'Imagine buying an image of yourself!'

'It will be an excellent reminder for the future.'

'Bay, I——' Sabrina pivoted slightly to the side, feeling the play of his eyes over her profile, cold and chilling. 'Th-there's been a mistake. Howell came to get me because ... well, because it isn't for sale.'

'Why not?' He didn't sound upset by her stammering announcement. 'I thought the purpose of this show was to sell what was on display.'

'It is, but not this piece,' she protested. 'That's why we put the price so high, so no one would buy it.'

'I'm buying it,' Bay answered evenly.

'No! I'm not letting you have it!' She lashed out sharply in desperation. 'You've taken everything else from me. Please let me keep this!'

'Taken from you!' he laughed harshly. His hand snaked out to wrap his fingers around her wrist. 'What have I ever taken from you? Aren't you forgetting that I'm the one who was used? Why not take my money? You've taken everything else of value I had to give!'

'Pity? Sympathy? Charity?' The end of her cane tapped the floor sharply in punctuation to her angry words. 'When were those humiliating things ever of value? And to whom? Certainly not to me! You

184

never cared about me! Not really! I was only a charity case to you!'

'You still don't believe I felt sorry for you?' A weary sign came from deep within.

'You certainly don't love me,' Sabrina sniffed.

'And if I had,' his hand closed firmly on the back of her neck, turning her stiffly composed face towards him, 'would it have made any difference?'

If only he hadn't touched her, Sabrina thought, a fiery trail racing down her spine, maybe she could have withstood the agony tearing at her heart. Now she felt herself go limp inside, pride unable to support her, and she swayed against his chest.

'If you'd loved me just a little, Bay,' she sighed wistfully, inhaling the spicy fragrance clinging to his jacket, 'I might not have minded loving you so desperately. But what girl wants to be with a man who only pities her because she can't see?'

'You are blind, Sabrina,' he said. A great weight seemed to leave his voice. The hand slipped from her neck to the back of her waist while the other hand gently stroked her cheek. 'I never pitied you. I was too busy falling in love with you to waste time with that emotion.'

'Oh, Bay, don't tease me,' she cried in anguish, twisting free from his tender embrace. 'Haven't I shamed myself enough without having you make fun of me?'

'I'm not teasing. Believe me, the hell I've been going through these last months hasn't been funny at all,' Bay stated.

'I'm blind, Bay. How could you possibly love me?'

she pleaded with him to stop tormenting her.

'My brave and beautiful blind queen, how could I possibly not love you?' His tone was incredibly warm and caressing. The sincerity of it frightened Sabrina.

'You aren't trying to trick me again, are you, Bay? Don't do this to me if all you want is the bust I did of you. I'll give it to you gladly if it will make you stop lying.'

A pair of hands closed over her shoulders and she was drawn against his chest. He placed her hands on his heart, rapidly thudding against her palm. Her own heart had to race wildly to keep in tempo. Cupping her face in his hands, Bay bestowed soft kisses on her closed eyes.

'Being blind doesn't make you feel less of a woman when I hold you in my arms, darling,' he whispered tightly.

'You never let me guess, not once,' Sabrina murmured, leaning her head weakly against his heart.

'I wanted to a hundred times in a hundred ways.' Strong arms held her close as if afraid she would try to escape again. 'I loved you almost from the beginning. Maybe it started that night we took refuge from the rain in my boat, I don't know. But I told myself I had to take it slow. You were proud, stubborn, defensive and very insecure. I didn't try to convince you in the beginning that I was in love with you, because you wouldn't have believed me. That's why I set about trying to help you build confidence in yourself. I wanted you to learn that there was nothing you couldn't do if you set your mind to it. Arrogantly I thought after that was accomplished I would make you fall in love with me. You can imagine what a blow it was to my self-esteem when you informed me that you didn't need me any more.'

He smiled against her temple and Sabrina snuggled closer. 'I needed you. I wanted you desperately,' she murmured fervently. 'I was terrified you would guess and feel even sorrier for me.'

'I never felt pity. Pride, but never pity.'

'Pride?' She turned her face towards him, questioning and bewildered.

'I was always proud of you. No matter what challenge I made, you always accepted it.' Lightly he kissed her lips.

'Accepted with protest,' she reminded him with an impish smile.

'No one could ever accuse you of being tractable. Stubborn and independent, yes, but never tractable. You made that plain the first time we met and you slapped my face,' Bay laughed softly.

'And you slapped me back.' Sabrina let her fingertips caress his cheek. 'It made me angry. Eventually it made me love you.'

His fingers quickly gripped her hand and stopped the caressing movement, pressing a hard kiss in her palm. 'Will you tell me now why you ran away from me at Pamela's?' he demanded huskily. 'The truth this time.'

Her heart skipped a beat. At the moment she didn't want to talk, not after the sensually arousing kiss in her sensitive palm.

'I heard you talking to a girl named Roni. She said you'd brought me with you because you felt sorry for me and because you hoped to make her jealous. You didn't deny it, Bay. I kept hoping you would at least say I was your friend, but you just let her keep rattling on about me being a charity case and a poor unfortunate. I thought she was telling the truth. That's why I ran away,' she admitted.

She heard and felt the rolling chuckle that vibrated from deep within. It was throaty and warm and strangely reassuring.

'One of the first things I'm going to have to remember when we're married is how acute your hearing is,' Bay declared with a wide smile of satisfaction against her hair. 'If you'd eavesdropped a little longer, you would have heard me tell Roni to take a flying leap at the moon and that I didn't appreciate her comments about the woman I was going to marry.'

'Bay!' Her voice caught for a moment on the tide of love that welled in her throat. 'Are you going to marry me?'

'If that's a proposal, I accept.'

'D-don't tease,' she whispered with a painful gasp.

His mouth closed over hers in a tender promise. Instantly Sabrina responded, moulding herself tightly against every hard male curve. Hungry desire blazed in his deepening kiss as he parted her lips to savour every inch of her mouth. His love lit a glowing lamp that chased away all the shadows of her dark world.

Long heady moments later Bay pushed her unsteadily out of his arms. She swayed towards the chest rising and falling so unevenly beneath her fingers. His hands rigidly held her at a distance.

'Darling, I love you so,' Sabrina whispered achingly. 'Please hold me a little while longer.'

'I'm not made of iron, my love.' The sternness of his voice only indicated the deepness of his love. 'A little while longer would be too long.'

The corners of her wide mouth were tugged upward in a tiny smile of immense pleasure. 'The door has a lock, Bay.'

'And there's a horde of people who must be wondering what's happened to the star of the show,' he reminded her tersely.

'I don't want to be a star,' she answered.

'Your work——' Bay began.

'——will fill the moments you are away from me. That's all it will ever do for me,' Sabrina declared in a husky murmur.

'You're not making it easy to be sensible,' he growled, letting her come back into his arms.

'I know,' she whispered in the second before his mouth closed passionately over hers.

REILLY'S WOMAN

BY
JANET DAILEY

WORLDWIDE BOOKS
LONDON • SYDNEY • TORONTO

*First published in Great Britain in 1977
Reprinted in Great Britain in 1994
by Worldwide Books, Eton House,
18-24 Paradise Road, Richmond, Surrey TW9 1SR*

© Janet Dailey 1977

ISBN 0 373 59201 9

99-9405

Printed and bound in Great Britain

CHAPTER ONE

THE pages of the magazine were flipped with an impatient finger. The articles couldn't hold Leah Talbot's attention as she kept glancing at the clock on the wall above the reception desk.

Outside, the gold ball of the sun was dipping closer to the horizon. Its light cast a pale yellow hue on the wings of the small planes parked on the hangar apron outside.

The clatter of the typewriter stopped. The dark-haired woman behind the reception desk rose from her chair, turning to her co-worker, an older woman with light hair that had been rinsed to a brassy shade to conceal the grey.

'Want a cup of coffee, June?' the dark-haired woman inquired. The older woman nodded without glancing from the account books spread across her desk. With two cups in hand, the brunette walked to the waist-high counter door, deftly swinging it open with her hip.

She smiled politely at Leah. 'How about you, Miss Talbot? Would you like a refill?'

Glancing at the empty styrofoam cup sitting on the table in front of her, Leah hesitated, then shrugged,

5

'Why not?' A faintly cynical grimace touched her sensually curved mouth.

Absently Leah smoothed the lightweight material of her camel tan skirt as she picked up her cup and, sidestepping her luggage, followed the woman.

'Getting tired of waiting?' The woman's question was rhetorical and sympathetic.

Breathing in deeply, Leah carried the thought further. 'And getting impatient to leave.'

The glass coffee pot sat in its heated nest on a table. Several vending machines stood adjacent to it, offering snacks of candy and cold sandwiches.

'You are going to visit family, aren't you?' The woman filled Leah's cup, then turned to the two she had brought.

'Yes, my brother Lonnie.' The heat from the hot liquid flowed through the sides of the cup. Leah held it gingerly. Her hazel eyes turned to the windows and the slowly sinking sun. Impatiently she flicked her light brown hair behind her shoulder.

'Perhaps you should telephone him and explain about the delay,' the woman suggested.

'There's no need.' Leah gave a brief shake of her head. 'He doesn't know I'm coming. It's a surprise for his birthday tomorrow.' She glanced at the persistently moving hands of the clock. 'At least, I hope it will be. First I have to get there.'

'What's your brother doing in Austin? I mean,' the woman laughed, 'there are quite a few other towns in Nevada I would pick first.'

6

'His letter indicated that it wasn't a bustling metropolis,' Leah smiled. 'He's only there temporarily, though. He works for a mining company. He's part of a team and they sent him to Austin to do some tests in the area.'

The coffee pot was set back in place. 'What about the rest of your family?' The woman picked up the cups and began wandering towards the reception counter, her gaze resting curiously on the attractive young woman walking beside her.

'There's only my parents. They're in Alaska now.' At the woman's lifted brow, Leah explained, 'Dad is in the Air Force.'

'That explains why someone as young as you is so accustomed to flying,' the woman replied.

Twenty-two didn't feel so young, but it probably seemed young to the brunette, who was in her late thirties. Nor did Leah correct the woman's suggestion that she was flying from habit. Time was the key factor in her choice of transportation and it was slipping away.

'How much longer do you think it will be before we leave?' Leah glanced at the clock, her impatience returning.

The woman shrugged, setting down one of the cups to open the counter door. 'I don't know. As soon as Mr Smith arrives, I suppose.'

The answer was hardly welcome. She had been waiting for Mr Smith's arrival for the last two hours. His tardiness seemed to be upsetting only herself.

Everyone else seemed to accept it as natural, but then he was a frequent customer of this charter flying service.

Settling on to the vinyl-covered couch, Leah acknowledged that the worst thing that could happen would be for Mr Smith not to show up. Her portion of the chartered flight to Austin had virtually emptied her meagre savings account. Only by sharing the cost of plane and pilot with this Mr Smith had she been able to afford the flight.

Luck had been sitting on her shoulder the day she had called to inquire about the price. When she had been told how much it would be, Leah had been ready to shelve the idea as too expensive. Then an inquiry as to when she wanted to go prompted the discovery that a charter flight had already been booked for that Friday with the same destination.

Leah had been on pins and needles until it was confirmed that Mr Smith was willing to share the expense. With a sigh she admitted that the waiting wasn't over yet.

A connecting door into the waiting lounge opened and a man stuck his head inside the room. Brown hair had begun to recede from his wide forehead, creased now with a studious frown of absent concentration.

'Hey, Mary, have you heard any more from Reilly since he called to say he'd be late?'

'Sorry, Grady.' The brunette lifted her hands in an open-palm gesture. 'Haven't heard a word.'

He sighed. 'What about my other passenger?'

8

'She's here.' The receptionist motioned towards Leah sitting on the couch.

His gaze swung the width of the room to Leah. Immediately that distant look left his expression. He stepped into the room, a smile splitting his broad cheeks.

'You are Miss Talbot?' His smile deepened at Leah's answering nod. 'Well, this is a pleasant surprise. I was afraid I was going to be stuck with a toddering old maid who would be scared to death of flying.' He thrust a large hand out to her. 'I'm Grady Thompson, your pilot.'

'How do you do, Mr Thompson,' Leah replied as her hand was wrung in a vigorous shake.

'No, make it Grady,' the pilot insisted with a bright twinkle in his eyes.

He was of medium height with a stocky frame. The paunch around his waist became more noticeable as he sat on the couch beside her. He was in his forties, old enough to be her father, but that didn't stop him from flirting. Yet his rakish, good-natured charm made it impossible for Leah to feel offended or repulsed.

'Okay, Grady,' she smiled naturally. Her light brown hair caught the golden fire of the sunlight streaming through the windows.

He studied the streaks of gold for a second, then shifted his gaze to her classic profile, partially outlined as she turned to him. None of her features was striking, not the arching curve of brow, nor the bright gleam in her hazel eyes or the healthy glow of

9

her complexion. Yet the total picture was decidedly attractive.

'If you're calling me Grady,' the pilot tipped his head to the side, 'I can't keep calling you Miss Talbot.'

'It's Leah,' answering the question he had only implied.

'Tell me, Leah, are you a friend of Reilly's?'

'Reilly is Mr Smith?' A brow arched briefly to confirm her guess.

'Obviously you don't know him,' Grady chuckled. 'If you aren't a friend of Reilly's then what's taking you out to the middle of Nevada's nowhere?'

'I'm going to see my brother—providing your Mr Smith shows up,' Leah added wryly.

'Reilly is not anybody's Mr Smith.'

The dry undertone of his voice aroused Leah's curiosity. 'It sounds as though you know him quite well.' Tactfully she pried for more information about her mysterious, and late, flying companion.

The pilot took a long, considering breath and leaned against the back cushion of the couch. 'I think the whole point is just the opposite. I doubt if anyone knows Reilly "quite well". He's a law unto himself, a lone wolf. He's part Indian, which may account for it.'

'Oh, I see,' Leah murmured. 'Why is he going to Austin?'

'Business. He has connections with some of the mining interests around Austin and Tonopah. I usually fly him to one place or the other,' was the reply.

Fleetingly Leah wondered if this Reilly Smith worked for the same company that her brother Lonnie did. It was also entirely possible that he worked for one of their competitors. No matter, Leah shrugged inwardly. The only thing she was really interested in was when was Mr Reilly Smith going to show up.

'Do you live here in Las Vegas?' Grady changed the subject to one that interested him more.

'Yes.' Before the usual question could be asked, Leah added, 'I'm a secretary to one of the executives of a local bank,' and hoped Grady wouldn't add the usual comment that she would look good in one of the chorus lines that were the trademark of the lavish shows at the hotels on the Strip.

'And your brother lives in Austin?'

'Only for the time being.' Leah went on to explain his temporary assignment in Austin.

'Has it been a while since you've seen him?'

'No, we were together at Christmas, but tomorrow is his birthday and I wanted to surprise him.'

'You must think a lot of him to go to all this expense,' Grady observed.

'Lonnie and I are very close,' agreed Leah.

Left unspoken were the details of her hopscotch childhood, skipping from one end of the world to the other. Under those circumstances, it was natural that she and Lonnie would be close. Despite the years that separated their ages, they were like twins.

'What's your boy-friend have to say about all this? And don't tell me a girl like you doesn't have at least one boy-friend,' the pilot teased with a knowing wink.

'Let's just say that he questioned my sanity.' A self-mocking laugh accompanied her reply as Leah remembered Marv's reaction.

He too worked in the accounting department of the same bank she did. She hadn't decided yet where their relationship was going, so for want of a better word, she accepted the classification of Marv as her boy-friend.

In truth, none of her co-workers nor her room-mate Nancy had actually encouraged the trip. They had all claimed that they understood her desire to see her brother again, but none of them seemed to think it was wise to spend all of her savings for that goal.

Of course, they didn't seem to possess that close feeling of kinship with their brothers or sisters. If she had been spending the money to see a boy-friend, they probably wouldn't have questioned her decision. But a brother! The thought brought a wry smile to her mouth.

'Your boy-friend was probably jealous that you weren't spending the weekend with him. I would be.' Again Grady ran an admiring eye over her features.

Leah darted a quick glance at the wall clock. 'I'm beginning to think I won't be going anywhere this weekend,' she sighed.

Reaching into her bag, she removed the opened pack of cigarettes and tapped out a filter-tip. As she started to search for the lighter, a flame sprang from the match in Grady's hand. She smiled her thanks and placed the cigarette between her peach-tinted lips, bending her head towards the flame.

'Don't worry, Reilly will be here. If there was a question that he might not make it, he would have said so when he called earlier,' the pilot assured her. 'In the meantime, why don't I take your luggage out to the plane and stow it in the baggage compartment?'

'Okay,' Leah agreed. 'At least, I'll be one step closer to leaving.'

With a cheering smile, Grady patted her knee. 'Don't give up. We'll make it off the ground yet.'

Then he was picking up her blue weekender bag and the cosmetic case and walking towards the door leading to the hangar apron. With his departure, the minutes started to drag again.

The smoke from her cigarette spiralled above her head. Inhaling briefly on the filter-tip, Leah exhaled more smoke impatiently. The blue-grey cloud swirled upwards.

The outside door opened. Her gaze swung indifferently towards the sound, expecting to see the pilot returning. It was a stranger who entered.

Her mind had a preconceived idea of what Reilly Smith would look like—in his late forties, a supposition based on the belief that only an older, senior member of a mining team would charter an aircraft, short and stocky in build.

This man didn't meet the description. He was six foot, leanly built but not slender and roughly ten years younger, in his mid-thirties. Jet black hair framed the boldly defined features of his bronzed tan face, prominent cheekbones leanly hollowing to powerful jawline. A face carved by the wind and sun.

His dress was a casual leisure suit of rugged brown denim. A complementing shirt patterned in yellow and brown was open at the throat revealing the large nugget of turquoise attached to the beaten silver choker around his neck.

Despite this contrast between the man and her image, Leah was certain this was Reilly Smith. The quiet pride of his carriage, the sensation of aloofness, and the effortless, animal stride convinced her she was right.

Mary, the dark-haired receptionist, confirmed it. 'Finally you arrive, Mr Smith!' Her hands rested akimbo on her hips. 'Miss Talbot was about to decide you were a figment of her imagination.'

For the first time since entering the waiting lounge, his gaze acknowledged her presence in the room. His eyes were startlingly green, the smooth, impenetrable colour of jade.

A disturbing shiver of awareness trembled through Leah as his cool gaze appraised her assets, admired them openly, then smoothly dismissed them in favour of the business at hand.

'I was delayed,' he said, which was neither an explanation nor an apology. 'My cases are sitting outside. Are you ready to leave, Miss Talbot?'

After waiting for going on three hours, Leah marvelled that he had the nerve to ask if *she* was ready! Sharply snubbing out her cigarette in the ashtray, she suppressed the impulse to remind him that he was the one who was late.

She kept her reply to a calm. 'My luggage is already in the plane, Mr Smith.' But the clasp of her handbag snapped shut rather loudly as she closed it and rose to her feet.

Stepping outside the building, a desert wind tugged at the hem of her camel-coloured skirt, briefly lifting it to reveal a shapely leg. Leah held the open front of her matching tunic-styled waistcoat together with one hand while her other hand carrying the bag tried to keep the teasing wind from billowing her skirt.

As an afterthought, she realised that she probably should have worn slacks. Habits die hard, and she had lived in too many foreign countries where slacks on women were viewed with disfavour.

Her shoes clicked loudly on the concrete while the man walking beside her made barely any sound at all. A sideways glance noticed that her heels didn't gain her much height. The top of her head came somewhere around his chin.

Automatically her gaze slid to the left hand carrying his bags. There was no wedding band on his finger. Somehow Leah had known there wouldn't be—perhaps because of Grady's statement that Reilly Smith was a lone wolf.

Shifting her gaze straight ahead, Leah mused silently that there were probably a lot of girls who would like to change his status. He was a compellingly handsome man. Not that it mattered to her. She was making this trip to see her brother.

A few yards ahead, Grady was standing beside the orange and white wing of a Cessna 310. The twin engine plane looked sleek and racy. A smile flashed across the pilot's face as he saw their approach.

'Didn't I tell you he'd make it. Leah?' he declared in a hearty voice, then to the man at her side, 'Hello, Reilly.'

'Hello, Grady.' It was a warm and friendly voice, unlike the impersonal tone Leah had heard earlier. A brisk handshake followed the exchange of greetings.

'Let me stow your gear.' Grady reached for the two bags gripped in the man's left hand.

'I'll take the briefcase on board.' Reilly Smith relinquished only the larger of the two bags, retaining the attaché case. His green eyes made an arc in the deepening lavender sky. A single star winked feebly in the purple twilight. 'What's it look like up ahead, Grady?'

The pilot briefly scanned the sky, then shrugged and returned his attention to his passengers. 'There's a front moving in. We still have a chance of reaching Austin before it does. If not, it might get a little rough, but we'll make it.' With his free hand, Grady

16

motioned towards the open door of the plane. 'Climb aboard.'

The two small steps made it easy for Leah to climb on to the wing even in her skirt. Manoeuvring past the front seat to the second seats was more awkward. Reilly Smith followed with an ease that she envied.

He sat down in the seat beside her. Considering the apparent friendliness between himself and the pilot, Leah had partially expected him to sit in front with Grady. As she fastened her seat belt, she noticed the briefcase he had brought on board and realised he probably intended to work.

Grady climbed agilely aboard and swung himself into the pilot's seat directly ahead of Leah. His quick glanced encompassed both of them before he buckled his seat belt.

'Did you two introduce yourselves?' The question didn't break the rhythm of his pre-flight checklist.

'More or less,' Leah answered.

'She's flying to Austin to visit her brother.' The information was given as the first of the plane's engines growled to life, the propeller hesitating, then spinning into a blur.

Leah cast a sideways glance at her companion. 'My brother works for a mining company. He's part of a team that's been temporarily assigned to survey the Austin area.' This seemed like an excellent opportunity to see if Reilly Smith was a member of the same company or with a rival firm. 'Grady mentioned that you had connections with some of the mining interests. Perhaps you know my brother. His name is Lonnie Talbot.'

There was a disconcerting levelness to his jade eyes as they briefly met her look. The grooves at each side of his hard mouth deepened into a faint smile.

'No, I don't know him.'

The roar of both engines made conversation impossible. Leah was forced to set aside her curiosity for the time being. At least she felt secure in the assumption that Reilly Smith did not work for the same company as her brother.

In the pilot's seat, Grady was on the radio. 'Mc-Carren Ground Control, this is 92 George requesting taxi instructions.'

Excitement danced in her veins. After all the waiting, she was finally on her way. Looking out the window, Leah smiled with secret amusement at what Lonnie's reaction would be when he learned she had flown to be with him on his birthday.

Blue lights flashed outside her window as the plane rolled along the taxi strip to the airport runway. At the edge of the runway, the engines roared with thundering force as Grady made his run-up. Then the tower radioed permission for them to take off.

Grady half-looked over his shoulder, a grin on his otherwise serious face. 'Now we'll get this bird off the ground.'

Smoothly the plane pivoted on to the runway, the engines building power. Leah felt the surge of acceleration as the brakes were released and the throttle opened to full power. The nose was lifted off the ground. Seconds later the plane was airborne and climbing, the landing gear thumping into the belly.

Outside her window, Leah could see the blaze of city lights in the pre-night darkness. The brilliant neon lights of the hotels and casinos on Las Vegas's famous Strip were like an iridescently coloured ribbon.

Cool night air from the vent above her head ruffled the light brown wings of her hair. The infra-red lights on the instrument panel kept the darkness at bay, those lights and the reading light shining down on the seat next to hers.

Her fellow passenger was not gazing at the diminishing world below them, Leah noticed. His briefcase was opened on his lap. Common courtesy ruled that she shouldn't try to resume their conversation when he was obviously working. The urge was strong to look over his shoulder and see the contents of the papers he was studying. She resisted, averting her attention again to the window. Eventually the only thing she could see was her own reflection.

She considered taking out the paperback book she had brought in her bag, then decided against it. She was too intent on reaching her destination to concentrate on reading.

The airplane levelled off. Grady partially turned in his seat. 'Want to sit up front with me for a while, Leah?'

'Thank you, yes,' she agreed readily. Conversation would make the time pass faster.

As Leah unbuckled her seat belt, Grady smiled crookedly at the man sitting next to her. 'You don't have any objections to the switch, do you, Reilly?'

'None at all.' There was a faint mockery in the reply as silently laughing green eyes flicked a glance at Leah.

Briefly she wondered if Reilly Smith thought she was making a play for the pilot. Surely he could see that Grady was old enough to be her father.

'Don't bump into any of the controls,' Grady cautioned as Leah crouched in a half-erect position to negotiate the tiny aisle way to the empty front seat.

A helping hand gripped her elbow. With faint surprise, she realised it belonged to Reilly Smith. His touch was pleasantly strong and reassuring, but brief.

Dodging the control panel near the floor, Leah slid on to the right front seat, straightening her skirt over her knees. The change of seats had been accomplished without mishap despite the close quarters.

'Thank you,' she offered over her shoulder for the steadying hand. 'I hope Grady and I talking won't disturb your work, Mr Smith.'

'As a matter of fact, I think I'll quit for a while and get some sleep.' The snap of the briefcase lid followed his statement.

When the reading light went off, Leah fleetingly wished she had not moved from her seat. She would have liked to satisfy some of her curiosity about this Reilly Smith.

'It's amazing.' Grady shook his head, a wry smile on his face.

'What is?' Leah returned blankly.

'Him.' With a backward nod of his head, the pilot indicated the man in the seat behind Leah.

Self-consciously she was aware that Grady's voice carried easily to the man. She glanced over her shoulder to see Reilly Smith's reaction to the comment. He was leaning back in his seat, eyes closed. His chest moved in an even rhythm.

'He's already asleep,' Grady sighed. 'He just closes his eyes. No tossing, no turning, just sleep.'

'Must be nice,' Leah agreed, settling back into her seat. She glanced around at the instrument dials illuminated by the infra-red light. 'Is the plane on auto-pilot now?'

'Yup.' But Leah noticed the automatic way Grady kept checking the panel. 'Have you ever been in the front seat of a private plane before?'

'My dad has taken me up several times, but never in anything as sophisticated as this,' she admitted.

'Modern avionics courtesy of the computer age.' Grady smiled. 'It does everything but land the plane, and nearly does that. It's great, but all equipment breaks down eventually. Let's not talk about flying, though—I hear that all day long. Considering your young years and the length of this flight, I think there's time for you to tell me about your childhood.'

'It won't take long,' Leah laughed softly. 'My brother and I were Air Force brats.' She added a sketchy outline of her childhood life, moving from air base to air base.

'How in heaven's name did you wind up in Las Vegas?'

'The usual way. Dad was transferred to Nellis Air Force Base when I was in high school. I had graduated and just started a secretarial course when his orders came through for Alaska. I wanted to finish my training, so for that reason, and because it was time to leave the nest, I stayed.'

'The lure of the bright lights?' Grady mocked.

'Not a bit. I'm very happy being a secretary,' she stated positively. 'I have no desire to be an entertainer of any sort. The work is too hard and the hours are too demanding.'

'That's true enough,' he agreed. 'Are you like the rest of the Las Vegas residents, rarely stepping inside a gambling casino unless you work there?'

'Exactly!' Then she qualified her answer. 'When new shows open or a favourite celebrity of mine is appearing, I do go then. But on the whole, I leave the casinos for the tourists and the gamblers.'

'Say,' Grady paused, turning a curious look to her, 'did you tell me that you were in the South Pacific for a time?'

'Guam and Hawaii.'

'I was there when I was in the service—and I'm not going to tell you how long ago that was!'

A steady flow of questions began as Grady probed her memory to see if she had been to places he had visited, then compared her descriptions to what he remembered.

Gradually they talked themselves out and drifted into silence. Leah gazed beyond her window reflection at the star-sprinkled sky in the east. She felt sublimely relaxed.

'If you feel like nodding off,' Grady spoke quietly, 'you can crawl back to your old seat. At least there, you can stretch your legs out without fear of bumping any controls.'

With a contented sigh, she agreed. 'I think I'll do that.'

It was a bit easier negotiating the tiny aisle, although Leah took care not to waken the sleeping Reilly. As she turned to slide into her seat, she noticed the inky blankness of the sky directly ahead.

'It's very dark ahead, isn't it?' she questioned Grady softly.

'It must be that frontal system. I think I'll check with the weather bureau and see if I can get an update on it.'

He made the call while she buckled her seat belt. The answering transmission didn't carry clearly to her, but Grady passed the message back.

'The front beat us to Austin. You'd better buckle in tight—it might get a little rough.' Then he glanced over his shoulder at the sleeping figure. 'Reilly!'

'I heard you,' came the quiet reply. With calm

deliberation, Reilly straightened and tightened his seat belt.

'I thought you were asleep.' Leah spoke without thinking.

'I was.'

There was not a trace of sleepiness in his voice. She decided that he wakened as quickly as he went to sleep.

CHAPTER TWO

A BLACK void yawned ominously around the twin
engine plane. Jagged splinters of lighting rained fire in
the sky. Turbulent cross-currents of air alternately
tugged and pushed at the plane.

At each bone-shaking bounce of the plane, Grady
throttled back to avoid putting any more stress on
the structure than necessary. The buffeting only
increased in intensity.

'Reilly!' Grady called for him to lean forward, not
taking his eyes off the gauges and dials bouncing with
the plane in front of him. The dark-haired passenger
loosened his seat belt slightly and bent towards the
pilot. 'It's only going to get worse. I'm going to try to
fly around it. Okay?' he shouted.

'Okay.' The voice that agreed didn't sound at all
troubled by the weather.

Leah, despite all her trust in the competency of
their pilot and the airworthiness of the craft, found
tremors of fear shuddering through her. She tried to
forestall the guilt feeling of cowardice with knowledge that only a fool wouldn't be afraid.

Still, she held her breath as Grady slowly banked
the plane towards the east, trying to outrace the
storm and sneak in around it. Sliding a rounded look

to the man next to her, she decided that behind that expressionless face, he must have nerves of steel.

A severe downdraught sucked at the plane, nearly taking Leah's stomach when the plane groaned free. The pitch blackness that surrounded them was only broken by fiery tongues of lightning licking the air around them. The plane continued bucking through the turbulence.

'I can't get above this stuff!' Grady shouted. 'I'm going to take her down a couple of thousand feet and see if it's any calmer.'

No reply was necessary. Leah doubted if her dry mouth and throat could have made any. It felt as if they were diving, but she knew it was a controlled sideslip downward.

Through the mirrorlike reflection of the window, Leah watched the pilot gently levelling the wings out. Lightning flashed ahead of them, its brilliant yellow-white light lasting for several seconds.

'Sweet Jesus!' Grady's mutter of angry prayer reached Leah's ears at the same instant that she saw the mound of solid black rising in front of the nose.

It was a mountain. She registered the terrifying fact a second before she was thrown violently to one side as Grady executed a sharp right turn.

Another flash of lightning clearly outlined more mountains in their path.

'There aren't supposed to be any damned mountains at this altitude,' came Grady's savage mutter as again he banked sharply. 'This damned altimeter must——'

26

He didn't finish the rest. A jagged fork of lightning had briefly shown an escape route—a low saddle-back ridge connecting two peaks. Grady aimed the nose of the plane at where he thought it had been. Leah waited in frozen stillness for the next streak of lightning that would reveal if his aim was true.

It was late. They were nearly there when the flashing light revealed that he had misjudged the spot. The plane was going to crash into the side of the mountain.

Quickly Grady tried to correct for his error. Leah gasped silently in horror—oh, Lonnie! Fingers closed vicelike on the back of her neck, pushing her head to her knees and holding it there.

'Stay down.' Reilly's softly spoken order pierced her terror.

There was a sickening jolt on the right side of the plane. The right wing tip had clipped the mountain side, metal wrenching and tearing as half of it split away.

The plane pitched downward. 'Come on, baby!' Grady urged below his breath.

The belly of the plane bounced and thudded on solid ground. It sliced along for a few rattling feet, then the right wing again met an immovable object. Their speed sent the plane spinning like a top across the ground.

The screaming rip of metal seemed to surround Leah on all sides without end. Why was it all happening so slowly! her mind cried. Glass shattered above her head. There were more tearing, crunching sounds

27

of metal from her side—the left side.

There was a faint sensation of pain as blackness swirled in front of her eyes. Yet Leah remained semi-conscious, dissociated from what was happening. The roaring in her ears deafened her to all outside sounds.

Then the black mist began to recede. An iron hook of some kind was pulling her upward. A second later she realised it wasn't an iron hook, but a muscled arm.

'Come on. We've got to get out of here.' The firm voice seemed to come from some great distance.

But Leah knew she had to obey the command. She shook her head to chase away the lingering daze. The trembling awkwardness of her legs made the arm around her ribs provide most of her support.

Taking a shaky breath, she suddenly realised she was alive. It was Reilly Smith's arm that was helping her through the open door of the downed plane. As she squeezed through the narrow opening, stumbling over the seats, she wondered why he hadn't opened the door wider.

When her foot touched the loose gravel outside the door, she knew. The plane had stopped lengthwise against the side of the mountain. It was the mountain wall that wouldn't allow the door to open more than it was.

Wind whipped at her hair as she emerged. There was the sting of rain against her cheeks while thunder rumbled ominously overhead. She wanted to lean against the body of the plane and quietly sob her relief and gratitude at being alive, but the arm around her waist wouldn't let her.

'We can't stop here,' Reilly denied.

Accepting that there was wisdom in what he said, Leah didn't protest his guidance. The numbness was leaving her legs. Walking was still difficult over the uneven ground because of the high heels of her shoes.

Some distance from the plane, he halted in an open patch of mountain desert. The supporting arm was removed to press a hand on her shoulder, pushing her to the ground.

'You wait here,' he ordered. 'I'm going back to the plane. And stay down, or you'll make a good target for the lightning.'

Leah nodded, then found her voice. 'I will.' As he pivoted to leave her, she remembered. 'Where's Grady?'

There was no answer as her rescuer glided away into the dark. Perhaps he hadn't heard the question, she decided, or else he was going back to get the pilot.

Lightning crackled. In the illuminating light, she could see his shadowy outline. Beyond was the mutilated metal body of the plane. She shuddered at the miracle that they had survived in that wreckage.

The tiny pellets of wind-whipped rain was not a downpour, but as Leah waited in the darkness, she could feel it slowly soaking her clothes. She pulled the camel-coloured waistcoat closer together.

A shooting pain stabbed her left arm. Experimentally her right hand explored the area of pain. The sleeve of her blouse was wetly sticky and warm. Then her fingers felt the tear in the material and the gash in the soft flesh of her upper arm. She didn't remember being hurt. Instinctively her hand clutched the wound, checking the flow of blood. In this darkness she couldn't see how serious it might be. Only now that she had discovered it was it beginning to throb. Suddenly Leah felt very cold and very alone.

Her gaze tried to penetrate the black curtain of night for a glimpse of the man who had led her here. There was only the ghostly shimmer of white from the painted metal of the aircraft.

Thunder boomed. A flash of lightning followed before the rolling thunder stopped. Leah had promised to wait, but if Reilly Smith didn't return soon, she wasn't going to keep that promise.

An eerie pool of light was coming from the direction of the plane, floating along the ground through the desert scrub. It was several spine-chilling seconds before Leah realised it was coming from a flashlight. A sighing laugh slipped from her throat.

She could distinguish enough of the tall figure to see that he was carrying something over his shoulder. Grady? She waited, breathlessly, for the man to reach her.

Blinded by the light when it picked her out in the darkness, she shielded her eyes from the glare. The light moved away as the figure knelt beside her, swinging the burden from his shoulder. Leah stared at the bundle—a coat with its sleeves tied together to carry the loose objects inside.

'Where's Grady?' Her hazel eyes bored into the expressionless male face as she mentally braced herself for his answer.

'He's dead.' Long fingers began deftly untying the coat sleeves.

'No!' she whispered even as she accepted the truth of his statement. It wasn't something to lie about. She tried to swallow back the tremor in her voice. 'You didn't leave him in the plane?'

'Yes.' The rain bronzed his tanned features into a mask. The green eyes held no hint of grief in their jade depths when they swung towards her. 'Let me see what I can do for your arm.'

Absently Leah touched her wound, its throbbing vaguely uncomfortable. It seemed wrong to have left Grady in that gnarled mess of twisted metal. It was harder to adjust to the fact that he was dead, that warm, vital man.

'You'll have to hold the flashlight.' When his words brought no response from Leah, Reilly frowned. Sooty lashes thickened by the rain narrowed his gaze. 'Snap out of it!'

'W-What?' she blinked.

'I said you'll have to hold the flashlight so I can look at your arm,' he repeated curtly.

Her hazel eyes had started to mist with tears. She hurriedly blinked them away as her fingers closed over the cold wet metal of the flashlight. She directed the beam at her injury. Beyond the radiating circle, she saw Reilly Smith remove his pocket knife and open the blades.

'I'm going to rip the sleeve the rest of the way.' With the explanation given, the blade sliced through the material's seam. A quick rip and the sleeve was in his hand.

Using the remnants, he carefully wiped away the blood to see the extent of the cut. The jagged rip in her flesh wasn't a pleasant sight and Leah turned her gaze away. She could feel him probing the wound for any splinters of glass or metal. It throbbed with burning fire now.

He turned away, opening the metal lid of a large first aid kit that he had placed at his side. He took out a bottle of antiseptic and closed the lid before the rain could damage any of the contents. Water droplets glistened like diamonds in his jet black hair.

'This is going to hurt,' he warned.

Although prepared, Leah couldn't stop herself from emitting a choked gasp of pain as her arm jerked to avoid the fiery liquid.

'Hold still!'

'It hurts!' she snapped back, stating the obvious.

Reilly Smith ignored that. 'And hold the light still so I can see what I'm doing.'

Insensitive pig! Leah thought angrily. At least he could have said he was sorry but that he couldn't help hurting her.

Gritting her teeth, she focused the light again on her arm. This time she didn't cry out as he poured the antiseptic on the open wound, although the flashlight beam did waver slightly. Next came the bandage, which was expertly and efficiently accomplished.

'Thank you,' Leah offered as some of the pain began to recede.

'You're welcome.' A distant smile touched his mouth.

He took the flashlight and laid it on the ground, bathing their clearing with light. Unfolding the coat on the ground, he slipped a pistol into the waistband of his brown slacks and pulled his jacket over it to keep out the rain. A canteen and another small box were set to the side along with a folded square of red material. He stood up, shaking out the coat.

'This will keep the rain off of you,' he said, holding it out to Leah.

'In case you haven't noticed, I'm already soaked.' She hugged her arms tighter around her waist, feeling the biting chill of her damp clothes.

'I don't want the bandage getting wet.' He draped a man's raincoat over her shoulders, drawing the collar around her neck. 'At night, it's cold in the mountain desert—in the spring or any other time of year. It will give you some protection against the cold if not the rain.'

What she wanted was some dry clothes, but logically Leah realised that they would soon get wet, too. Gingerly she slid her injured arm in a sleeve and carefully eased her other arm into the second sleeve and buttoned the coat.

'Whose is this?' she asked unthinkingly as the coat drowned her in its looseness.

33

'Grady's.'

Leah paled. Suddenly the coat didn't feel the same. She started to unbutton it.

'You can wear it,' she murmured tightly.

'No.' His voice was firm as his watchful eyes studied her face. 'He isn't going to object, Miss Talbot.'

Her temper flared at his apparently flippant remark. 'How can you be so callous?'

'It's the truth—however hard it may sound,' Reilly Smith replied calmly. Her anger flowed over him without denting his aloof composure. 'There isn't anything more we can do for Grady. Our main concern now has to be ourselves. We'll have to use what's on hand to survive the night.'

His cold logic defeated her anger. She began rebuttoning the coat. 'You could build a fire to warm us up and dry us out,' she declared, a seed of rebellion remaining.

'It's raining,' he reminded her dryly.

'Well,' impatiently she pushed the wet brown hair away from her forehead, 'you are part Indian. Surely it shouldn't be too difficult for you.'

An eyebrow lifted in a measuring look. Her teeth nibbled selfconsciously on her lower lip. That had sounded very prejudiced and she hadn't meant it at all that way. His composure had got under her skin and made her thoughtless in her reply.

He reached down and picked up the folded red square. 'A fire could be built,' there was a hint of

34

cynical amusement in his voice, 'after I'd found some dry wood and started the kindling in the rain. Maybe after a couple of hours, I would have a fire blazing—if the two of us hadn't succumbed to exposure and shock, we might enjoy it.'

'I'm sorry, I didn't think.' Leah lowered her gaze to the ground. She took a deep breath and let it out slowly. 'We can't sit out here in the rain. Wouldn't we be better off in the plane?'

'The metal of the plane would act like a lightning rod. It's too dangerous.' The square of red was shaken out, rustling stiffly in protest. The opposite side of the material resembled aluminium. Its silvery finish glistened in the flashlight beam. 'Besides, higher up the mountain there are some loose tailings from an abandoned mine. The rain might bring it down and block the door by morning. Out here, we might get wet and cold—it wouldn't be any warmer in the plane—but we wouldn't be trapped inside the mangled wreckage.'

Again, Leah had to submit to the wisdom of his reasoning. But she was wet and cold, and getting colder. Her teeth had started to chatter and her arm was beginning to stiffen and feel sore.

'What are we going to do?' Her gaze wearily moved to him. Since all her thoughts seemed to have been wrong, it was time he suggested something.

'Stand up.'

His hand was at her elbow, lifting her upright. Leah stood, waiting uncertainly for his next move. The thin, blanket-size sheet was partially wrapped around her, rising above her head in a stiff half-hood.

'Hold the side,' Reilly instructed, pushing an edge of the material into her fingers. He hesitated, drawing her curious gaze. 'What we're going to do is wrap ourselves together in this blanket, using our body heat to keep us warm and the blanket to keep out as much of the rain as possible.'

'You're saying we should sleep together.' Leah repeated the essence of his words. She was shivering and trying to keep her teeth from chattering too loudly. 'It's the logic and practical thing to do, isn't it?' she added wryly.

'Yes,' he nodded with a faint smile on his wet face.

She was too cold and wet and miserable to care that her straitlaced parents would be horrified to learn their daughter was sleeping under the same blanket with a virtual stranger.

'By all means, let's do it,' she agreed, weakly returning his smile.

An arm slid around the bulky folds of the raincoat at her waist as he drew the stiff blanket behind and around him. At his signal, they eased themselves to the ground in unison.

Reilly lay on his back, drawing Leah's head and shoulders on to his chest and curving the rest of her against his length. Pellets of rain struck at the blanket, hammering to get in, but the waterproof material kept them dry.

At first she was conscious only of the cold wetness

of his hard form, then gradually she felt his body warmth steaming through his soaked clothes and she snuggled closer, shivering uncontrollably. His hands began rubbing her back, shoulders and waist, stimulating her circulation while taking care to avoid her injured arm that throbbed dully now.

'Is that better?' Warm breath stirred the air near her forehead.

'Much better.' She inhaled deeply in contentment. The musky scent of his maleness was heightened by the rain.

His hands maintained their slow, steady rhythm. A small fire was glowing inside her. She was beginning to feel human again. Her mind stopped dwelling on her physcial discomfort and started to wander on to other subjects.

'A search party will start looking for us tomorrow, won't they?' she said quietly.

'Yes.'

'How long do you think it will take them to find us?'

'It's hard to say,' For a minute Leah thought that was the only reply Reilly was going to make, then he enlarged upon his answer. 'There wasn't time for a mayday call to give our location. Grady had his hands full trying to keep from nosing into the side of the mountain. If he filed a flight plan, he flew off-course trying to avoid the centre of the storm. A search would initially cover the planned route, then widen its area if the plane wasn't found.'

'Then it could be late tomorrow before they find us?'

A moment of slight hesitation followed her question. 'There's a lot of rugged terrain a party would have to cover. It could be Sunday—or Monday.'

Leah shuddered, this time not from the cold. 'I'm glad I didn't let Lonnie know I was coming. He won't be worrying about me for a while anyway, wondering if I'm dead or alive.'

The authorities would first notify her parents. They, in turn, would contact her brother. With luck, by then she would be rescued.

'You were planning to surprise him?'

Leah nodded, her cheek moving against the damp denim of his jacket. 'For his birthday. It's tomorrow,' she sighed, then pulled her mind away from its depressing path. 'You were expected, weren't you?'

'Yes, by some business friends.'

'Who do you work for?' She tipped her head back against his shoulder, peering through the darkness of their cocoon for a glimpse of his face. The suggestion of intimacy at being in his arms seemed to banish the need for diplomatically worded questions. Her curiosity surfaced without disguise. 'An arch rival of the mining firm that employs my brother?'

'I work for myself,' he replied.

'You own a mining company?'

'No.' There was amused patience in his low voice. 'I design jewellery.'

As Leah digested the information, she remembered

38

the nugget of turquoise he wore around his neck. 'Turquoise jewellery?'

'Or Indian jewellery, whichever you prefer to call it.' The mockery was unmistakable in his tone.

Leah stiffened defensively. 'I didn't mean for my comment to sound derogatory earlier. I was cold and wet and thought a fire would be the logical remedy. I simply didn't know how to build one—not from scratch.' She hesitated, irritated that he had even indirectly referred to her thoughtlessly cutting remark earlier. 'Grady had mentioned that you were part Indian. I only referred to it because I thought you would have the experience at building fires which I didn't have.'

'You didn't need to explain. I'd already guessed that,' Reilly Smith returned complacently.

Sputtering inwardly, Leah longed to demand why he had let her make the apology if, as he said, he had already guessed. It was pointless to begin an argument about it, though, since initially the fault had been hers.

'Then why were you flying to Austin?' Leah swallowed her irritation and switched to a less personal topic.

'There are turquoise mines in the vicinity that I periodically visit,' he said with a thread of indulgence. 'I deal directly with them, purchasing the stones I want to use for mounting.'

'I didn't know that.' She frowned slightly, trying to remember if Lonnie had mentioned the turquoise mines in one of his letters. 'About the mines being there, I mean.'

'There's a line of turquoise deposits that runs almost directly down the centre of the State, starting around Battle Mountain through Austin. At Tonopah it curves north north-west. The line would look like a "J" if you drew it on a map.'

'I guess I always thought most of the turquoise was found in Arizona.'

'Arizona does produce quite a bit, but mostly as a by-product of their copper mining.' His fingers gently pulled her long, wet hair free of the coat collar, smoothing it over her back. 'I think it's time we got some sleep. It's going to be a long day tomorrow.'

The truth was Leah didn't want to stop talking. As long as her mind was occupied with other things, it couldn't dwell on the crash.

'I suppose you're right,' she sighed reluctantly, adding a silent 'again' to the admission. Her eyelids were beginning to feel heavy. 'What time is it?'

'Nearing midnight, I imagine. Are you comfortable?'

'Yes,' she nodded, nestling her head closer to his chest. 'Goodnight.'

'Goodnight.'

Silence closed in. Despite the crash of thunder and lightning and the tapping of rain, it was silence. There were none of the sounds of cars and people or street-lights shining through the window that usually lulled her to sleep.

The ground was hard and unyielding beneath her hip. Her pillow, Reilly's chest, rose and fell in even breathing. The steady rhythm of his heart beat against her ear.

If things had been different, she would have been sleeping in a strange bed tonight, but none as alien as this. And Lonnie would have been close by. Her throat tightened as she remembered that if things had been different, Grady would be alive, too.

'If we'd left earlier,' she murmured in a low, choked voice, 'we could have beaten the storm to Austin.'

'You would be with your brother. I would be with my friends and Grady wouldn't be dead.' Leah could feel the vibration of Reilly's low-pitched voice against her ear, unemotional and aloof. 'That isn't the way it is. It's best that you accept that.'

Tears slid down her cheeks as she bitterly admitted he was right again. But it didn't make it any easier to accept. Her lashes fluttered down, clinging to the tears on her lower lashes.

In the night, her troubled and uneasy sleep was interrupted by a rolling roar that seemed to vibrate the ground beneath them. She stirred, her eyes opening in a frowning blink.

'What was that?' she whispered bewilderedly. She tried to level herself up on an elbow, but the arm around her tightened and a hand pressed her head against his chest.

41

'It's nothing to worry about,' Reilly answered quietly. 'Go back to sleep.'

Not fully awake and with her muscles stiffly protesting any need for movement, Leah obeyed. It was probably just the thunder anyway, she told herself.

CHAPTER THREE

IT wasn't thunder.

The morning sun was in her eyes, but the light didn't blind Leah to the mound of chipped rock and rubble in front of her. A landslide had completely covered the plane.

Farther up the mountain slope on a rocky ledge, her gaze noted the black hole of a mine entrance. A fallen timber lay across in the opening, supporting only its own weight. Last night's rain had sent the loose tailings from the mine down the slope.

Leah remembered Reilly's warning about it. If they had taken shelter in the plane, they would have been trapped inside or smothered by the gravel debris.

This morning her bones ached from sleeping on the hard surface of the ground and her muscles were cramped from clinging to the warmth of Reilly's body. Yet somewhere under that mound of rock was the plane, and her discomfort seemed like a very small thing.

Soberly she watched Reilly Smith carefully working his way over the rubble. At each step, the ground shifted beneath his feet, miniature slides of loose gravel rolling away. Then he stopped, kneeling gingerly to push away the rock.

A patch of white was revealed and made larger. Using the length of his left arm as a barricade, he held back the gravel that tried to recover the patch. With painstaking slowness he pushed more rock away with his free hand, digging downward along the side of the plane.

His goal was the baggage compartment in the crumpled nose of the plane. The crash had buckled the door, popping it partly open at the bottom. Leah watched Reilly straining with only one free hand to open it the rest of the way.

When the last fragment of latch released itself, he quickly lifted it up, using it instead of his arm to hold back the gravel. Reaching inside, he wasted no time in dragging out his suitcase, then Leah's two pieces of luggage.

Gravel danced around both sides of the door in warning. He shoved the cases away, letting the rolling rocks carry them away from the plane. Leah held her breath as he slowly lowered the door. The trickle of rocks grew steadily louder as the angle lessened.

Above him, there was an uneasy shifting of rocks, but no fresh slide started when the door was down and immediately covered by slow-moving gravel. Turning, he inched his way down the slope in a half-sitting position to the luggage.

When he stood on firm ground again, Leah let out the breath she had been holding in a relieved sigh. Reilly picked up all three cases and walked to where she stood a safe distance away.

44

'Now we can change out of these clothes.' The grooves around his mouth deepened to suggest a smile.

'I can hardly wait,' agreed Leah definitely. Although she had dried out considerably from her soaking last night, her clothes still felt vaguely damp against her skin.

'Have you got a pair of jeans in there?' He set her bag and cosmetic case on the ground in front of her.

'Slacks,' she told him.

'You'd better put them on, and some flat shoes.'

Leah glanced around. The mountain side was sparsely covered with desert scrub. There was not a rock or boulder in sight large enough to use as a dressing curtain.

'Where can I change?' she asked finally.

An amused light danced in his green eyes. 'Wherever you want,' he shrugged.

'I mean somewhere private,' Leah retorted. 'I don't intend to strip in front of an audience.'

'I guess you'll have to crouch behind one of the bushes, then.' His expression changed to one of complete indifference as he bent to unsnap the lid of his suitcase. 'I'm more interested in changing my own damp clothes than being an audience for you.'

Pressing her lips tightly together, Leah knelt in front of her suitcase. Her injured left arm was held stiffly across her waist. It hurt badly this morning. She took care not to bump it accidentally as she unlatched the lid and began rummaging through the bag's contents for fresh underwear, slacks, and top.

'I wasn't suggesting that you would sit and applaud while I undressed,' she muttered tautly.

'Oh? What were you suggesting?' Reilly mocked cynically.

'Just a desire for some degree of privacy.' Leah rolled her change of clothes into a ball and placed a pair of flat-heeled loafers on top.

'You can have all the privacy our primitive surroundings will permit.' His strong, lean features were impassive.

'Thank you.' She flipped the lid of her suitcase shut with a snap.

Rising awkwardly with her bundle, she marched towards a thick clump of sage, her nose tilted into the air. Damn! she cursed silently. She had done it again.

His jesting remark to dress wherever she wanted had not had the suggestive meaning she thought. She had taken offence and defended her sense of modesty without cause. The indignant outburst had been unwarranted and unjustified. The result was that she had been made to look the ignorant fool.

Why do I always put my foot in my mouth? she sighed angrily.

'Miss Talbot.'

His low voice halted her steps. She turned hesitantly towards him, suddenly wary, knowing he deserved an apology yet still too angry with herself to make one that would sound sincere.

'What?' she asked, somewhat abruptly.

'Before you put a clean blouse on, I'd like to look at your arm.'

'All right,' she agreed, and resumed her course to the large bush.

Not until she had shed her damp clothes and put on clean underwear and the olive green pair of slacks did she realise that he had wanted to look at her wound before she changed her clothes and not before she put on a clean blouse. The ripped sleeve of her blouse would have given him free access to the bandage.

The lacy edges of her brassiere accented too much the cleavage between her breasts for her to let him see her in only that. It didn't matter that it covered more than her bikini top. She looked with disfavour on the damp, rumpled blouse she had been wearing. She couldn't stand the thought of putting it on again.

'You get yourself into some fine messes sometimes, Leah Talbot!' she muttered to herself.

Picking up the crisp olive and yellow print blouse, she wrapped it under her arms and around her breasts, holding it securely shut with her right hand. With a wry twist of her mouth she decided that she was decently covered and stepped from behind the bush.

The morning air was cool yet, sharply scented by last night's rain with sage. A shiver danced over her bare shoulders. Leah couldn't decide whether it was from the coolness or a chill of apprehension.

Reilly was in the clearing where they had spent the

47

night, his back turned to her. He seemed to be buttoning the clean white shirt that hung down over a pair of dark blue denims. The sunlight glistened blackly on his hair.

'Do you want to look at my arm now, Mr Smith?' Leah asked in a faintly defensive tone.

He glanced over his shoulder, then pivoted slowly, the shirt buttoned halfway. Without finishing his task, he reached down for the first aid kit.

'Yes, I will,' he answered smoothly.

Leah walked towards him, holding her head proudly to hide the nervous hammerings of her heart. His gaze moved lazily to the white bra straps over her shoulders. A dull red flush crept into her cheeks.

'I misunderstood what you meant earlier. I forgot about the sleeve,' she offered in self-protection.

'I realised that.' A dark glow entered his jade eyes, but she couldn't tell whether or not he was laughing at her. 'I was going to explain more fully what I meant, but I thought you might launch into another attack before I'd finished.'

'I'm sorry.' Leah lowered the angle of her chin by several degrees.

But Reilly was already removing the adhesive strips to examine her wound, accepting her apology without comment. The gentle probing of his fingers made her wince.

'Hurt?' His piercing gaze slid quickly to her face.

'Of course.' Her teeth sank into her lower lip,

nibbling at it to distract her mind from the pain in her arm.

'It looks clean. Does it feel like there's anything in it? A piece of glass?' he questioned.

'No. It's just sore.' Leah shook her head.

'I'll put a clean bandage on.'

She watched as he deftly changed the bandage to a fresh one. Her gaze strayed to the tanned column of his neck and the hollow of his throat where the nugget of turquoise rested. Then it was drawn down the partially unbuttoned front of his shirt where his muscled chest gleamed bronze and smooth like a statue's. It was several seconds before she realised he was finished. Caught staring, she flushed guiltily.

'Thank you.' Her fingers tightened on her blouse as his gaze moved over her face.

'You're welcome.' There was a mocking inclination of his dark head. Then Reilly turned his back to her. 'You can put on your blouse now.' With definite overtones of laughter in his voice, he added, 'As long as you promise not to watch me tuck my shirt into my levis.'

Laughing softly, Leah promised and turned her back to him. She carefully eased her injured arm into the sleeve of her blouse, then twisted to find the other sleeve.

As she buttoned the last button, Reilly asked, 'Finished?'

'Yes, you can turn around now.' A wide natural smile was curving her mouth when he turned around, the dark jade of his eyes glittering brilliantly warm.

'Do you feel better?' He reached down to pick up a denim jacket lying across his suitcase.

'Clean, dry clothes are a wonderful improvement,' Leah agreed. 'The only way I could feel better is if I'd already had breakfast.'

'The tin box sitting over there has some crackers in it,' he suggested. 'That's the best I can offer in the way of food until I can collect some firewood and get a fire going. There isn't much water in the canteen, so use it carefully,' he cautioned.

'I will.' She knelt beside the box and unlatched the lid. There was more than crackers inside. There were several packages of dried food that had to be mixed with water and sticks of beef jerky. 'I didn't know that charter flights carried food survival kits?'

'They don't as a rule,' Reilly answered. 'Grady was just superstitious.'

'Superstitious? What do you mean?' Leah frowned.

'He served overseas during the Korean war. He flew light reconnaissance aircraft. Survival kits were carried almost as standard equipment,' he explained. 'One day Grady forgot his and his plane was hit by gunfire. He crashed in some heavy foliage, breaking a leg. Luckily he was in friendly territory, but it was almost three days before he was found. He swore he almost starved to death. After that he never went up without the kit and he was never shot down again. When he'd served his term and was released from the service, he came back to the States and got a job flying. He kept on carrying a kit like this as a good luck charm.'

The partially unwrapped cellophane of crackers was in her hand. The appetite Leah had thought she had had receded. 'The kit didn't bring him very much luck this time,' she murmured sadly.

Reilly didn't comment on that. 'I pointed out to him once that those dehydrated foods wouldn't be much use in this desert country where the most valuable commodity is water. His reply was that he'd never have to use it anyway, but this way the food wouldn't keep spoiling all the time.'

Dully Leah swung her gaze to the rocky mound of earth that covered the plane. 'Can't we get him out of there?'

'No. It would take men and machinery and a way of holding back the slide.' She had known what his answer would be, but she had needed to hear it. 'I'm going to go look for some wood to build a signal fire,' Reilly continued, switching the subject back to their original topic. 'You stay here. You'll be all right.'

'Yes.' Leah was still staring at the gravelike mound that covered the plane.

'Keep an eye out for search planes. I doubt if they'll be this far east so early this morning, but keep watch.'

His firm voice reminded her that their concern must be for their rescue. The pilot was beyond help. Breathing in deeply, Leah returned her attention to the small package of crackers in her hand.

'I will,' she promised.

'Shout if you need me,' he added.

At Leah's nod, he smiled in reassurance and started up the mountain slope towards the abandoned mine. His lithe stride chose a new path, avoiding the unstable ground of the slide. Leah watched him until he disappeared on the rocky ledge high above.

Taking care not to tear the wrapper, she opened the cracker package. The salty square tasted dry and chalky in her mouth. She ate only one and tightly wrapped the others in the package. As she picked up the canteen, Leah remembered Reilly's statement that water was valuable.

Hesitating, she took a small swig to wash the cracker down, then re-capped it. It was ironic, she thought, how a person always felt more thirsty when they knew water was scarce. The arid landscape made the nearly full canteen seem like very little.

Setting it aside, she reached for her cosmetic case. She creamed her face with cleansing lotion before applying fresh make-up. When her long hair had been brushed free of the snarls of sleep and laid about her shoulders in a silken curtain of light brown, she felt almost whole again.

Her hazel eyes, bright again with renewed spirit, scanned the western sky. Not a single cloud broke the pale blue scene. The storm clouds of last night had completely disappeared.

A bird was soaring lazily above the desert valley

floor below the mountain. In the far distance, Leah could see the wispy ribbon of a jet trail. The desert seemed to stretch for endless miles. The awesome fact registered that she couldn't see one sign of human habitation, not a building and not a road.

A tremendous sense of isolation closed over her. The incredible silence of the desert mountains was loud. What if they weren't found? Before it overwhelmed her, Leah rose to her feet. She was not going to panic, she told herself. There was a search party looking for them. She was not stranded in this forbidding wilderness for ever.

She glanced at the rocky ledge where she had last seen Reilly. She wished he would come back soon. Shout if you need me, he had said. Right now, she needed to know he was still out there. But she stifled the desire to call out to him.

Activity was the answer. Sitting doing nothing, she had let her imagination run away with her. The search party would find them. It was only a matter of time. Meanwhile, the best thing was to occupy herself with some small task until Reilly returned. Favouring her injured arm, Leah glanced around to find that task. Her gaze fell on the damp clothes she had laid on top of her suitcase.

They would never dry in that heap. Her blouse was on top. Leah picked it up and carried it to a bush, spreading it out for the sun to dry. Then she returned for the next piece of clothing. Deliberately taking her time, she made a project out of it, smoothing out the wrinkles and spreading all four corners of the garment over the bush. It served to prolong the task.

When her clothes were laid out to dry, she started on Reilly's. She was straightening the sleeves on his brown jacket when a loosened stone rolled down the slope behind her. Turning, she saw Reilly working his way down, his arms laden with small, broken chunks of wood. The bulk of it seemed to be pieces of timber from the mine.

'Hello!' Her greeting echoed the happiness and relief she felt at his return. Mostly it was happiness. 'I see you found some wood.'

'There's more up there, so we won't have to worry about wood for the time being.' He flashed her a quick smile, the mask of aloofness gone. 'I found something else, too.'

'What?' Leah held her breath.

She sensed that whatever he had found pleased him. It was responsible for the brilliant light in his eyes that seemed to radiate a satisfied glow over his compelling features. Maybe he had seen a road or highway on the other side of the mountain.

'Water,' Reilly stated, dumping the wood on to the ground near the centre of the clearing. He looked back up the mountain. 'There's a rocky outcropping on the east side beneath a slight overhang. It's shaped like a basin. Last night's rain filled it about half full.'

'Then it's safe to drink?' It wasn't a sign of civilisation he had found, but her cottony tongue said it was nearly as good.

'It's rain water.' The corners of his eyes crinkled to match the smile curving the male line of his mouth.

'I feel like drinking the canteen dry to celebrate,' she laughed.

'Be my guest.' He motioned towards the canteen as he kneeled beside the pile of wood.

'Now that I know I can drink, I don't feel very thirsty,' she shrugged.

Reilly picked out a thin plank of wood and used it as a scraper to clear a fire circle. 'Would you gather some stones to make a fire ring? Some of those near the slide should do.'

Hampered by her sore arm, it was a slow job collecting the medium sized rocks to form an outer protective ring. When Reilly had the ground cleared to his satisfaction, he took out his pocket knife and began splintering wood for kindling. The tiny mound of wood chips lay in the centre of the circle.

'Do you have any paper?' Reilly asked.

'Some tissue in my cosmetic case,' Leah volunteered.

'That should work fine.' While she went to get it, he removed a box of matches from his inside jacket pocket.

She handed him one of the white tissues and watched him stuff it beneath the wood chips. Removing one match, he struck against the side of the box. He cupped the flame protectively with his hand as he carried it to the tissue and kindling. The white

55

tissue charred, then burst into flame. A teasing breeze swirled the tiny fire.

Reilly nursed it carefully so the fire wouldn't be blown out. 'If there's one guarantee in lighting a fire, it's that no matter which way the wind is blowing when you start, it will change direction the minute the fire has started.' He slid a glittering look at Leah, amusement in the crooked smile. 'Invariably blowing the smoke at the person who started the fire.'

'Is that a piece of Indian lore?' She laughed at the truth in his comment.

'Naturally.' As the kindling started to burn, Reilly added slightly larger pieces of wood, stacking them in a pyramid around and above the small flame.

There was only a small breeze blowing, a mere breath of wind. Leah looked around the clearing at the dry-looking sagebrush that stretched over the mountainside. Here and there a pinyon tree dotted the slopes, but they were very few.

'There isn't any chance of starting a grass fire, is there?' she asked, trying not to imagine the horror of trying to escape from that.

'Very little,' Reilly answered. 'The fire ring will keep the flames from spreading as long as the wind isn't strong. Strangely enough, it's rare to have a fire sweep through the desert, considering how dry and flammable some of the plants are.'

'Why?' Leah tipped her head curiously to one side, absently tucking the opposite side of her hair behind her ear.

'Mainly because it's so dry,' was his cryptic reply. Then he explained, 'There's so little moisture in the desert that the plants can't grow close together. Their root systems are wide and deep to absorb every available trace of water, so they choke out any new plant that tries to grow. The distance between plants keeps any fire that starts from spreading.'

He sat back on his heels, waiting for the pyramid-like stack of wood to catch fire. Leah understood what he had meant last night about it being a slow process to build a fire, without the aid of kerosene or starter fuel.

'Now that we've found water, we can mix up some of that dehydrated food,' he stated.

'I'll see what we have.' Leah opened the metal box and began looking at the packages inside. 'Here's some beef stew, but what shall we heat it in?'

'There's some twisted fragments of metal from the plane wing over by the slide. Maybe one of them can be used as a makeshift pan.'

'I'll see.' She started to get to her feet, but he motioned her to sit back down.

'On second thoughts, I'd better look,' he said. 'I don't want you accidentally cutting yourself on the metal edges.'

He stacked two more pieces of wood, larger than those propped against each other, making sure there remained openings at the bottom to keep a circling draught of air.

Leah didn't object as he rose smoothly to his feet. With only one hand operating effectively, she had already discovered gathering rocks for the fire ring that she was very clumsy.

Within a few minutes Reilly had returned with a twisted piece of metal. Using two of the rocks around the fire, one as a hammer and one as a hard surface, he beat away the sharp edges around the outside. Then he turned the angularly hollowed centre upside down on top of the rock and hammered a flat bottom in the pan. When the sides were fairly straight, he examined it for a moment, then glanced at Leah.

'Do you think it will work, cook?' A mocking eyebrow was lifted in question.

'So I'm the cook, am I?' Leah nodded in an amused, knowing manner.

There was a wicked glint in his dark jade eyes. 'Cooking is squaw's work, isn't it?'

Leah smiled and shook her head, silently amazed that they could be joking about the Indian blood that flowed in his veins after she had made that challenging and unwittingly derogatory remark last night.

'I've heard that it is,' she admitted.

'Will the pan do, then?' He held it out for her inspection.

'I think so.' Leah took the pan and set it on the ground beside her. 'Hand me the canteen, will you? I'll start mixing the stew while you get the fire hot.'

First, Leah rinsed out the makeshift pan with a little water, wiping it dry with some tissue. By guess, she roughly measured the amount of water required into the pan and added the dried soup.

'What can I use to stir this?' She glanced at Reilly, her face breaking into a sudden smile. 'Better yet, how are we going to eat this without a spoon?'

'Here's my pocket knife.' He handed it to her with the blade closed. 'I guess we'll have to stab the meat and potatoes with the blade and drink the liquid.'

'The pan will have to work as a community bowl, too, I guess,' she laughed shortly, and stirred the dry ingredients into the water.

It was almost an hour later before Reilly could separate a few glowing coals from the fire bed to heat the stew. He propped the pan an inch above the embers on some flat rocks.

It wasn't long before the liquid started bubbling, emitting an appetising aroma.

In the interim, Reilly had fashioned two shallow bowls from the metal fragments of the plane, explaining that the sides of the pan would be too hot to drink from. When the stew was heated through, he took the shirt Leah had draped over a bush and folded it to use as a potholder to remove the pan from the coals.

Carefully he poured part of the stew into the two bowls and handed Leah's to her. Leah refused his offer to use the knife, choosing to scoop out the chunky pieces with a cracker. Neither utensils were efficient, but they both served their purpose.

'Cigarette?' Reilly offered when they had finished

their meal, removing a pack from his shirt pocket and shaking out a filtered tip for her.

'Mmm, please.' Leah accepted the cigarette, bending forward as he lit the end with the burning tip of a stick from the fire.

They smoked their cigarettes in a comfortable silence. Leah finished hers first, then tossing the butt into the growing camp fire.

'I suppose I should clean the dishes,' she sighed.

'Might as well,' Reilly agreed. 'We might have to use them tonight.' His comment drew her attention to the sky, empty of any search plane. 'Sand will work better than water to clean.'

Drawing her gaze away from the sky, Leah picked up the pan and poured in a handful of small sand. When it was scoured clean she rinsed away the grit with a little water and started on the shallow bowls. Reilly picked up the canteen and emptied it into the pan.

'Why did you do that?' she frowned.

'I'm going to refill the canteen from the basin. While I'm gone I want you to have water on hand to pour on the fire in case you see a search plane,' he answered.

'But it will put the fire out,' Leah protested.

'It will also make a lot of smoke which with luck the pilot would see and come to investigate,' Reilly pointed out.

'I see.' Dimples edged into her cheeks. 'The old Indian smoke trick.'

'Right,' he winked, and started walking towards the slope.

She scoured the two bowls clean, rinsing them with a handful of water from the pot and wiping them dry with a tissue. With that done, she checked the clothes she had draped over the bushes and found that they were dry. She folded hers up and put them in her suitcase. Reilly's she stacked neatly on top of his suitcase. With only the partial use of her left hand, the task had taken some time, yet still Reilly hadn't returned. The sun was making its fiery presence in the sky felt. Leah added some more wood to the fire and sat down away from the blaze to wait.

Finally she saw him on the ledge above. He started down the fairly steep slope with the canteen in one hand and a four-foot-long board in the other.

'I wondered what was taking you so long,' Leah called when he was half way down. 'You made a sidetrip for more firewood.'

At the base of the slope, Reilly made his reply. 'No, I'm not going to use this board for firewood.' He set the canteen beside the box of packaged food. 'I'm going to try and split it in two and make lean-to poles out of it. It's going to get hotter and we'll need to get out of the sun.'

After splitting the board down the middle with the pocket-knife as his wedge, he whittled each end to a point. The stiff, blanket-like sheet they had used last night had grommets in each corner. The stakes supported two of the blanket's corners and Reilly weighted the other two to the ground with rocks.

'A strong wind would probably blow it down, but it keeps out the sun,' he declared, then bent down to sit inside his lean-to and waved Leah to join him.

She moved eagerly to its shade, revelling in the coolness after the burning rays of the sun. Reilly picked up one of the sticks from the firewood pile and began whittling on it with his knife.

'What are you making now?' she asked curiously.

'I thought I'd try my hand at carving a spoon.'

Laying on her back with her arm as a pillow, she watched him shaving away the outer layer of wood with his knife. The steady rhythm of the slashing blade was slightly hypnotic. Soon she found her eyelids growing heavy.

'Why don't you take a siesta?' Reilly suggested when she tried to blink away the tiredness. 'I'll keep a watch for any search planes.'

'I think I will.' She stopped fighting the drowsiness and closed her eyes.

CHAPTER FOUR

LEAH slept through the heat of the afternoon. The same rhythmic sound that lulled her to sleep was the first one she heard when she wakened. Reilly was sitting in the long shadow of the lean-to, whittling on a stick that now bore considerable resemblance to a wooden spoon.

Blinking the sleep from her eyes. she started to push herself into a sitting position. Unconsciously she used both arms as a lever and gasped sharply at the pain that stabbed like a burning knife in her left arm. Quickly she switched all her weight to her right arm.

'That was stupid,' she muttered.

'Is your arm bothering you a lot?' Reilly's green eyes narrowed with piercing scrutiny.

'Only when I do something like that.' She sat upright, cradling her left arm in her lap as the shooting pain began to recede. Her mouth felt scratchy and dry as if coated with wool. A frown marred her forehead as she glanced around the circle. 'I need a drink. Where's the canteen?'

'In the shade behind you.'

Leah had to shift slightly to reach it. Uncapping it, she took a long swallow. The water was warm but

63

deliciously wet. The funny taste left her mouth.

'How are you getting on with the spoon?' At her question, Reilly's knife stopped its slashing as he held it up for her to see. 'It looks like a spoon.' The knife resumed its work. A fly buzzed noisily about her head, pulling Leah's gaze to the empty sky. 'There hasn't been any sign of a search plane?'

'No.' He didn't elaborate. After several minutes of silence, he set the spoon-shaped piece of wood on the ground, folded back the knife blade and slipped it into his pocket. 'We'll need some more firewood for tonight. I won't be gone long.'

As he started up the slope, Leah scooted from beneath the lean-to and stood up to scratch her legs, arching her back to ease the stiffness from lying on the hard ground. The action tipped her head back, and a black object in the sky overhead caught her eye.

A buzzard was slowly circling. Leah shuddered, bringing her gaze swiftly to earth to focus on the slide. She was glad that the rock and debris had buried the plane and Grady. The desert scavenger was wasting his time.

She didn't want to let her thoughts dwell on its menacing presence, so she turned towards the western horizon. Shielding her eyes from the glare of the late afternoon sky, she studied the empty blueness. There was not a speck of anything. Surely by now the rescue party would be widening their search grid, she thought.

Her parents had probably received the notification that she was missing—and her brother, too. Oh, Lonnie, what a rotten birthday present! Tears misted her eyes at the dispiriting thought of the agony her family was going through.

An explosive sound ripped the air. Her first reaction was that a car had backfired before she realised that the idea was ludicrous because there were no cars. It had to have been a gunshot.

In a flash of memory, she recalled the pistol Reilly carried in his waistband of his levis. What could he have been shooting at? A snake? Terror gripped her throat. This area was probably crawling with venomous rattlesnakes.

'What if he's been bitten?' The thought, uttered aloud, made it seem all the more possible.

Spinning, she raced towards the slope. Her widened hazel eyes scanned the rocky ledge where he had disappeared from sight.

'Reilly! Reilly!' she screamed.

His reply was instant, and calmly clear. 'It's all right,' he called.

A few seconds later he appeared at the rim of the ledge, tall and bronzed and cloaked with an air of competency. Her knees threatened to buckle from under her at the sight of him. Perspiration plastered his white shirt against his muscular chest. His hair glistened blue-black in the sun.

'I heard a shot.' Leah's voice trembled.

An arm raised to show a jackrabbit dangling lifeless from his hand. 'Tonight's dinner,' he explained offhandedly. 'I'll be down as soon as I get the fire-wood.'

Then he disappeared again. He had looked so compellingly masculine standing there, a fact Leah had noted before, it had never struck as forcibly as it had a second ago. She suddenly began to wonder about the women in his life and whether there was a special one that belonged to him.

Remembering the strong arms that had held her in sleep last night and the hard length of his body lying beside hers, she realised she envied the woman, if there was one. As a lover, Reilly—— She stopped, shaking her head wryly. Her thoughts were becoming decidedly intimate.

Turning away from the slope, she walked back to the clearing. She knelt beside the box of food supplies, forcing her mind to concentrate on the task of deciding what could be served with the rabbit Reilly had shot. Setting aside a dried vegetable pouch, she added a packet of peaches to the water left in the pan.

When Reilly came down the slope a few minutes later laden with an armload of wood, she was still stirring the peaches, trying to hasten their absorption of the water. It was difficult not to look at him with the new sensual awareness that she felt.

She did her best to ignore it, though. 'I hope you don't expect me to clean that rabbit. I wouldn't know the first thing about skinning it,' she said, eyeing the limp animal distastefully.

66

'Then you can watch me,' Reilly grinned crookedly.

'No, thanks.' She turned quickly back to her peaches, catching the gleam of devilry that sparkled in his look. 'You fix the rabbit and I'll take care of the rest of the dinner.'

She kept her attention firmly riveted on her task. Blood didn't make her squeamish, but the sight of that small carcase being cleaned wasn't all that pleasant.

'When I heard the shot, I had visions of a rattlesnake attacking you,' she said.

'It's too hot for them to be out. They come to hunt just before sunrise and shortly after sundown,' Reilly explained. 'Besides, rattlesnakes don't attack. They're relatively timid reptiles. The only time a person has to worry about them is if he's unwary enough to stumble on one.'

'Remind me not to go wandering about, then,' she said with mock seriousness.

Reilly chuckled quietly, a pleasant sound that Leah found she liked very much. Glancing surreptitiously at his chiselled features, so lean and powerful, there was a lot she liked about him.

Later, after their meal of roasted rabbit, they sat and watched the orange sun wavering above the horizon. The western sky was painted a brilliant scarlet orange, the distant mountain range set afire with its flaming light.

There was so much emptiness in the wilderness land Leah studied. It was as if she and Reilly were the only two people on the whole of the earth.

She stared unblinkingly at the sunset. 'Do you think the search planes will find us tomorrow?'

'Possibly.'

A thin thread of fear stretched over her nerves. She turned. 'What if they don't find us, Reilly? What if we're stranded here for ever?'

He held her gaze for a long moment, looking deep into her hazel eyes. Then he smiled faintly and shook his head. 'We won't be. We'll get out of here.'

'Of course,' she sighed, silently chiding herself for giving in to that momentary twinge of fear.

The plane had crashed only twenty-four hours ago, hardly enough time to start panicking that they wouldn't be found. One day, her mind echoed; it seemed much longer than that.

Standing, Reilly added two more small logs to the dying fire and took down the lean-to so the stiff blanket could be used as a cover. While the dwindling sunlight still gave enough light to see, he smoothed away the top layer of stones where their bed would be.

With the departure of the sun, the air became instantly chilled. Leah moved closer to the small fire, staring into its flames. Its toasting warmth couldn't reach her back. When she started shivering Reilly suggested it was time they went to sleep. A blanket of stars was overhead as she curled against him.

The second day was longer than the first. A great part of the first day had been occupied recovering what they could from the plane, finding water, building a fire, improvising cooking utensils and erecting the lean-to. None of that needed to be done the second day and time rested heavily on Leah's mind.

The heat of the sun seemed more intense, the perspiration prickling her skin. All day long, her gaze restlessly searched the sky for the rescue plane. The inactivity of waiting scraped at her nerves, although Reilly's outward composure of stoic calm didn't seem affected by it.

Only once had she seen anything. Jumping to her feet, she had pointed excitedly to the flash of sunlight on metal wings. 'There! It's a plane, isn't it?'

As he stood beside her, his piercing gaze had searched the sky until he, too, saw the slow-flying plane far in the distance. 'Yes, it's a plane,' he had agreed calmly.

'I'll let them know we're here.' She had turned sharply to get the canteen to douse the fire and send up the smoke signal that would reveal their location.

Strong fingers curled around her wrist, halting her. 'It's too far away now.'

Leah had waited, her gaze riveted on the plane, praying fervently for it to fly towards them. But it had continued on its course southward, growing smaller until it had disappeared.

'It will come back,' she had declared in a low voice to conceal her disappointment and the fraying edges of despair.

But it hadn't.

That night Leah slept badly. The hard ground couldn't provide a cushion for her aching muscles already stiffened by two previous nights on the uncomfortable bed. Reilly slept with infuriating ease, wakening only twice to reach from beneath the covers to add wood from a nearby stack to the fire.

Awakening from a fitful doze, Leah discovered it was morning. She groaned at her lack of restful sleep and laid her head back on Reilly's arm to stare disgustedly at the brilliant blue sky. Her left arm throbbed painfully. She shifted against him, trying to ease her arm into a more comfortable and less painful position.

As she twisted on to her side, her gaze focused on his face. She almost hated the way he was sleeping so calmly. The impulse rose to waken him and deny him of sleep as she had been. While she was seriously contemplating it, his sooty lashes lifted partially open, screening his eyes to a smoky jade colour.

'Good morning,' he said in a voice that was disgustingly refreshed and relaxed.

Irritation flashed in her eyes. 'Is it?' she snapped, and tugged at the stiff edge of the blanket to free it of his hold. 'I don't know what's particularly good about it.'

When he released it, she hurled the cover aside and scrambled awkwardly to her feet. Smoothly he joined her with an ease that betrayed not a trace of a sore or protesting muscle or joint.

'You didn't sleep well.' Amusement danced in his look.

'That's an understatement! But then you slept

sound enough for both of us,' she muttered sarcastically.

'I don't think so.' Silent laughter edged his voice. 'There was a wiggling in my bed all night.'

She glared at him, scraping the tousled light brown hair away from her face. She was tired and cross and taking it out on Reilly. It was unfair, but she couldn't seem to stop herself.

'You're lucky it didn't bite you,' she retorted.

She knelt beside her suitcase, rummaging through it to find a clean blouse to replace the rumpled one she wore. Silently she swore that if he laughed openly at her grouchy reply, she would throw something at him.

As if sensing the slender thread that held her temper in check, Reilly didn't enlarge on the subject. 'Put some water on to boil so I can shave, will you?' It was more of an order than a question.

Leah reacted unconsciously to the tone. 'Heat your own water!' Then she cursed silently for being so ill-tempered when it wasn't his fault she hadn't slept. Her guilty sideways look caught the sharp narrowing of his eyes. 'Never mind,' she grumbled, 'I'll do it.' But she couldn't seem to stop her tongue from tacking on. 'After all, it is squaw's work, isn't it?'

The harsh line of his mouth warned her that she was pushing her luck. 'Are you trying to start an argument?' Reilly demanded.

'No,' Leah sighed irritatedly.

'Good.' He pivoted and walked into the brush.

71

She scraped a few glowing coals from the fire and added more wood to the rest. The pan of water was balanced on the four supporting rocks around the separated embers.

With that accomplished, she shrugged off her blouse, the gash in her left arm burning constantly. She carefully eased the clean yellow blouse over it. She was buttoning the last button when Reilly returned. Sliding a glance at the pot, Leah saw the water was steaming.

'Your water is hot,' she told him somewhat coolly.

'Thanks,' was his equally indifferent reply. With a handkerchief from his suitcase, he set the pot off the coals, then paused. 'Would you like to wash first?'

Shaking her head negatively, Leah opened her cosmetic case and took out the bottle of cleansing lotion to cream her face. The mirror in the lid of her cosmetic case was turned at just the right angle so that she saw not only her reflection, but Reilly's too.

It was a curiously intimate experience to watch a man shave. Long, sun-browned fingers gripped the razor, its blade slicing through the foamy lather and one day's stubble of beard. Each stroke of the blade revealed more of the bronzed skin below his cheekbones and the strong line of his jaw until the handsomely chiselled features were fully exposed.

As he rinsed away the traces of lather, Leah voiced the thought that had just occurred to her. 'I thought Indians didn't shave.'

'They didn't.' Reilly wiped the razor dry and replaced it in his suitcase. His voice was emotionless and distant. 'They plucked out the hair on their faces.' Leah winced at the thought. 'Is your arm bothering you this morning?' he asked in the same tone.

'A bit,' she shrugged with one shoulder, carefully favouring the burning wound in the other arm.

'Let me take a look at it.' He started towards her.

'There's no need,' Leah refused quickly and sharply. It was his aloofness that made her reject his suggestion, combined with the lingering crossness of a sleepless night. 'It's sore mostly because it's healing.'

Reilly hesitated thoughtfully. 'We don't have much bandage left in the kit. I'd rather not change yours for a couple of days if it isn't bothering you too much.'

'I said it was just healing pains,' she repeated.

'Very well.' He accepted her explanation with a faint grimness. 'I'm going to get some more firewood. Have something to eat while I'm gone.'

'I'm not hungry.'

'It might make you feel better,' he replied tautly.

'Improve my disposition, you mean,' Leah flashed at his suggestion of criticism. 'Well, I'm not hungry.'

A moment of tense silence followed her challenging statement.

'I realise you didn't sleep well last night,' Reilly spoke in an ominously quiet voice, 'but I suggest, Miss Talbot, that you stop taking your frustration out on me.'

Miss Talbot, she thought with a dejected sigh as his long strides carried him towards the slope, not Leah

73

any more. She deserved the set-down, she reminded herself, but it didn't make it any less cutting.

With light make-up applied and her long hair brushed to a silken shine, she slipped off her shoes and shook out the sand. Removing her socks, she grimaced at the sand and dirt that had collected between her toes and on the bottom of her feet. They felt hot and sweaty, too.

The pan of warm water sat invitingly near, flecks of shaving foam still floating on top. She hesitated for only a second. It would be foolish to put on a clean pair of socks without washing her feet.

Treading carefully over the rough ground on her bare feet, she retrieved the handkerchief Reilly had laid over a bush to dry. With it as a washcloth and the small bar of soap from her cosmetic case, she started washing her feet in the pan of water. She rinsed the soap away with water from the canteen and wiped her feet dry with the tail of the rumpled blouse she had taken off earlier. The dirtied water she dumped on the sand.

It was nearly as good as taking a bath, she thought contentedly. When they were rescued, she decided she was going to laze in a bathtub full of bubbles for an hour, or possibly more. She tugged on her clean socks and shook the sand out of her shoes a second time.

As she slipped on the first shoe, she heard a humming sound. She frowned, listening intently, trying to recognise the cause. She couldn't tell which direction the sound was coming from, yet it seemed to be growing louder.

Her eyes widened in recognition. It was the drone of an aeroplane engine. She looked immediately towards the western sky. It was unbelievably near their position and flying towards it. The breeze from the east must have carried the sound until it was nearly above her.

With an excited shout to Reilly, Leah grabbed for the canteen and dumped the water on the fire. Only a trickle came out, sizzling to a tiny puff of smoke as it touched the fire. She stared at the insignificant puff in disbelief.

'You fool!' she muttered. 'Why did you use all that water to wash your feet?'

The roar of the plane's engine came from overhead. Wrenching her gaze away from the fire, she looked above her head. There was no indication that they had been seen as it flew onward to the east into the sun.

'Here we are!' she shouted, running after the plane's shadow and waving her arms frantically. 'Here we are! Down here!'

Reilly came racing down the slope, a miniature avalanche of small rocks rolling before him. 'Pour water on the fire!' he shouted.

Leah stopped. 'There isn't any water. I used it all.'

His expression hardened at her statement, but there was no comment on her stupidity. Without breaking stride, he hit the level ground at the bottom of the slope. He paused long enough to pick up the wrinkled red cloth that had been their blanket and tossed it to her.

'Wave that in the air!' he snapped out the order. 'The aluminium side up!'

As she obeyed, she was conscious of Reilly kneeling beside her cosmetic case, but she was more aware of the plane flying away from them. Then Reilly was standing beside her, the rectangular mirror from the lid of her cosmetic case in his hand.

While she waved the blanket until she thought her arm would drop off, he wigwagged the mirror in the sun, trying to pinpoint the flashing light on the plane. But the plane never wavered from its course.

'Come back!' Leah screamed. Her arm hung limply at her side, without the strength to raise the blanket one more time, her injured left arm cradled across her waist.

It disappeared into the sun. A tear slipped from her lashes, then another and another until there was a silent, steady stream down her cheeks. Her lips were salty with the taste of her tears.

'They didn't see us,' she whispered in a choked, tight voice.

Her chin trembled as she turned to look at Reilly. His hands were on his hips in a stance of angry disgust. He was staring into the emptiness where the plane had been. He turned, turbulent green eyes briefly meeting hers before he walked back to the fire.

'I'm sorry, Reilly.' Leah followed him. The stiff blanket was still clutched in her fingers, trailing along the ground behind her. 'It's all my fault. I didn't realise I'd used all the water to wash my feet.'

'Your feet?' he repeated dryly, his speaking glance saying all the things he didn't put into words.

'They were dirty,' she offered lamely in defence.

Reilly began stacking the few remaining logs on to the fire. His silence was more crushing than any verbal condemnation. Finally Leah couldn't take it any more, and her anger and hurt erupted like a volcano.

'Why don't you say something?' she accused. 'Why don't you shout at me and tell me what a stupid idiotic thing it was to do? We both know it was, so why don't you say it! Get angry or something! Don't just keep putting wood on the fire as if nothing had happened!'

'There wouldn't be any point,' Reilly answered calmly, rising to his feet and brushing his hands on his thighs. Except for the grim tightness of his mouth. an impersonal mask had slipped over his face. 'I'm going to go and fill the canteen and bring down the firewood.'

A broken sigh of frustration slipped from her constricting throat.

'What if the plane comes back while you're gone?'

'Wave the blanket and yell for me.'

When he had disappeared up the slope, Leah collapsed on her knees. Her fingers relaxed their death grip on the blanket and it lay beside her, the shiny aluminium side catching the sun's rays. She was exhausted and emotionally drained.

She wanted to bury her head in her arms and cry

silently at her stupidity, but she didn't dare. There was a chance that the plane might fly back this way. She couldn't risk being caught unaware a second time.

Sniffing back the tears, she wiped the salty dampness from her cheeks and started scanning the skies. Her ears strained to hear the drone of an aeroplane engine. There was only the desert mountain silence until the rolling of stones down the slope heralded Reilly's return.

After setting the armload of wood on the ground a few feet away from the fire, Reilly handed the canteen to Leah. 'Have a drink.'

She looked at it as if it were poison. She was hot and tired and very thirsty, but no matter how parched her throat might be, she didn't want to drink the water that might get them rescued.

'No,' she refused with quiet firmness.

Exasperation straightened the line of his mouth. 'A swallow isn't going to do any harm. Take a drink,' he ordered.

Reluctantly Leah obeyed, taking a small sip and letting it roll around to wet her dry mouth before swallowing it. Moistening her lips with her tongue, she handed the canteen back to him, aware of the alert greenness of his eyes watching her, but unable to meet it.

The canteen was set in the shade of the firewood. Without a word Reilly walked over and picked up the thin blanket lying on the ground beside Leah. She frowned, wondering what he intended to do with it, then saw him erecting the lean-to.

Her frown deepened. 'Won't we need the blanket to signal the plane?'

Reilly didn't turn away from his task as he answered. 'It can be torn down in seconds if we see the plane. In the meantime it will be of more service as a sunshade.'

Leah stared at the crackling fire. It burned cleanly, a thin wisp of smoke rising and disappearing in the clear desert air almost immediately. Shimmering heat waves danced above the fire.

'The plane flew almost directly over us,' she said quietly. 'I didn't hear it coming until it was almost here. Why couldn't they see us?'

'In the first place,' Reilly secured the last corner of the lean-to, 'they were flying into the morning sun. Their vision was impaired. And in the second place, they were looking for aeroplane wreckage.' His head nodded in the general direction of the slide. 'Ours is buried beneath that.'

'They would have seen the smoke signal, though,' she sighed, gazing into the morning sky. 'It's my fault.'

'Stop feeling sorry for yourself,' Reilly ordered firmly.

'I'm not!' Leah protested indignantly.

'Yes, you are, and it's not going to change anything.'

'I never said it would,' she retorted.

'Then let's stop discussing what happened and be prepared in case the plane flies back this way.'

Leah paused. Something in his voice made her ask, 'Do you think it will?'

'I don't know.' Nothing in his expression revealed what Reilly really thought or believed.

CHAPTER FIVE

A CLOUD blocked out the western sun. A halo of gold formed around its grey-white shape, then streamed to earth to bronze the sage-covered ground.

Leah's blouse was damp with perspiration, clinging to her like a second skin. Her arm ached with an agonising throb. That morning's exertion when she had tried and failed to use it to wave the blanket at the plane had increased its soreness.

Wearily she pressed her right hand against her forehead for a few seconds, then lifted her head, her hand pushing the hair away from her face. All day they had waited and the plane had not returned. It was nearing sundown.

Her clouded hazel eyes moved to Reilly, relentlessly watching the sky yet seeming to be miles away in thought. 'How long do you think they'll continue looking for us?' She voiced the fear that had been recurring all day.

The remoteness remained in his bland jade eyes as he glanced at her. 'It's hard to say. An extensive air search is expensive and time-consuming,' he replied. 'They'll probably look for a couple more days at most. After that, they'll ask local pilots to keep a lookout for any sign of wreckage and send out one or two search planes of their own.'

The knowledge was sobering. The possibility of being stranded in this wilderness for more days seemed probable. Leah knew she couldn't think about that without sinking into a morass of guilt feelings. And Reilly was right, that wouldn't solve anything.

'I think I'll get us something to eat,' she murmured.

Food didn't interest her. At lunch, she had chewed indifferently on a stack of beef jerky, knowing that she had to eat something. It was the latter motivation instead of hunger that prompted her to cook the evening meal. The side benefit would be taking her mind off their situation.

After three days, the choice of dried food dishes had dwindled considerably. Leah glanced through the few that remained, searching for one that at least sounded appetising.

Out of the corner of her eye, she saw Reilly crouching in front of the suitcases. Curious, she shifted slightly to see what he was doing, and her lips parted in surprise. It was her suitcase he had opened and was searching through the contents.

'What do you think you're doing, going through my suitcase?' she challenged, rising angrily to her feet and striding to his side. He didn't even look up. 'Those happen to be my personal things and you have no right going through them!'

He set a stack of her lingerie to one side and started going through her assortment of outer clothes. She tried taking them out of his hands to jam them back in her suitcase, but he picked them up and discarded them quicker than she could stop him.

'Did you hear what I said?' she demanded finally.

'I'm not stealing anything,' Reilly answered her finally. 'I'm trying to find if you have anything suitable for walking.'

'You could ask!' Leah retorted bitterly. She tried to fold the items he had discarded. 'You don't have to rummage through my things!'

'I've seen women's clothes before. There's no need to let your modesty embarrass you.' He held up a pair of corded slacks of wheat tan and a long-sleeved blouse of white with tiny gold and brown diamond patterns crisscrossing it. 'These should do.'

Leah sat back on her heels, staring at his impassive face bewilderedly. 'Should do for what?' she frowned. A piece of his earlier remark came filtering back. 'What did you mean "suitable for walking"?'

'We're leaving,' Reilly announced calmly, and turned to her cosmetic case. 'Do you have any face cream in here?' he asked as he snapped open the lid.

'Yes.' She reached in and picked up the jar. 'Why do you want it?' The answer to that wasn't nearly so important when his announcement sank in. 'How are we leaving?'

'On foot, of course.' He flicked a brief glance at her, then opened the jar and removed a dab of cream with his forefinger, rubbing it experimentally between his finger and thumb. 'This cream is going to protect your pale face from the sun.'

'On foot? You must be crazy!' Leah stared out over the vast desert mountain wilderness.

'It would be crazier to stay here.' The cosmetic case was abandoned as Reilly opened his own suitcase.

'I know you think I'm stupid——' Leah began hotly.

'I think nothing of the sort,' Reilly interrupted evenly.

'But I do know,' she continued with barely a break, 'that when you're lost and people are looking for you, you're supposed to stay in one place and not going wandering off. We don't even know where we are!'

He removed two of his dirty shirts from the suitcase and closed the lid. 'I have a rough idea.'

'Wonderful,' Leah murmured sarcastically. When he rose to his feet she followed as closely as his shadow. 'Does that mean we're somewhere in Nevada? I could have made that guess.'

Reilly stopped shortly, nearly causing her to run into his broad back. His gaze was as hard as steel when he looked at her.

'We're on the east side of the Monitor Range, which would put us roughly sixty miles from the nearest town as the crow flies. In this terrain, on foot, it would probably be ninety miles.'

In this emptiness, it seemed impossible that they were even that close to civilisation. 'We could die out there,' Leah argued.

'We could die here,' he pointed out.

'Yes, but'—his reply put her off her stride for a second—'here, we at least have a chance of being

84

found, of signalling the next plane.'

'When will it come, Leah? Reilly studied her rebellious yet frightened expression. 'Tomorrow? The day after? Three days from now? When?'

'I don't know.' Her hand lifted to wave the question aside. 'But it will come. My parents and Lonnie won't stop looking until they find me. I know they won't!'

'I agree, but time is still the factor.'

'Why?' she demanded.

'Because in three, maybe four more days we won't have the food, the water, or the strength to walk out of here.' The lowness of his voice, his calmness, seemed designed to impress on her the gravity of their situation.

Wildly, she looked up the slope in the direction where he had said he had found the water. 'But——'

'The water I found in the rock basin is drying up.' Reilly explained. 'It's evaporating in this heat.'

Foolishly Leah had regarded their water supply as inexhaustible. She had forgotten Reilly's comment that water was invaluable in desert terrain.

A tide of helplessness washed over her. 'You should have told me.'

'Perhaps.' Reilly adopted the same indifferent attitude about discussing what had already been done as he had when Leah had used all the water to wash her feet. What had been done was done, and as far as he was concerned, there was no purpose in rehashing the reason.

85

'If we tried to walk for help,' Leah still didn't en-
dorse the idea despite the logic of Reilly's reasons,
'how would we know which way to go?'

'We'll go south.'

'Why?' she persisted stubbornly. 'Why not west?
When we flew off course, we came east. Surely we
should go back that way.'

Reilly breathed in deeply, as if his patience with
her questions was thinning. 'The mountain ranges
run in a north-south line. I don't know how many of
them we would have to cross before we reached
either a highway or a town. Finding a safe way over
them and down would take too much time. That
same reason rules out going east. To the north, I can
see mountains. If we went that way, we would have
to travel along the ridge. But south, we have a valley.
The walking will be easier and we can make better
time.'

'We could also get lost,' Leah pointed out.

'I won't get lost,' he assured her dryly.

His confidence irritated her. He was absolutely positive he was right. With all of her arguments dismissed,
she retaliated with lashing sarcasm.

'How stupid of me to forget that you're part Indian,' she inserted cuttingly. 'Of course you wouldn't
get lost.'

His carved features darkened ominously. 'You're
quite right.'

She pressed her lips together. Her barb had somehow fallen short of its mark. Exhaling an angry
breath, she glanced away.

'I don't care what you think,' she muttered. 'I don't think we should leave here. The search plane could find us any time.'

'We're leaving in the morning at first light,' Reilly stated calmly.

Leah tossed her head back defiantly meeting his cool gaze. 'You can leave if you want. I'm staying here.'

'No, you are not.' His jaw tightened.

'And how are you going to stop me?' she asked pertly. 'I somehow don't think you're strong enough to carry me all the way and I'm certainly not going to go with you willingly. That puts us at something of an impasse, doesn't it? I won't go and you won't leave without me, so that means we'll stay here.'

'You're making a mistake.' His eyes had narrowed into a lazy, measuring look.

'I don't think so.' This time it was she who brimmed with self-confidence.

'All right,' he nodded curtly in acceptance. 'You can stay here. I'll leave in the morning.'

Her eyes widened in amazement. 'What?'

'It's probably the best solution anyway. I can make better time without you along and you can be here to signal the plane in case it flies back over this area again. If it doesn't, then within three day's time, at the outside, I shall have reached help and be able to send someone back for you,' Reilly concluded, satisfaction gleaming in his eyes.

'You mean you'd leave me—here—alone?' Leah repeated in disbelief.

'It's the logical thing to do. This way we can cover

both possibilities for obtaining help,' he paused, as if studying the idea more thoroughly. 'I'll have to take the canteen with me, but you can use the pan to fetch water. You can keep the dried food with you since I won't have a water supply to depend on. I'll take the beef jerky, though.'

'No!'

A black eyebrow shot up in surprise at her vigorous protest, a studied arrogance in the action. 'I shall need some food,' Reilly commented dryly.

'I don't care about that,' Leah frowned. 'You aren't honestly going to leave me?'

'Why not?' He tipped his head to one side. 'Are you going with me?'

'No.'

'Then you must be staying here,' he shrugged, and turned away.

Her fingers closed over the hard flesh of his arm, halting him when he would have walked away from her. She stared into his impassive face, lean and compelling handsome in its proud, carved lines.

'You really would leave me here by myself, wouldn't you?' Leah murmured.

A faintly bemused smile crooked his mouth as if he didn't understand why she had doubted it. 'Yes,' Reilly answered simply.

'Well, you're sadly mistaken if you think you're going to leave me here alone while you go traipsing off,' she vowed. 'If you go, then I'm going, too.'

'But you were going to stay here to signal the plane,' he reminded her with a wry shake of his head.

'I'm going with you,' Leah stated emphatically. 'I don't care how impracticable it is. You can't make me stay here.'

The instant the last sentence was spoken, her teeth bit into her lip in angry memory. Only minutes ago she had been insisting that he couldn't make her go with him in the morning.

'In that case,' Reilly drawled, 'I guess you'll leave with me.'

As he started to turn away, Leah caught the roguish glint in his eyes. 'You tricked me,' she hissed accusingly. You never intended to leave me here by myself!'

He paused, an eyebrow raising in a complacent arch, glittering eyes dancing over his face. 'Did you really think I would leave my squaw behind?' he mocked with decided jest.

She released his arm, and the open palm of her hand swung in an arc towards the deepening grooves beside his mouth. Reilly didn't attempt to check her slapping swing. He simply drew back so that she missed her target.

When her hand had swished by, he captured her wrist in his fingers, smiling openly at her burst of temper. Leah tried to twist free of his steel grip. Her left arm was throbbing too painfully to be of any help.

He held her easily. Her angry struggles only brought her closer to the firmness of his chest. A throaty chuckle rolled from his lips.

'I don't think it's funny!' Leah tossed back her head to glare at him coldly.

The amusement faded from his gaze as he stared down to her. The brilliant fire that leaped into his eyes dazzled her, halting her attempts to pull free. Her heart skipped a beat when his attention shifted lazily to her mouth.

His thumb slowly rubbed the inside of her wrist. His other hand came up to absently smooth the hair from her face. It stayed to cup the back of her neck. A shiver of anticipation raced up her spine. She was already swaying towards him when his hand exerted pressure to draw her lips to his.

His mouth closed over hers warmly, masterfully firm in its possession. Her muscles melted closer to the lean hardness of his tapering length. His kiss ignited a slow-burning flame in her midsection that languidly trailed through her limbs.

Yet when the moment came for the embrace to deepen with passion, Reilly relaxed the pressure at the back of her neck that had drawn her on tiptoe to him. Weakened by his kiss, her legs couldn't support her in that precarious stance and lowered her away from the male lips.

The gold tips of her lashes fluttered partially open. Through their veil, she gazed unsteadily at him. Her breath was coming in uneven spurts. The look in his eyes was gentle and friendly yet seemingly masked.

'We're in this together all the way, Leah,' Reilly said quietly. 'We both leave in the morning.'

'Yes,' she nodded.

His hand uncurled from her neck, a finger trailing lightly over her cheek as he smiled, forming crinkling lines at the corners of his eyes. Leah couldn't help wondering if the kiss had been a means of persuading her to agree without more arguments.

Reilly moved a step away, reaching into the pocket of his shirt and taking out the pack of filtered cigarettes. He shook two out and lit them one at a time.

He handed one to Leah. 'Shall we smoke the peacepipe?' A smile played with his mouth.

'Why not?' she smiled, and shook her head wryly, wishing she felt as normal and unmoved by the kiss as he did.

There was the barest tremor in her hand when she accepted the lit cigarette to betray the shaken state of her senses. Her lips still felt the warm imprint of his mouth as she inhaled deeply on the filtered end.

It was a good thing, she decided, that they were leaving in the morning. She was definitely attracted to Reilly physically. More days alone in their isolated camp and a few more expert kisses might increase the temptation of night. At least the exhaustion of the trail would dull her awareness of her virilely masculine companion.

A gauzy cloud drifted between them from Reilly's cigarette. 'When we've finished smoking,' he said idly, 'you can go ahead with your dinner preparations while I organise what we'll need to take with us tomorrow.'

The remaining daylight hours were filled with activity. The three-quarter moon had barely risen when Reilly announced that they should go to sleep early to rest up for the long walk ahead of them.

In his arms beneath the blanket, Leah felt the stirring of her pulse in response to the male length of him moulded against her. Since the afternoon's kiss, she had expected him to attempt to make love to her tonight.

Expected was the wrong word. She had anticipated that he would make love to her, and with dangerous honesty, she admitted that she had been partly looking forward to it. The even rise and fall of his chest beneath her head was disappointing.

What manner of man was Reilly Smith? she asked herself. She knew she was an attractive woman, yet in three days he had kissed her once. Even then, although it had been an ardent kiss, it hadn't been exactly passionate.

Other men that she had dated would have quickly tried to take advantage of this situation she and Reilly were in—thrown together constantly by the isolation, forced to sleep together to endure the cold mountain desert night. Not that she had dated a lot of lecherous men. It was just that, under these circumstances, it would be easy for a man to take advantage of her.

Yet Reilly hadn't. It certainly wasn't because he lacked experience—the mastery of his kiss this afternoon wouldn't support that theory. When they had first met in the waiting lounge of the flying service, there had been admiration in his eyes when he looked at her.

Her own response to his kiss had indicated that she was not indifferent to him. So why hadn't he pursued her unwritten invitation?

Leah sighed angrily and shifted her throbbing left arm to lie across the muscular flatness of his stomach. She was being ridiculously feminine. She should be glad that she wasn't having to fight off his advances every second instead of wishing he would make one.

Forcing her lashes to close, Leah ordered herself to go to sleep. After last night's fitful dozing, she drifted off almost instantly.

Strong fingers pushed the hair away from her temples. 'It's time to wake up,' the male voice spoke insistently.

The cover was pulled away from their heads. Leah shivered at the intruding cold and tried to snuggle deeper into the curve of Reilly's shoulder. The same fingers curved under her chin.

'I said it's time to wake up,' Reilly repeated with indulgent humour.

Moaning in protest, she peered through her lashes at the outside world. Except for the crackling fire, there was utter silence. Overhead sparkled the brightest stars Leah ever remembered seing, thousands of them glittering with profound brilliance against a curtain of black.

'It's still dark,' she grumbled.

'It won't be for long. Come on.' His arm tightened around her side, drawing her up in a sitting position as he pushed himself up.

'We're honestly getting up at this hour?' Leah protested, barely stifling a yawn.

'It's nearly daybreak. You'd better get the water boiling so we can have what's left of that instant oatmeal,' he ordered, pushing her the rest of the way out of the bed.

'Who's hungry?' she muttered.

'You will be when we start down the mountain if you don't eat something now.'

Leah admitted silently that he was probably right, but she wasn't interested in food. What she really wanted was another couple of hours' sleep. Instead she poured water from the canteen into the metal pan and balanced it on the rocks beside the fire to boil.

The lonely wail of a faraway coyote echoed through the stillness. Leah huddled closer to the small fire, seeking its warmth. The eerie call drew her gaze to the landscape. The three-quarter moon frosted the ground with a silvery glow.

A ribbon of bubbles started to form in the pan of water, forcing her to leave the fire's circle for the oatmeal, bowls, and the two carved wooden spoons. A glance at Reilly saw him folding their stiff blanket into a small square, adding it to the other small items they would backpack with them.

When the water boiled, Leah stirred the oatmeal

into it. It was difficult to gauge how much water was needed without a measuring cup, but this morning the oatmeal was neither lumpy nor runny. With the last portion, she had found the right mixture.

'Breakfast is ready,' she called softly, spooning some into her bowl and giving Reilly the largest amount.

While they ate, a pink hue touched the eastern horizon as dawn began its silent appearance. The coppery pink pushed back the night, making way for a golden haze. By the time Leah had cleaned their dishes with sand, the entire sky was bathed in the half-light of sunrise.

Reilly handed her the canteen. 'Drink all the water you can hold, then I'll go and fill it up.'

After several swallows, she paused. 'What are we going to do for water along the way? This canteen doesn't hold that much.'

'We'll have to count on finding it.' He waited for her to take another drink. 'If there's water on the desert floor, it will probably be along the base of the mountains. Once we get down into the valley, we'll stay close to them.'

After drinking as much as she could, she handed the canteen to him. While he disappeared up the slope, she changed into the clothes he had deemed suitable for the long walk. She was tucking in the tail of her blouse when he returned.

His green eyes swiftly appraised her appearance. 'You don't have a hat, do you?' His mouth tightened grimly when she shook her head negatively. 'A scarf?'

'Yes.' She rummaged through her suitcase until she found the gold and brown silk scarf and held it up for him to see.

Reilly studied it for a considering moment. 'It will have to do. Tie it around your head like a turban. At least it will protect your head from the sun.'

Leah did as she was told. It was difficult with the searing pain in her arm. 'I don't see what good it will do,' she protested.

'If you'd ever had your scalp sunburned, you wouldn't say that,' he replied dryly.

'What about your head?' She glanced at him pointedly, only to find he was tying a blue bandana around his jet-dark hair.

His was done more swiftly and more expertly than hers. When he had finished, Leah could see the inherent traces of his Indian ancestry. The inborn stamp of ruthless nobility was more striking than before.

He opened the jar of cold cream and offered it to her. 'Put it on thick,' he ordered.

'Why?' Leah frowned and scooped out a generous amount.

'To protect your face from the sun,' he answered patiently, and did the same.

The white cream looked strange against his sunbrowned skin. 'Since when did Indians need protection from the sun?' she teased.

'Everyone needs protection from the sun,' Reilly grinned, 'including Indians. One tribe of Plains Indians used to rub sunflower oil all over their bodies for that purpose.' He watched Leah smear the cream over her face. 'Your nose is already a little red. I'd leave a coating of cream on it for extra protection.'

His carved features glistened like a bronzed statue in the soft morning light. There was nothing to wipe the excess cream from her hands, so Leah followed his suit and used her trouser legs.

'There isn't anything more you need out of the suitcase, is there?' Reilly questioned.

'No.'

'I'm going to set them over by the rock slide, then we'll get loaded up.'

While he walked to the slide area where the plane was buried, Leah carefully touched the area around the wound on her left arm. It was burning as if a hot knife was being held against it and sore nearly down to her elbow. Yet it didn't feel as if her arm was swollen. She wondered if she should ask Reilly to take a look at it

His cautioning comment of yesterday morning that they didn't have much bandage left and his desire for an early start on the trail while it was still cool made her decide not to bother him. The wound was obviously healing, and it had been an ugly gash.

'Are you ready to load up?' His long supple strides had carried him back into the clearing, his gaze touching her briefly.

'Why not?' Leah shrugged.

He had fashioned two crude shoulder packs out of his shirts. The lighter one, containing the blanket and cooking utensils, he tied on her back. The heavier and more cumbersome one with the first-aid kit, food box, and flashlight, Reilly fastened on himself.

'Here.' He handed her one of the sticks that had been used to support the lean-to.

'What's this for?' she frowned. 'To chase the snakes out of my path?'

'It's a walking stick. It'll come in handy on some of the steeper stretches of the mountain.' He walked over to the fire and stirred the ashes with the other stick, covering the remains with gravel and sand. 'Are you ready?' he asked.

'I guess so.' She shifted the pack on her shoulders to a more comfortable position, then laughed. 'I feel like a squaw carrying a papoose on her back.'

Reilly laughed softly, a dark glint in his jade eyes that was oddly disturbing. 'Then let's hit the trail, squaw woman.'

Waving her stick, Leah motioned for him to lead the way. Reilly started off, setting an easy pace, but one that could be maintained.

The level ridgetop gave way to the sloping mountainside. A lean jackrabbit darted swiftly out of their path while a lizard sunning himself on a rock stuck out his tongue as they passed. The sun was a yellow sphere above the horizon.

CHAPTER SIX

RIVULETS of perspiration ran down her neck to the hollow between her breasts. The straps of the crude backpack chafed at her shoulders, adding to her discomfort.

The blazing sun was nearing its noonday notch, the fiery rays beat relentlessly down. Leaning heavily on her stick, Leah paused, winded, to catch her breath. The backs of her legs achingly protested the sight of the downhill grade still before them. All morning long they had zigzagged down the mountain and there was further yet to go.

'How much farther is it, for heaven's sake?' Leah cried in a tone of exasperated anger.

Reilly halted several yards ahead, squinting his eyes against the sun to look back at her. 'Distances are deceiving in open country.' He wiped the sweat from around his mouth with the back of his hand.

'You're telling me,' she muttered.

'Do you want to rest here or wait until we get to the bottom?'

When will that be—next year? Leah wondered tiredly. 'How long has it been since we stopped last?' Since starting down the mountain, they had stopped every hour for a ten-minute rest.

'About twenty minutes ago,' Reilly answered.

It seemed like a year, but Leah gritted her teeth and pushed onward with her stick. 'Let's go down.'

She wondered why they didn't just sit on their rumps and slide down to the bottom. The grade was certainly steep enough, but Reilly maintained his zig-zag course, doubling the distance while lessening the severe downhill strain.

Her left arm was hurting her more now. Its weight swinging freely at her side seemed to increase the pull on the knitting wound. She tucked her left hand in the waistband of her slacks to form a natural sling. It helped, although it made balancing on the rockier stretches awkward.

Both shoes were rubbing against her heels. Leah knew she would soon have blisters to contend with. She shifted the pack on her back, but it slid back to the already chafed area. So she trudged on, putting one aching foot in front of the other.

Except for an occasional glance to be sure Reilly was still ahead of her, she concentrated on only the ground ahead of her feet. She stopped looking to see how far they had to go. She tried to blank out all her aches and pains and the dryness of her mouth and throat.

Time became meaningless. Leah didn't know if she had walked for an hour or four hours when the ground finally levelled out beneath her feet. Reilly was already shedding his pack.

'We'll rest here for a couple of hours and stay out

of the worst of the heat,' he announced.

If she had had the energy, Leah would have cheered. Instead she sank to her knees, shrugging the chafing pack off her right arm and gently easing it off her throbbing left.

Dully she watched Reilly take a quick swallow from the canteen before handing it to her. The sound of the water sloshing against the sides was beautiful. She was so thirsty she knew she could drink it dry. But her thirst reminded her how precious water was and she settled for a swallow.

Opening her pack, Reilly removed the blanket and picked up the stick she had dropped on the ground. He looked disgustingly fresh, she thought, as if he could walk down ten such mountains without drawing a laboured breath.

'Why don't you look as tired as I feel?' she sighed as he swiftly set up the lean-to.

He smiled faintly. 'Probably because I don't spend five days a week behind a desk.' The last corner of the lean-to was secured. 'Come on, get out of the sun.'

Leah willingly crawled into the shade, stretching out on her back. Her only wish was to never move again. Then Reilly was bending over her, his green eyes mocking and gently amused.

'Here, gnaw on this for a while.' A stick of beef jerky was in his hand.

'I haven't the strength to eat anything.' She waved it aside with a flick of her fingers.

'Eat!' It was an order not to be disobeyed as he placed the meat stick between her parted lips.

Reluctantly she obeyed, knowing he stubbornly wouldn't leave her alone until she did. Her jaws were weary from chewing by the time she had finished. Sighing, she closed her eyes to rest and was almost instantly asleep.

A hand shook her shoulder. She forced her eyes open to focus on Reilly, squatting beside her on the right. The pack was again strapped to his back, the canteen in his hand.

'It's time we left. Have a drink while I repack,' he offered.

Leah pushed herself up, fighting the blackness that swirled sickeningly in front of her eyes. She took a hesitant sip of water and handed the canteen back. While Reilly started taking down the lean-to around her, she pressed a hand to her burning forehead and waited for the dizziness to subside.

I feel awful, she thought to herself.

Her left arm felt like a balloon, but she inwardly shrugged that thought away as the cause of her nausea. There wasn't a part of her body that didn't ache.

The sun had begun its westward trek, but the heat, even in the shade, was scorching. If anything was to blame, she decided it was the feverish heat and her general exhaustion. She moved slowly to her feet, not wanting any quick movement to bring the dizziness back.

Reilly had the blanket back in her pack and ready to strap on. While he was adjusting it in place on her back, he accidentally brushed the area near her wound. Leah winched at the knife-sharp pain.

'Does it hurt?' he asked instantly, his alert gaze missing nothing.

'Everything hurts,' she grimaced.

He handed her the walking stick. 'Are you ready to go on?'

At her brief nod, Reilly took the lead. Although he set the same slow pace as before, Leah had trouble keeping up. At each step, pain jarred through her body. Twice he had to wait for her to catch up.

The rays of the sun seemed to set her skin on fire, burning through her clothes until she felt drowned in a river of perspiration. Waves of weakness kept eroding her strength. Her parched throat made swallowing difficult.

The ten-minute rest break at the end of the first hour was all too short. The one swallow of water hadn't begun to quench her thirst and her throat felt as dry as the desert sand. Her mind cried that she couldn't go any farther, but with feverish determination, she pushed herself up.

In memory, she could hear her brother Lonnie chiding, 'I told you girls couldn't keep up.' His voice sounded so clearly in her mind that she had to brush a hand in front of her glazed eyes to keep his image from dancing before her.

At Reilly's concerned look, she smiled tiredly. 'I'm

all right,' she said hoarsely, more to convince herself than him.

'Hold this pebble in your mouth,' he instructed as he handed the small stone to her. 'It will keep the saliva working and help your thirst.'

It did help to moisten her mouth as they started out again. Leah tried hard to follow the path Reilly was taking, but she kept weaving from one side to the other. The fire raging inside kept feeding her growing weakness. She tried focusing her gaze on Reilly, using his broad shoulders as a lifeline to draw her onward. The world was spinning before her eyes and she kept losing sight of him in the intermittent moments of reeling blackness. She could feel herself beginning to lose consciousness and was terrified.

'Reilly!' Her cry for help was a croaking whisper, made thicker by the pebble in her mouth. She stumbled and leaned heavily on the stick to regain her balance. Before her reeling senses collapsed under the raging heat and unquenchable thirst, she called to him desperately again. 'Reilly.'

Then she had no more strength. Her knees started to buckle beneath her and only the stick was keeping her upright. As she fought to keep the blackness away, she sobbed because she didn't think he had heard her. She had fallen so far behind.

The stick wavered in its support and she began to sink slowly to the ground. A pair of strong arms circled her waist, easing her down gently.

'Reilly,' she breathed, unable to see him clearly

yet recognising the feel of those arms that had held her in sleep these last nights. 'I'm sorry, I can't make it any farther.'

'Don't talk,' was his low reply. He propped her against his chest.

The canteen was held to her lips, but most of the water trickled down her chin when she couldn't make her mouth swallow the precious liquid. He started to brush the damp tendrils of hair from her face, then stopped abruptly, his rough hand cupped on her cheek.

'My God, you're burning up with fever,' Reilly muttered.

Quickly he stripped the pack from her back and unbuttoned her blouse. The pain was excruciating when he started to pull the sleeve back from her wound. Leah cried out sharply, sickening blackness swirling more thickly in front of her.

Through it, she heard the angry hiss of his breath. 'You crazy woman!' he snarled. 'Why the hell didn't you tell me how much this was hurting?'

Her tongue moved heavily to reply. 'It's healing.'

'Healing? Like hell—it's infected!'

With a groan of defeat, Leah surrendered to the threatening blackness, letting it carry her away to oblivion. The sensation followed that she was floating above the ground, cradled against Reilly's chest by a pair of strong arms. Her consciousness returned long enough for her to realise that Reilly was carrying her before she drifted away again.

A beautiful dream world closed around her. She was lying beside a mirror-smooth pool of clear water where green grass grew thickly along its banks. Overhead the branches of willow trees veiled the scarlet fire of a setting sun. Their leaves were green, a more brilliant green than the jade colour of Reilly's eyes. A blessed coolness bathed her burning forehead. A trace of woodsmoke was in the air.

Then she was being lifted and her blouse removed. She moaned a protest at the interruption of her serenely peaceful vision.

'Hold as still as you can,' was Reilly's gentle request.

Her lashes fluttered open, her eyes focusing on his jet dark head framed by a willow bough. 'I'm having the most wonderful dream,' she murmured. 'There are trees and water and grass.'

'It isn't a dream,' Reilly told her as he removed the bandage from her arm and began washing the infected wound. 'Evidently a Basque shepherd has at some time partially dammed a small spring to water his sheep.'

It was real, she sighed to herself, and drifted again into unconsciousness.

The green world vanished, and she was stumbling over sun-scorched earth. The fiery rays of the sun blinded her eyes and burned her skin, its relentless blaze never once slackening.

At intervals, the coolness of water touched her parched lips. Sometimes it was Lonnie holding the canteen to her mouth, teasing her as he had done when they were children when her short legs were unable to keep up with his long, lanky strides.

Other times it was Reilly telling her to lie still and rest. He couldn't seem to understand that she was condemned to walking beneath the searing sun. So she kept walking, surrounded by a furnace of heat.

The rising of the moon brought no relief. Its silvery glow burned white-hot from the sky. The desert night did not cool as it had always done. Perspiration boiled on her skin.

The sun was worst. Leah cried aloud when it returned to the sky, yet there was no escape from its fierce temperature. The only protection she had to prevent her from being consumed by the flaming tongues was her clothes. To her terror, she felt them being removed and struggled wildly to stop it.

'Leah, can you hear me?' Reilly's firm voice pierced her nightmare world.

'Yes.' She sobbed with relief that she hadn't been abandoned. Her glazed eyes opened to discover that she was again in the green oasis, Reilly bending beside her, stripped to the waist.

His compelling gaze wouldn't let her slip back into the blackness. 'I have to take off your clothes.' Each word was spoken slowly and distinctly so that Leah would understand despite her delirium.

Her head lolled to one side in an effort to protest. She couldn't let him see her naked. It was against every moral principle her parents had instilled.

'No, you mustn't,' she pleaded in a fever-choked whisper.

'Listen to me.' His voice was low and insistent. 'There's no need for you to be ashamed and embarrassed that I'll be seeing you unclothed. An Indian does not look at a naked body as a form to be sexually glorified. It's one more part of nature and nothing more.' Reilly let that statement settle in her mind before continuing. 'Now I have to get your temperature down. The water from the spring is cool and I'm going to bathe you in it.'

The raging fire that engulfed her was caused by a fever. Leah understood vaguely why she hadn't been able to escape the burning heat. Yet her modesty still wouldn't let her give in to his logic.

'Leave——' She was so weak she could hardly get the words out. 'Leave my clothes on.'

'I can't. You must have something dry to put on when you come out,' Reilly answered. 'Don't fight me, Leah. You're going to need your strength.'

Her mind resisted, but her body surrendered itself to his expert hands. In a semi-conscious haze, she was aware of Reilly bodily lifting her into his arms and carrying her to the water, her head resting against his naked shoulder.

Then she was immersed in water, cooling ripples washing her from head to toe. An arm around her waist kept her from sinking into the refreshing depths of the dammed pool. The overhanging branches of a small willow shaded them from the sun.

Time was in limbo, beyond measurement for Leah. At some point in her fever-induced stupor, she became aware that Reilly too was unclothed, but it didn't matter as long as the deliciously cool water continued rinsing her fiery skin.

Stirring restlessly, she tried to escape the stifling cocoon that held her tightly. She wanted the refreshing water of the pool to cool her again. A hand gently stroked her temple and settled along her neck. She was lying on the ground in Reilly's arms, the blanket wrapped around them.

'Sleep,' he murmured near her ear. 'Your fever has broken. You need to sleep.'

With shuttered eyes, Leah relaxed against him. The warmth of his body turned into a safe haven instead of a furnace that she needed to escape from. She slept without dreams or nightmares.

Reilly awakened her once in the daylight to feed her some broth. She instantly went back to sleep. Later there was the sensation of him lying beside her.

The next time she opened her eyes, Leah discovered she was alone under the blanket with the sun well up in the sky. The snapping sound of a fire drew her gaze to the centre of the miniature glade. Reilly was crouched beside the fire, stirring the contents of the pan sitting near it.

His bronzed torso was shirtless, his muscled chest and shoulders rippling a golden copper in the sunlight. A pair of snug-fitting denim levis covered the lower half of him. As if sensing her gaze, he glanced over his shoulder. The boldly chiselled face was more forcefully handsome than she remembered. Lazily his eyes met her look.

'Hello.' The grooves around his mouth deepened with the familiar smile that crinkled his eyes.

'Hello,' Leah returned, feeling self-conscious without knowing why.

'Are you hungry?' He poured the liquid from the pan into one of the small bowls.

'A little,' she admitted, and tried to shift into a sitting position, only to discover she was weaker than she had realised.

'Lie down. I'll feed you,' he said, lithely rising to walk over to her.

'That's squaw's work, isn't it?' An impish smile curved her lips.

The line of his male mouth crooked in response. 'It is, but an Indian is sometimes forced into the role when his woman is crazy with fever.'

Her heart lurched at the term 'his woman'. He couldn't have meant her to take it literally since he had only been responding in jest to her lighthearted question. Yet it certainly was a heartstopping thought.

Setting the bowl on the ground nearby, Reilly took his backpack, cushioned it with his shirt, and put it beneath her head for a pillow. Cross-legged, he sat beside her and picked up the bowl.

'How many "moons" have I been out?' Leah asked after swallowing a spoonful of broth put to her lips.

'Three nights.' Another spoonful was held to her mouth.

'That long?' she breathed in surprise.

'Try eating without talking,' he suggested with amusement. 'It will be much faster.'

When half the bowl was gone, Leah couldn't manage any more and Reilly set it aside, not forcing her to eat more than she wanted.

'How does your arm feel?' His dark head was tilted to one side, his gaze intently studying her.

Tentatively she moved her left arm, testing it carfully. It was sore, but without that aching throb. She smiled with relief.

'Much better,' she nodded.

'You'd better let me have a look at it,' he said. 'I don't trust your opinion any more.' The roguish glint in his eyes removed the sting from his comment.

Without any protest, Leah began unbuttoning her blouse. She was on the third button before she realised she wasn't wearing a bra. Red stained her cheeks a crimson hue as she darted a covert look at Reilly.

'Do you remember that when you were delirious with fever I undressed you to bathe you in the pool?' A black eyebrow arched briefly with question.

Her fingers fumbled with the buttons, neither undoing them nor buttoning them back up. 'Yes, I remember.' She averted her gaze.

'Your shoulders were chafed from the backpack, so I didn't put your bra back on,' he explained.

'I see,' she murmured, staring at her fingers clutching the blouse front.

His thumb and forefinger captured her chin and lifted her head to meet the gentle amusement dancing in his eyes. 'So did I. Everything there was to see.' Her flush deepened, as did his voice with mockery. 'It's pointless to turn prudish now, don't you think?'

Leah's answer was to unbutton her blouse the rest of the way, heat flaming through her veins. While Reilly eased her left arm out of the sleeve, she discreetly shielded her breast with her hand. The blood pounded in her ears.

If he found her action amusing, he made no outward sign. Expertly and impersonally, he examined the wound and rebandaged it, helping her back into the blouse.

'This time I think it will heal,' he announced, turning away while she rebuttoned the front. 'I could wring your neck for not telling me it was bothering you.'

'I thought it was healing,' Leah defended selfconsciously.

'From now on, let me be the judge.' He picked up the bowl and rolled to his feet in one fluid moment, reminding her again of his animal grace. 'You'd better get some more rest.'

'I've been sleeping for days as it is. I think I should get up before I become permanently bedridden,' she stated, fighting the waves of weakness as she tried to sit up.

'There's time enough to try your legs tonight, but you rest this afternoon,' Reilly insisted.

She lacked the strength to get up on her own. She had to lie back down. Despite the hours of sleep she had had, she was soon dozing off again.

A purple dusk had settled overhead when she awoke, casting its violet colour on the smooth water of the dammed pool. Chunks of meat sizzled on a spit above a low camp fire. Again Reilly's sixth sense alerted him to Leah's wide-awake state.

'The food is about ready,' he stated. 'Do you want to sit by the fire?'

'Yes,' she answered emphatically.

When he had lifted her to her feet, Leah's long legs felt like quivering sticks of jelly beneath her. She wavered unsteadily towards the fire. She doubted she could have made it even that short distance if it hadn't been for the support of his steadying hand at her waist.

Shakily, she sat cross-legged in front of the fire, realising the full extent of her weakness. Even her hand trembled when she took the bowl of greens Reilly offered her.

'What is this?' she asked.

'I found some rushes growing on the far side of the pool,' he answered, spooning the rest into his bowl. 'They may be a bit stringy, but they're edible and nourishing.'

Actually Leah thought the dish was quite tasty— different and stringy as Reilly had warned, but otherwise good. But it was the tender white quail meat, roasted to perfection on the spit, that really aroused her appetite. She felt positively stuffed as she finished the last piece and licked her fingers in satisfaction.

'That was delicious,' she sighed.

'You liked it?' A sideways glance moved briefly over her face.

'Mmmm, did I ever!' Leah pressed a hand against her full stomach. 'How did you manage to catch the quail? Did you set a snare?' Unless she had slept very soundly, she hadn't heard any gunshot.

'Quail?' A crooked grin lifted one corner of his mouth.

'That's what it was, wasn't it?' She eyed him curiously.

'No,' Reilly drawled the word. 'I don't mean to ruin your meal, but it was rattlesnake.'

Closing her eyes, Leah quickly swallowed a lump that had suddenly risen in her throat, then took a couple of shaky, calming breaths. Slowly the colour returned to her face as the brief nausea passed.

'Is the meal still delicious?' He had been watching her changing expression with wicked laughter in his eyes.

'Maybe not quite as good as it was when I thought I was eating quail,' Leah admitted.

Reilly smiled, lighting a cigarette and handing it to her, then lighting one for himself. Their cigarette smoke mingled with the wispy trail from the fire. Although the shock of actually eating snake had worn off, Leah wanted to divert the conversation from food.

'Do you know that in all the time we've been stranded, you've hardly told me anything about yourself? I've rattled on about my parents and Lonnie and my vagabond childhood, but I know very little about you, except that you design turquoise jewellery.'

There were a lot of other things she had observed about him, his calmness in a crisis, his knowledge of the desert, but no actual facts about his life.

'What would you like to know, for instance?' he asked dryly, yet not refusing to divulge personal information about himself.

'I don't know.' In truth, Leah wanted to know everything, but she tried to sound lighthearted and nonchalant. 'For instance, how did someone who's part Indian get a name like Reilly Smith?'

'You were expecting something more like John Black Feather,' Reilly chuckled, exhaling a gauzy cloud of smoke.

'Something like that,' she laughed easily at his jesting reply.

'My mother was a half-breed. It's from her that I received my Indian ancestry. The name is from my father, who was Irish.' At the questioning arch of Leah's eyebrow, Reilly smiled and nodded. 'Yes, although his surname was Smith, he was strictly Irish.'

'How?'

'It was common practice years ago for men with questionable pasts to change their names. That's what my father's father did. My father never knew what his real name was, but the family rumour said that my grandfather had killed a man in a bar-room fight back East. No one ever proved whether it was fact or fantasy. One fact is known and that is that he married an Irish lass named Maureen O'Reilly, who was my grandmother. My father left off the "O" when he named me.'

'Are your parents alive?'

'No. My father was killed in a car accident shortly after I was born. And my mother wasn't able to keep me with her, so I was raised by her parents on a reservation. She died when I was eight.' Reilly studied the tip of his cigarette for a few silent seconds, then glanced at Leah and smiled, almost absently. 'Anything else you want to know?'

Leah stared into the fire. Remembering Grady's comment that Reilly was a loner, she was surprised that he had already told her so much about his past. But his last question had invited her to ask more and she definitely wanted to know more.

'What was it like growing up on a reservation?'

'Simple.' Knowing that reply was insufficient, he continued, 'I went to school with other Indian children, took care of my grandparents' sheep, and helped with other chores. Their home was in an isolated area of semi-desert land. My grandfather made turquoise jewellery as a hobby and a way to supplement their meagre income. Whenever I had my work done, he would let me help.' A corner of his mouth lifted wryly in memory. 'My help was mostly cobbing.'

'What's that?' she frowned.

'Separating the turquoise from the host rock with

a pair of pliers or a hammer and lead block,' Reilly explained. 'My grandfather got most of his ore from an abandoned mine in the hills that had been commercially worked out years ago.'

'But that's how you got interested in jewellery?'

'Yes.' He flicked the cigarette butt into the fire, then looked away to study the first timid stars in the night sky. 'In many respects I grew up thinking like an Indian with some of the old customs and traditions, yet I always knew I was mostly white. I never really belonged.' When he paused, Leah didn't fill the silence, but waited. 'I've never decided whether it was the Indian quarter of my blood desiring freedom that prompted me to leave the reservation or the materialistic white part of me that gave me driving ambition and the desire for a different life.'

'You can't divide yourself,' Leah murmured. 'You're the end product of both worlds, whole and complete.'

In her mind, she added more. He was a strong and competent man, creative and intelligent, resourceful and proud. Sewing all those qualities together was a strain of unshakable confidence in himself that gave him an inner peace.

'We're becoming too philosophical,' he told her firmly. 'I think it's time we went to bed. I'll move it closer to the fire.'

While he retrieved the blanket a few feet away, Leah stared at the fire only inches from her knees. 'Why do you always make such a small fire?

Wouldn't it be warmer if it was larger?'

Reilly spread the blanket beside the fire within arm's reach of the woodpile so the fire could easily be fed during the night.

'The white man makes a large fire, then has to sleep several feet away because it's too hot. The Indian makes a small fire and lies down beside it.' He held out his hand to help her to her feet, the flickering reflection of the fire dancing in his eyes.

CHAPTER SEVEN

THE serenity of the pool was soothing, clear and cool without a ripple to disturb its smoothness. The small water willows curved above it to admire their reflection on its surface. A faint breeze stirred the rushes at the far end while water giggled over the dammed side of the pool to follow the course of the narrow silver stream.

Leaning against a slim tree trunk, Leah plucked at a blade of grass. She was not as weak as she had been yesterday, but her strength was quickly sapped.

A string rested in a curved line on the water, the unravelled threads from one of Reilly's shirts that he had plaited together. The string was attached to one of the lean-to poles and a pin from the first-aid kit was fashioned into a hook on the other end.

A faint, questioning smile touched the edges of her mouth. 'Do you really think there are any fish in the pond?'

'No.' Reilly darted her a sideways look, the grooves around his mouth deepened. 'But it's an excellent excuse to sit and think.'

'Think about what?'

'Things.' He shrugged with one shoulder.

'What things?' Leah prompted.

119

The line of his mouth straightened, leading her to believe that his thoughts were serious ones. He didn't answer immediately.

'This is a good place.' His alert gaze swept the area. 'There's plenty of water, and firewood too from that deadfall over there.'

'And it's peacefully beautiful,' Leah added to his practical assessment. 'We were lucky to find it.'

'Against the earth tones of the desert, a patch of green stands out for miles. And where there's green, there's water,' he replied. 'I noticed it when we were almost at the bottom of the mountain.'

Turning her gaze to the mountains that ringed them on three sides, Leah tried to locate the saddle-backed ridge on which their plane had crashed. Each mountain and ridge bore a likeness to another and she couldn't find it.

'Where were we?' she asked.

'About thirty miles back and up.' Reilly pointed towards a mountain peak that didn't seem very far away. 'Do you see the small dip on the other side of that peak? That's where the plane crashed.'

Sighing, she leaned back against the tree. 'I imagine we've been given up for dead after all this time.'

This was the eighth day. It seemed like such a short amount of time, yet, conversely, it seemed like forever.

'It will be another three or four days before you'll have the strength to try to walk out of here,' he stated grimly.

'At least here we won't have to worry about a supply of water,' Leah offered. 'And let's hope we'll have food.'

This morning Reilly had announced that the three remaining packets of dried food would be used only as a last resort. They would eat what they were able to forage. He had placed snares along the game trails leading to the watering hole. If that failed, he would hunt with his pistol and there was always the abundant supply of snakes to fall back on. Although Leah doubted she would be able to eat them with the same degree of pleasure as she had when she hadn't known beforehand.

'With the two of us, the food we have now would last only three days. It would last six days, if there was only one,' he said quietly, slowly trailing the string through the water.

Something in his tone made her stiffen. 'What's that supposed to mean?'

His impassive face turned to meet her challenging look. 'That you stay here while I go for help.'

'We've been over that before,' she stated tautly.

'Circumstances are different. You aren't capable of travelling, not for several days.' Reilly averted his attention back to the fishing line. 'I noticed a dirt track about ten miles from here. It heads down the centre of the valley floor. It will either lead to the highway or a ranch house.'

'How far?'

'I don't know. I haven't seen any smoke to the

south in the morning that might indicate the existense of a ranch house,' he answered thoughtfully. 'The second day we were here I walked over to the track. There wasn't any sign that it had been used for several weeks or longer. It might have been abandoned when the mine was. But it leads somewhere.'

'I won't stay here alone, Reilly. I mean it.' Her teeth were clenching in determination.

'The longer we stay out here, the more risk we'll be taking that something will happen. You'll be safe here by yourself.'

'You said we were in this together,' Leah reminded him. 'I won't let you leave without me.'

'You're too weak to go now.'

'I am not!' she protested vigorously even though she knew what Reilly said was true. 'I can walk just as far and just as long as you can! There's nothing wrong with me. My fever's gone and I'm as healthy as a horse!'

To prove her allegation, she rose swiftly to her feet and took a quick step towards him, but the sudden movement instantly made her dizzy. She pressed a hand to her reeling head and swayed unsteadily.

With split second reaction, Reilly was on his feet, hands gripping her waist in support. She leaned heavily against him, fighting to regain her sense of balance. He lifted her in his arms and set her back against the slim trunk.

'Now will you admit I'm right?' His green eyes mocked the pallor of her face. 'You are too weak.'

'I moved too quickly, that's all,' Leah defended,

resting her head against the tree to gaze at the man kneeling beside her. 'I swear that you're not leaving without me, Reilly. If you go, I'll follow.' There was a tight lump in her throat as she spoke, but her voice was otherwise controlled.

Grim amusement was carved in his features. 'I believe you mean that.' Pivoting on his knee, he started to move away.

But Leah needed assurance that he had changed his mind and wouldn't leave her. She clutched at the material of his shirt to halt his departure.

'Reilly?' She leaned forward, earnestly searching his expression with questing hazel eyes.

Motionless, he held her look, revealing nothing of his thoughts or decision. A smouldering light of anger burned in his eyes and a male hand slid slowly, almost unwillingly, along the back of her waist.

Her heart fluttered uncertainly, excited and afraid. Then his mouth was savagely crushing hers in a punishing kiss. The pain lasted only brief seconds as Reilly switched the kiss to sensual demand. Response flamed through Leah's veins, melting her against the solid wall of his chest.

The weight of his body pressed her backwards, pinning her on the carpet of grass while he continued to explore her mouth with arousing thoroughness. Shudders of primitive rapture quivered within her. She had not guessed that his masterful kiss would be as glorious as this. Her senses were reeling under the assault of his desire.

The soft flesh of her body moulded itself willingly

to the male length of him. No part of her was immune to his fire. His caressing fingers explored her neck and shoulders, blazing a trail that his mouth followed. Quicksilver gasps of air were all she was allowed before a new shiver of experience stole her breath.

In a mindless haze, she knew she had lost control and was powerless to regain it as long as his lips kept returning to dominate hers. Unexpectedly, Reilly rolled on to his back, drawing her on top of him. There he cupped her face in his hands and held it away from him.

Her parted lips were swollen and trembling from his kisses. She knew her eyes had darkened from the desire he had aroused. Her lashes fell to veil the completeness of her response. Yet she couldn't deny the truth of what she felt.

'I've wanted you to do that.' Her voice throbbed with the disturbed beat of her heart.

'Leah.' His husky tone too betrayed his inner passion, yet his was controlled. 'You've never known a man, have you?'

The gently spoken question frightened her as his embrace had not. The silken curtain of her hair had fallen forward. It shielded the flames that licked her cheeks as she drew away from his unresisting hands and scrambled shakily to her feet. She could feel his piercingly alert eyes watching her, but she was unable to meet them. Keeping her back to him, she stuffed her trembling hands deep in the pockets of her slacks and drew a quivering breath.

'Have you?' repeated Reilly.

124

The question came from directly behind her, his animal silence bringing him to his feet unheard by her. In the next instant, his hands were resting lightly on each side of her waist. She breathed in sharply to keep from turning and seeking his embrace.

'I . . . I really don't see why I should answer that,' she swallowed, closing her eyes and wishing she could close the rest of her senses to his nearness.

'I want to know,' he replied simply.

'You could have found it out for yourself. I could scream my head off and there's no one for miles to hear me. What stopped you?' Leah challenged, but with a faintly hysterical note.

'Dammit, Leah!' He spun around, exasperation snapping in his green eyes.

The pinched lines around her nose and mouth must have betrayed her inexperienced state because Reilly immediately loosened his steel grip on her waist, the fire in his gaze banking at the sight of the apprehension that clouded her eyes.

Reilly smiled gently. 'You don't need to be afraid.'

'Of who?' she blinked. His touch was curling her toes. 'Of you? Or me?'

His muscular chest rose in a deep breath, his eyes narrowing into green slits. 'You shouldn't say such things.'

'Why?' Leah challenged. 'I can't deny that a moment ago I wanted you to make love to me!'

'Well, try!' he snapped savagely, releasing her from his pole.

The anger that had flashed across his face for that

125

split second was completely gone when Leah focused her gaze on him. The mask of unshakable composure covered his lean features.

Leah felt trapped in a labyrinth with no escape in sight. She was thoroughly confused and puzzled by his actions. Reilly had wanted her—she wasn't so inexperienced that she didn't know that. Yet when he had discovered she was a virgin, he had rejected her. Why? Because she wasn't sufficiently experienced for his tastes?

Hot tears filled her eyes. 'I don't understand you, Reilly Smith!' she lashed out at him angrily.

A furrow of absent concentration darkened his brow as he glanced briefly in her direction. 'It's simple,' he replied harshly. 'When I'm in the desert, I think too much like an Indian.'

The cryptic answer made more sense than his actions. Leah rubbed the back of her neck in frustration and tried to check the welling tears. She held them back, but she couldn't keep her chin from trembling.

A sigh came from Reilly. Grass whispered beneath his feet as he rose and walked to her. His hands touched her shoulders and Leah drew away. He simply grasped them more firmly a second time.

'Please don't try to convince me that you're some saint,' she declared caustically, tossing back her head to glare at him defiantly through her mist of tears.

'I'm not virtuous by any means,' Reilly agreed with iron control, 'although I don't intend to brag about the number of women I've known.'

'That's a relief!' Her tongue tasted bitter with sarcasm.

'If a maiden is taken by a man before marriage, in the eyes of the Indian, she becomes unclean and is shunned.' The faint cynicism in his tone seemed to be directed at himself. 'That's a quaint custom to be observed in these promiscuous times, I'll admit. Nevertheless,' he drew the words out slowly, 'as far as you are concerned, I'm compelled to respect my grandfather's teachings. We have been through too much together these past days for me to be the one to take away your innocence.'

A tremulous smile touched her mouth. His words chased the clouds away from her heart and let the radiant light of joy shine through.

'That's why you asked,' she breathed.

'Yes.' Reilly smiled without humour.

Slipping her arms around his middle, she sighed contentedly, nestling her head against his chest. His arms tightened to hold her close, a firm hand slowly caressing her shoulders and back as his mouth roughly moved against her hair. His fingers raked through her hair, drawing her head back. His mouth closed over hers in a hard, lingering kiss. The melting of her bones began all over again.

When he released her, his eyes burned possessively over her face. 'I think it's time you took charge of the fishing while I check the snares,' Reilly said huskily.

'Let me go with you,' Leah whispered.

His fingers covered her mouth as he shook his dark

127

head. 'I want to be sure you've had plenty of rest so you'll be able to cook dinner tonight.' He pushed her to the ground near where his pole lay.

Leah didn't resist and sat quietly on the bank while he walked away. She knew she was falling in love with him, if she hadn't already. Was it because she couldn't have survived in this desert wilderness without him? She thought not. She admired his competency, resourcefulness and strength, but her feelings for him went beyond that. Nor was what she felt strictly physical.

So, eliminating all the other possibilities, she was in love with him. She tried to caution her heart that eight days was a very short time to fall in love with someone. Her heart answered that she and Reilly had been through more than some couples experience in a lifetime together.

The only uncertainty that remained was how Reilly felt about her. If for him, it was more physical attraction, too? Leah sighed, knowing that no one would ever put words in his mouth nor elicit an answer he wasn't prepared to make. But, for the moment, the knowledge of her love for him was enough.

One of the snares had trapped a rabbit. Reilly had cleaned it and shown Leah how to roast it on the spit. Again, their menu had contained a side dish of greens, an item that Leah had decided was going to become a staple part of their diet.

The exertion from doing their few dishes left her

slightly weak. She set them near the fire to dry. Brushing a hand wearily through her gold-brown hair, she wished longingly for a hot bath and a shampoo.

'Tired?' Reilly asked gently.

'A little,' Leah admitted. She sat down beside him in front of the fire, curling her legs beneath her. 'Mostly I was thinking that I was a mess.'

An arm circled her waist and drew her against his shoulder, locking his hands across her stomach as he kept her faced towards the fire. Leah stared into the flames, a feeling of intense bliss stealing over her.

'Aren't you going to say that I'm not a mess?' she teased with a soft sigh of contentment.

'I'm not going to state the obvious,' Reilly chuckled.

'Now that's a tactful reply!' Her head moved briefly in mock exasperation, but there was amusement in her tone.

A coyote sang his lament to the winking eye of a crescent moon. On a faraway hill, another coyote joined in the chorus. Overhead, the stars blazed brightly in the velvet sky.

His chin brushed the top of her hair. 'Did you want me to say that your hair is perfumed with sage and smoke? That its colour reminds me of the dappled coat of a doe fawn in the morning sunlight?' The husky murmur of his voice quickened her heartbeat.

'Is that really what you think?' Leah held her breath.

Reilly smiled against her hair. 'Your eyes are the

the colour of the fawn's, round and trusting, fringed with sunbrowned lashes.' A hand circled her wrist to make her arm join his as he drew her more tightly into the circle of his arms. 'Your bones are deceivingly dainty as a fawn's.'

'I think'—she was sinking in a quicksand of heady emotions, yet not wanting to struggle to the point where she could break free '—that one of your ancestors kissed the Blarney Stone, Reilly Smith.'

'Do you?' he mused softly against her hair. 'It comes naturally from both sides of my heritage. Some of the greatest orators in our history were Indians—Red Cloud, Spotted Tail—if only someone had listened.'

There was no bitterness in his statement and nothing that required a response. The desert silence moved in, drawing them into its magic circle of ageless enchantment.

It was a long time before either of them moved until Reilly finally decreed softly that it was time they got some sleep. The only thing that made Leah willingly agree was the knowledge that she would return to his arms beneath the blanket.

This night, as he cradled her in his arms, she lifted her head for a kiss. The firm pressure of his mouth on hers started a slow glow of warmth through her limbs. The small fire remained even after he had dragged his mouth from hers, leaving it tingling and moist from his kiss. The steady beat of his heart beneath her head soon lulled her to sleep.

Cool air invaded the blanket cocoon. Leah frowned

at its chill, keeping her eyes tightly shut, and tried to snuggle closer against Reilly's muscular length. He wasn't there!

She was immediately awake. Soft morning light filled the camp. The flames of the campfire were hungrily devouring the fresh wood that had been added. Throwing back the cover, she sat up. There was no sign of Reilly.

The canteen was gone. Her gaze flew to the waterhole several yards away, thinking Reilly was there refilling the canteen with water. He wasn't. Scrambling to her feet, Leah scanned the area around the campfire again.

A cold dread filled her heart. 'He couldn't. He wouldn't!' she murmured aloud, protesting against the chilling thought.

But it was entirely possible. Reilly was nowhere to be seen. That left only the desert. Shuddering, Leah realised that he had not promised he wouldn't leave without her. In fact, he had never said that he wouldn't go.

Her gaze shifted towards the centre of the valley. He had sneaked away at first light, probably thinking she would be too frightened and weak to follow.

Leah clenched her teeth tightly together. 'You're in for a surprise, Reilly Smith!' she muttered.

Deciding that he couldn't be very far ahead of her, she kicked sand on to the fire, quickly stirred the smouldering embers, and kicked on more sand. If she hurried, she could catch up to him.

There was no point trying to carry the few items

with her. Their weight would slow her down. Reilly had the canteen and that was the important thing.

Not allowing time to question the wisdom of her impulse, Leah abandoned the campsite without a backward glance. Her only thought was to catch up with Reilly as quickly as possible. She started running, wanting to make up the distance that separated them.

The desert brush whipped at her legs and thighs. A startled flock of mountain bluebirds skimmed the bush tops in flight. All her attention was focused on the land ahead of her.

Leah's scream ripped the air as an unknown force yanked her backwards. Her motion stopped with an impact against a hard, immovable object.

'Where the hell do you think you were going?' Reilly demanded, shaking her savagely by the shoulders.

She stared at his glaring, angry face in disbelief.

'Reilly!' She started laughing and crying at the same time, ceasing her instinctive struggle of self-protection.

'Answer me!' His eyes glittered coldly.

'I thought——' her breath came in short, laughingly relieved signs, 'I thought you'd gone for help. I thought you'd left me.'

'You crazy——' Reilly snapped off the rest of the words, leaving it dangling, unfinished in the air. 'And you were coming after me.'

Leah bobbed her head, trying to calm her shaky breath. 'I told you I would,' she reminded him.

His fingers loosened their digging grip into her bones. 'You might have checked to be certain I was gone,' he replied tightly, 'instead of racing off into the bush like a madwoman.'

'I looked for you,' she defended. 'Where were you?'

'Checking the snares.' He released her entirely, standing in front of her, his hands on his hips, his expression grim and unyielding.

Her hazel eyes rolled guiltily away from his censorious gaze. She had completely forgotten about the snares in her panicked certainty that he had left her.

'I didn't remember them,' she admitted.

Reilly breathed in deeply, his action letting her know what he thought of that. 'Let's go back to camp and restart the fire.' His mouth thinned sardonically. 'You were so intent on following me, would you like to follow me back to camp?'

Leah nodded. There was no doubt he was angry with her. In retrospect, her action was foolhardy and impulsive. She could very easily have got lost.

'How——' She had to hurry to keep up with his long strides. 'How did you know where I'd gone?'

'I didn't,' he replied curtly, 'but I heard the racket of something charging through the bush, and I decided it was either you or a stampeding herd of cattle.'

'I was stupid,' sighed Leah.

He slid her a chilling look. 'If you expect me to disagree, woman, you're wrong.'

Until his anger cooled, Leah decided it was better

to keep silent. It became an oppressive silence, as she patiently rebuilt the fire. When it was burning freely once more, he began cleaning a gamebird he had caught in the snare. Not a word nor a glance did he direct at Leah.

There was little for her to do except sit and watch him, squirming inwardly at the uncomfortable silence. The feeling kept growing that she was being unfairly punished. Finally she decided that it was time for a truce to be offered.

As Reilly started to put the cleaned bird on the spit, Leah stepped forward. 'Let me do that. It's squaw's work.' She tried to lessen the crackling tension by drawing on their stand-by joke.

'You aren't a squaw.' The aloof indifference in his voice cut like a knife.

'Reilly, I'm sorry. What more do you want me to say?' she demanded.

With the bird secured on the spit, he stood up, his chiselled features carved into uncompromisingly harsh lines. 'Do you realise you could have got yourself killed out there? If not from snakebite or a broken neck, then from thirst or starvation! You didn't take anything to protect you from the elements! You didn't take any food or water!'

'I wanted to catch up with you!' Leah shouted in answer to his loud accusing voice. 'I didn't want to be slowed down carrying things. Besides, you had the canteen! Was I supposed to go racing through the desert carrying a pan of water?'

'You shouldn't have been racing anywhere! And if I *had* left, then you should have stayed here! And I took the canteen to refill it at the waterhole on my way to check the snares!'

'But I didn't know that!' she protested angrily.

His eyes narrowed as he let out a long, exasperated breath. 'I ought to take you over my knee and spank the living tar out of you for what you put me through,' he declared through gritted teeth.

'What about what I went through?' Leah retorted. 'I thought you'd gone off and left me!'

'So you followed, not knowing where you were going and not taking anything with you. You would have been lost—or dead before the day was out,' Reilly said harshly.

'At least then you would have been rid of me and you wouldn't have been thinking about me any more! Aren't you sorry you went after me and brought me back!' she cried bitterly, brushing her hair away from her face as she turned away.

She was spun back around and pulled against his chest in one fluid motion. Her startled mouth opened to protest and it was covered in a brutal kiss. Love rushed, unchecked, to respond to the punishing ardour of his mouth. Her senses whirled in the vortex of Reilly's embrace until she didn't know down from up and didn't care.

Then his mouth was buried in the sensitive cord along her neck. 'You would test the patience and endurance of a saint,' he muttered against her skin.

His warm breath was a disturbing caress as she wound her arms tightly around his middle for support. The wild tempo of her heart was making clear thinking difficult. She inhaled deeply of his intoxicating male scent and sighed.

'You're not a saint,' she murmured.

His hands firmly set her away from him. The dark fire glittering in his eyes did nothing to steady the erratic beat of her heart. His mouth crooked wryly.

'Don't remind me.' There was no more cold anger in his expression. 'See what you can do about keeping our breakfast and lunch from being burned up while I wash.'

The fire was trying to char one side of the dressed fowl. Leah was forced to rescue it as Reilly walked towards the narrow stream formed by the water spilling over the dam's walls. As she turned the spit, she watched him crouch beside the stream, splashing the cold water on his face and the back of his neck.

Smiling at his action, she glanced at the sun. Its fiery heat hadn't yet begun to scorch the ground. In fact, it was only pleasantly warm.

CHAPTER EIGHT

AFTER they had eaten, Reilly had suggested that Leah rest in the shade through the hot hours of early afternoon. She tried, knowing that it was important to regain her strength, but she couldn't relax.

A fever burned inside as she watched him repairing one of the snares. It wasn't a fever caused by infection, unless love was infectious. If it was, she hoped Reilly caught the disease, too.

No matter how often she closed her eyes, they opened, her gaze straying to Reilly. Her senses would tingle with the awareness of him. The ache to be in his arms would start again and all thought of rest immediately vanished.

It wasn't any use. She stopped trying to force inactivity upon herself. She recognised the inherent temptation of their present situation, the two of them alone in a miniature paradise, the succulent apple waiting for the bite that would lead her into true womanhood.

Pushing herself up from the cool carpet of grass, Leah briskly rubbed her hands over her hipbones. Reilly's questioning look flickered curiously over her determined expression.

'I'm going to wash my clothes down at the stream,'

she announced. 'If you want, I'll do your shirt.' She tried to sound offhand and partially succeeded. 'I'm not in the mood to lie around doing nothing,' she explained in unnecessary defence of her decision.

His shirt was already unbuttoned and hanging loose in front. With a nod of acceptance to her offer, he slipped it off and tossed it to her, immediately returning his attention to the damaged snare.

'You can wear one of the shirts we used for a backpack while you're washing your clothes.' His dark head remained bent over his task.

'Thanks.' Only he seemed not to hear her reply.

Behind the screen of a thick bush, Leah stripped away her outer clothes and donned the robe-like shirt, its tails reaching halfway down her thighs to provide relatively decent coverage over her underwear. Rolling back the sleeves, she set to work rinsing and rubbing to try to clean their clothes minus the assistance of detergent.

Finally she decided they were as clean as she was going to get them under the circumstances. With the back of her hand, she wiped the beads of perspiration from her forehead and lip, then picked up the wet clothes and carried them to the large stands of sunburnt brush on the edge of their spring-made glade.

The sun will fry them in minutes, she smiled to herself, feeling the scorching rays of the sun the instant she stepped out of the shade. More perspiration collected between her shoulder blades as she laid the clothes over the bushes. She glanced longingly at the dammed pool of water, about three times the size of a bathtub.

She retreated into the shade. 'Reilly? Would it hurt anything if I got my arm wet?'

'Why? Did you get it wet?' He frowned, but didn't glance up.

'No,' Leah denied quickly. 'If it wouldn't hurt anything, I was going to take a short dip in the waterhole to cool off.'

'You'd better let me take a look at it first.' As he lifted his head, his gaze slid over her in absent appraisal.

'Just a minute.' She turned her back to him and slipped her left arm out of the rolled shirt sleeve, wrapping the left side of her shirt in sarong fashion across her front.

There was a flicker of amusement in his green eyes at her action as he rose to his feet to examine the wound. His touch against her skin was strictly impersonal when he eased the bandage away.

'You're going to have a scar from this, do you know that?' he commented, adjusting the bandage back in place.

'It doesn't matter,' Leah shrugged. It was difficult to breathe naturally with Reilly standing so close. The nakedness of his bronzed chest ignited all sorts of wayward desires. She tried to shut them out as she tossed her head to look at his face. 'Will it hurt if I get it wet?'

His gaze fastened itself on her mouth. For a heart-

139

stopping moment Leah felt herself start to sway towards him, aching with every fibre of her being to feel his caress. The silver and turquoise necklace gleamed dully against the tanned column of his neck.

'Briskly he turned away. 'I don't think so, but if I were you, I'd try to keep it out of the water. There's no need to take a risk at this stage. The waterhole isn't deep. Unless you slip, you shouldn't have any trouble keeping the bandage dry.'

'How do you know it isn't deep?' Leah arched a curious eyebrow, frowning slightly.

'I bathed you in it once to bring your fever down, remember?' Reilly reminded her with lazy mockery in his tone as he again bent over the snare. 'And I've used it myself a few times—in the mornings before you were awake.'

No wonder he always looked so fresh and impervious to the rigours of their less than luxurious conditions, she thought. But there was hardly a need to make a vocal comment on the fact.

'I'll be careful not to slip,' she promised diffidently.

At the waterhole, Leah glanced over her shoulder. Reilly's back was turned towards her, deliberately or indifferently, she didn't know which.

Removing the shirt the rest of the way, she stepped into the pool, using an overhanging branch of a willow for balance. The deepest point, near the far end of the pool, brought the water to her waist. The temperature of the water in that area was several degrees cooler than the rest of the pool. She decided that she was near the spring's inlet.

It was awkward keeping her left arm out of the water while she tried to rinse the upper half of her body and her hair. It was a slow procedure but refreshingly cooling. She resisted the impulse to linger, splashing and playing in the water, and crawled on to the bank. Reilly was still working on the snare.

Quickly she towelled the moisture from her skin with the shirt she had been wearing, blotting the excess water from her undergarments. The rest of her clothes would be dry. Slipping the now damp shirt on, Leah retraced her path to the bushes, collected the washed clothes, and changed swiftly into her own.

The seams of her slacks were still damp, but that coolness and her damp underwear countered the sun-baked heat of the dry material of her slacks and blouse.

'Here's your shirt,' she told Reilly as she returned to the circle of their camp.

'Hang it on the lean-to.' His jet dark head nodded towards it while his attention remained with the damaged snare.

Leah hooked the collar over one of the poles. 'Haven't you fixed that yet? You've been working on it all afternoon.'

'Whatever it was that was caught in it worked on it all night,' he replied absently.

Kneeling beside the stack of their meagre possessions, she sifted impatiently through them, finally sitting on her heels and glancing at Reilly.

'Do you know where the comb is?' she asked.

'In the food box.'

She found it and began raking its teeth through her tousled and snarled hair. The sun had bleached pale streaks through its light brown colour, increasing the golden highlights. As she tugged the comb through her hair, she watched a cloud shadow racing across a distant mountain slope. A ghost moon occupied a corner of the daylight sky.

There had not been a sign of a search plane in the last two days. There couldn't have been one previously or Reilly would have mentioned it. There was no one who knew where they were or that they were alive.

Leah thought of her father, stern yet compassionate, but always correct and proper. His air of reserve was a contrast to her mother's warm, outgoing personality, which helped her make new friends with ease every time her husband was transferred.

With his cold logic, her father would have calculated Leah's chances of surviving the plane crash and nine days in a desert wilderness. She guessed that his conclusion would be that there was little hope that she was still alive. He would be devoting himself to consoling her mother. Lonnie, she knew, would never give up the search until he found her. He did not accept the inevitable as their father did.

Her father's calculations could not have taken into consideration Reilly's presence. He couldn't know of Reilly's knowledge of the desert or his ability to live with relatively little hardship in primitive conditions.

A smile played with her mouth as she visualised her parents' reaction if they were able to witness this scene—Reilly sitting there trying to repair a broken snare to catch their night's meal and herself combing her hair after washing their clothes in a stream and bathing in a pool.

The clock could have been turned back a hundred years. The only modern possessions they had with them were a flashlight, an emergency ration of food, a pistol, and a pocket-knife. Everything else they had made or improvised—the pan, the bowls, the spoons, the snares, the lean-to.

'Why are you smiling?' Reilly was studying her, his impassive face tipped to one side in idle curiosity.

'I was imagining my parents' astonishment if they could see us now, living here in the desert like natives.' Her smile deepened with wryness.

He nodded understandingly, his gaze briefly sweeping the sky before returning to the snare in his lap. His action wiped the smile from her face.

'There isn't much hope any more that a plane will find us, is there?' Leah said. 'We'll have to walk out of here, won't we?'

'Yes.' A simple, clear-cut answer.

Her gaze shifted to the sage-coloured valley and the corridor of mountain that enclosed it. The valley seemed to run for ever. It was difficult to remember that somewhere beyond the horizon, there was a modern highway with cars and trucks and buildings and homes with electricity, running water, and central heat and air-conditioning. The neon world of Las Vegas was an absolute fantasy in the cruel beauty of this wilderness.

A snarl at the back of her head caught the comb's teeth. She tried working the comb through the knotted hair and she gasped at the inadvertent yank on her scalp. The sound drew a look from Reilly.

'A rat built a nest in my hair,' she answered the silent question in the green eyes.

While she tried to work out the snarl, she watched him set up the snare to test his repairs. At the first pressure, it snapped at the very place he had mended. Reilly gathered it up and tossed it in the banked fire.

'Can't you fix it?' Leah protested as a tiny flame licked greedily over the snare.

He shook his head in a negative answer. 'The other three will have to be enough.' His sideways glance noted her struggles with the comb. 'Want some help?'

'Please,' she sighed with frustration. 'I can't see what I'm doing,' she rubbed the tender portion of her scalp that had become sore from repeated pulling of her knotted hair, 'although I certainly can feel it!'

Rising, he walked to her, taking the comb from her hand as she knelt behind her. With gentle care, he worked the hair free of its snarling knot piece by piece, then smoothed the hair into the rest curling around her shoulders. He offered the comb to Leah.

'Would you comb the rest of it . . . to be sure there aren't any more knots?' It was only an excuse to keep him near. The breathless tremor in her voice must have betrayed her inner wish.

'Leah, no.' His answer was grimly firm.

He tossed the comb on the ground in front of her. She turned sideways, her hazel eyes wide and shimmering with the aching need of her love for the sustenance of his touch. The parted softness of her lips issued an invitation that his jade eyes couldn't ignore.

His narrowed gaze ripped away from her mouth to look deep into her eyes. 'You're playing a dangerous game, Leah,' he muttered.

'I know,' she swallowed tightly, her voice unreasonably calm, 'but——'

'This situation provides enough temptations without you offering more,' he added flatly.

Leah averted her gaze, lowering her chin in reluctant agreement. 'You're right, of course,' she admitted, but it didn't soothe her wildly leaping pulse.

A sun-browned hand lightly cupped her cheek and chin, turning it back to meet his gaze. Desire smouldered through the sooty veil of his lashes as it swept possessively over her upturned face.

'I should have left this morning and gone for help.' She moved her cheek against his fingers, her lashes fluttering briefly from the magic spell of his touch. 'I would have followed you.'

'I know.' Her lips curved into a faint smile.

An irresistible force bent his dark head towards her. At the touch of his mouth against hers, Leah turned into his arms, sliding her hands around his neck into the black thickness of his hair.

The demand of his kiss tilted her head backwards while his moulding hands arched her against him. A fire to equal the burning rays of the sun flamed through her veins, the roar of its blaze raging in her ears. The male scent of him was intoxicating fuel to the fire that consumed her.

Boneless, she gasped as his mouth explored the exposed hollow of her throat, sending volcanic shudders through her body from his sensually arousing caress. Pushing aside the collar of her blouse, his mouth tantalised her shoulder, trailing up the sensitive cord in her neck to nibble at her ear lobe. Then he teased the corner of her mouth until her lips sought his kiss.

The iron band of his arms eased her to the ground. Leah's hands slipped to his muscular shoulders to draw him with her, then remaining to revel in the nakedness of his hard flesh. Crushed beneath his weight and smothered by his kiss, she could hardly breathe, yet there was no thought to struggle. Never before had she been so completely alive.

The sun blazed white-hot in the sky. Behind her closed eyes, the light of love was as intensely bright as the sun, searing in its insatiable fire and illuminating every corner of her heart. It was beyond physical. If Reilly never touched her again, Leah knew the invisible linkage of love bound her to him for eternity.

Wordlessly, she responded to his embrace with all

the fervour the magic knowledge had given her. The soaring joy that sang in her veins lifted her to a horizonless world. Reilly's kiss hardened as if he had been carried there, too.

Then just as suddenly, as if the height was too dizzying, he rolled on to his side, his hand slipping away from her breast to rub his face and mouth. One arm couldn't let her go. It remained to hold her firmly against his chest.

Dazed by the rapturous discovery, Leah could only listen to the pagan drumbeat of his heart and the raggedness of his breathing. Much slower, she descended from the spiritual plateau to the physical reality of their nearly consummated embrace. Irrationally she knew she would have gloried in his possession of her and cared not about any future consequences.

His control was almost frightening when she considered how readily she had abandoned her own under the possession of her love. The wonder of it kept her silent for several minutes.

'Reilly.' Her voice was warm and throbbing.

His hand cupped her cheek, a thumb touching her mouth to ask for silence. 'Leah'—she could hear the conflict with his physical need in his husky voice—'be still.'

It would have been easy to disobey his order and persuade him to countermand it. The delicious temptation teased her thoughts. but the wisdom behind it was unquestionable. So she lay unmoving in the half-embrace of his arm until she felt the tension easing from his muscles and knew he was again in total command.

'Tell me about your boy-friend,' he said quietly.

Her eyebrows drew together in confusion, 'Who?' Leah blinked.

'Marvin, the man you've been dating.'

Tipping back her head, she gazed into Reilly's impassive features. 'How did you know about him?' she frowned.

'You mentioned him when you were delirious.' He smiled, but it didn't reach his eyes.

It was strange, but she couldn't remember what Marvin looked like. It seemed years ago since she had seen him. The vague image she could summon was of a pale, insignificant man compared to Reilly, lacking the masculine vitality and virility that were a dominant part of the man who now held her in his arms.

'He works at the same bank I do,' she answered indifferently. 'I've been out with him several times, which, I suppose, classifies him as a boy-friend. What did I say about him?'

'Nothing.'

She believed him. There was little she could have said about Marv except that he was nice and possessive in an irritating kind of way. A stab of jealousy shifted her thoughts to an adjoining track.

'Tell me about your girl-friend,' she requested tensely.

148

'I don't think that terminology would fit.' His mouth twisted cynically as he shifted on to his back and stared at the pale blue sky.

An agonising pain knotted her insides. 'Your mistress, then,' she suggested with underlying bitterness. 'Tell me about her. Does she ... live with you?'

His dark head shifted to the side to look down at her nestled in the crook of his arm, his hair pitch black against the green of the long grass.

'I live by myself,' he answered, a remoteness in his tone. 'My mistress is my work. I know women, but I don't have a woman.'

His reply should have made her feel content. Instead she felt a vague dissatisfaction. It was several seconds before she realised why. The implication of his answer included her in the category of women in the plural. A lump rose in her throat.

'You ... you mentioned you lived in Las Vegas,' she murmured, needing to change the subject. 'Where?'

'I have a house in the foothills outside the city.'

'Why ... er ... why did you pick Las Vegas?' Leah tried to sound nonchalant.

'It's centrally located for my work. I'm not far from the mines or the outlets for my work in California and Arizona.'

'Do you spend much time at your home?'

'A good deal, yes.'

Again, Leah tilted back her head to see his face, smiling bravely despite the tears scalding the back of her eyes. 'When we get back, shall I see you?'

The pause before he answered was electric. The jade mask of his gaze revealed nothing to her searching eyes. 'I imagine we'll have dinner one evening,' Reilly seemed to choose his words carefully, 'to celebrate our safe return.'

It was better than nothing. Averting her gaze, she slid her hand over the naked flatness of his stomach. 'I'd like that,' she agreed with aching softness.

Her wrist was seized and her hand jerked away from the firmness of his flesh. The motion continued, turning her on to her back, her arms pinned above her head as Reilly hovered above her, dark anger flashing in his eyes.

'Don't do that!' he snapped harshly. 'Do you think I'm made of stone?'

'I'm sorry.' She knew she should be frightened by the suppressed violence in his expression, but she wasn't. 'I can't help it, Reilly, I——'

'Yes. you can!' Abruptly he released her wrists and got to his feet. His expression was cold and grim as he towered above her. 'You know as well as I do what's happening between us!' He turned away, savagely rubbing the back of his neck. 'We've been alone out here too long. The world we lived in before the crash seems far removed from today. But we're going to get back,' he added firmly. 'When we do, those days we've spent together will be the time that seems unreal.'

'Is that what you think?' There was a calm

curiousness to Leah's voice. Having concrete instead of desert sand beneath her feet would not alter the love she felt for him.

'It's the way life is.' It was a statement not issued to be debated. With a long stride, Reilly grabbed his shirt from the lean-to pole. 'I'm going to check the snares.'

Was he telling her something? Leah wondered as she watched him go. Was he saying not to fall in love with him because he was not in love with her? She picked up the comb from where he had tossed it and began running it through her hair, digging the teeth into her scalp to stop the chilling numbness from totally possessing her.

By early evening, Reilly hadn't left her to walk for help. He was too wise in the ways of the desert to get lost checking the snares he had set some distance from the waterhole.

As dusk settled over the sky, Leah clutched the flashlight tightly in her hand. If he wasn't back by the time the sun touched the rim of the mountain, she was going out to look for him. She added another log to the fire and glanced at the mountain.

There wasn't a whisper of a sound, yet something made her spin around. Where there had been nothing but cobweb shadows cast by the willows Reilly stood, returning to the camp with the animal silence of his ancestors.

Only when she saw him did Leah realise how numbly she had waited for him to come back. Relief weakened her knees, keeping her from racing into his arms. Relief, and the withdrawn expression in his face. His gaze studied her slowly, sliding finally to the flashlight in her hand.

'I . . . I was coming to look for you,' she explained shakily. 'I thought if you weren't back by sundown, that you had got hurt somehow.'

His expression didn't alter as he slipped the pistol from his waistband and returned it to the first-aid kit. Then his swinging strides carried him to the fire.

'Where did you go?' Leah asked when he offered no explanation for his long absence.

Except for perspiration stains on his shirt, there wasn't a mark on his leanly muscled physique. His impassivity chilled her to the bone.

'The snares were empty.' He took a long drink from the canteen, avoiding her searching eyes. 'I went hunting—unsuccessfully.'

Leah hugged her arms about her to ward off the sudden attack of misery. 'I'm not hungry.' She stared into the fire.

'You're going to eat anyway,' he stated firmly.

A sighing, bitter laugh escaped her throat. 'Yes, I have to get my strength back, don't I?'

'Yes, you do.' His gaze narrowed on her huddled form for a slashing second.

Leah looked at his carved profile, so aggressively male. His black hair had grown longer since the crash and now curled over the short collar. The shirt was opened in the front, revealing the hard bronzed chest.

Muscles rippled as he recapped the canteen. The ache to touch him was a physical pain.

'Reilly——' Her voice throbbed with need.

Was it her imagination or had his face grown paler beneath his tan? A muscle twitched alongside his lean jaw, but he didn't glance at her.

'I'll refill the canteen while you decide which one of the packages you want to fix tonight.' He turned away from the fire.

His movement brought Leah to her feet. 'I'm not hungry now.'

'Reilly, will you listen to me?' she demanded in frustration. He crouched along the pool's bank, letting the canteen float on the water. 'Reilly, I'm in love with you.' She thought she would have burst if she had held the admission back much longer.

Her statement brought no reaction. He didn't even blink an eye at her words. He just watched the water flowing into the canteen. Somehow Leah had to make him understand that she meant it.

'I know you think this physical attraction we feel is a—a natural result of our situation,' she hurried on. 'We've been a man and woman alone together for several days under intimate conditions that have put us outside the normal conventions of society. But it isn't just sexual attraction, Reilly. I'm in love with you. I'm telling you now, and whenever we do get back to civilisation, I'll tell you again. Nothing is going to change the way I feel.'

He capped the canteen and straightened. 'We're leaving in the morning,' he announced unemotionally.

Leah's head recoiled at his unexpected response. 'I ... I thought we were going to wait another day or two until ... until——'

'——you were stronger,' Reilly finished the sentence for her, not sparing a glance in her direction. 'Before I got back to camp, I decided there wasn't any point in delaying longer. I think you've recovered enough to travel. If necessary, I'll carry you out.'

'Haven't——' she shook her sunstreaked hair helplessly, 'haven't you heard anything I said?'

His eyes hardened on her with cynical amusement. 'What do you expect me to reply to it?'

What had she expected? In white-hot humiliation, she didn't know. She hadn't thought he would suddenly admit that he might care for her, too. But his crushing indifference to her declaration of love sliced deeply with agonising pain. The only thing that she knew was that she wanted to hurt him back.

Her hand swung in a lightning arc, her open palm striking his lean cheek with stinging force. The attacking hand was captured by punishing fingers that twisted her arm backwards until Leah thought it would break. His expression had darkened with savage rage.

'You're hurting me!' she cried out, frightened by the temper she had aroused.

'Am I?' His lip curled in satisfaction.

The fingers shifted their pressure without easing the excruciating pain. The action forced Leah against him, her hips pressed against his muscled thighs while his other hand brutally wound her hair around his fingers and pulled her head back.

Leah tried to struggle, but at her first attempt Reilly twisted her arm further, checking her protest before it started. As her lips parted to moan her pain, he ruthlessly covered them with his own, grinding them against her teeth until the taste of her own blood was on her tongue. He licked it away with savage pleasure.

Tearing his fingers free of her hair, he tugged at her blouse front. Dominated by his devouring mouth and the cruel twisting of her arm, Leah was helpless. The buttons that resisted his fingers were torn off, as was the cotton front of her bra.

Although she was terrified by his assault, it was having a devastating affect on her senses. When his hand closed roughly over her breast, she felt it swell to his caress. His warm, male scent filled her head. The stirring male hardness revealed his ultimate need of her. Leah's free hand slid inside his shirt to feel the pagan drumbeat of his heart.

Mercilessly Reilly thrust her away, his green eyes glaring at her contemptuously even as his bared chest rose and fell in disturbed breathing.

'It won't work,' he taunted harshly. 'I won't be tricked into raping you!'

'I——' Tears swam in her eyes. There was nothing she could say. His accusation wasn't true, not the way he meant it.

The numbed nerves in the arm Reilly had twisted screamed to life when she tried to cover her semi-nakedness. With one hand she tried to button her blouse, but most of the buttons were gone.

A hissing release of breath came from Reilly. 'Your clothes are ruined. You'll have to wear one of my shirts.' Fingers savagely raked the virile thickness of his black hair as he walked impatiently to get the shirt she had worn earlier as a robe. Avoiding direct contact with her tear-filled gaze, he tossed it to her. 'I'll start dinner.'

An ominous silence descended on the camp. Later, with shoulders hunched to defend her inner anguish, Leah ate the tasteless food. Her hurt anger kept her from making any attempt to break the silence. It was not the uneasy silence between two strangers, but rather it held the tense hostility of two enemies.

When the scarlet sunset gave way to the purpling night, she crawled into the stiff blanket. She didn't ask Reilly if he would be having an early night before facing tomorrow's walk. She knew without being told that she wouldn't sleep in his arms that night.

Tears washed her face as she turned her back on the fire and Reilly. Even though her pride was severely wounded, she knew nothing had changed. She still loved him as deeply as ever. Nothing would change that.

The swan-dive of a falling star arced across the heavens. Leah watched it until the crystal brightness of a tear got in the way. She pulled the blanket tighter around her shoulders, but the chill was from inside.

CHAPTER NINE

LEAH'S knuckles whitened around the end of the lean-to pole, now a walking stick. There was a poignant tightness in her throat as she gazed for the last time at the mock oasis where she had admitted her love for Reilly.

Dawn's early light had lengthened the shadows over the pool, making it look dark and mysterious. It was almost as if the doors were closing on paradise.

The campfire was drowned and the ashes scattered. Soon the desert wind would wipe away any trace of the presence and the waterhole would again belong to the wildlife of the Great Basin.

'Let's go,' Reilly said flatly, adjusting with a shrug of his shoulders the pack strapped to his back.

Forcibly turning herself away from the scene, Leah nodded in agreement. She didn't look at him—she avoided it whenever she could. The voltage in his green eyes invariably jolted her with its aloofness.

Reilly probably felt none of the sadness she did about leaving this place where, for a short time, they had been so close in body and spirit. Her family was waiting at the end of their walk, whenever that would be, but Leah knew that if she had been given a choice, she would have stayed here with Reilly. Admittedly, it was a romantic fantasy that was neither logical nor practical.

But she loved him. Oh, God, how she loved him, she thought dispiritedly.

As before, Reilly led the way. The pace was slower than the last time. She knew it was done to conserve her strength. There wasn't any pack on her back this time. Everything they had with them, Reilly carried.

The first few hours of walking, each one punctuated by ten-minute rest stops, Leah felt quite good, not tiring as quickly as she thought she might. Then the sun neared its zenith and heat began prickling her back.

Reilly set up a noon camp in the middle of the desert valley along the rutted dirt road they had been following for the last several miles. Leah tumbled exhaustedly beneath the lean-to he had immediately erected, swallowed a mouthful of water and closed her eyes.

The nap helped a little. Before they started out again, Reilly inquired distantly as to how she felt. Leah shrugged aside his indifferent question with a stiff, 'I'm fine.'

For a while she was, but her energy dissipated sooner than it had this morning. Each step seemed to jar her teeth. The ten-minute rest stops seemed to get shorter. She could feel the encroaching weakness, but she gritted her teeth and pushed on.

Reilly stayed close beside her, never more than a few paces ahead. The freshness of his stride goaded

Leah to keep walking, reminding her that she was holding him back. If she wasn't along, he would be miles farther than they were now. Bitterly she knew how determined Reilly was that they should find help. He didn't want to spend an hour more than he had to with her.

Turning an ankle on a rock, Leah stumbled and fell to her knees. His hand was under her arm to help her to her feet. She wrenched it away from his hold.

'I can make it,' she insisted sharply, and pushed herself upright. Sand had bit into her palms. She rubbed it off on to her slacks.

'Did you twist your ankle?' Reilly studied her quietly with his remote gaze.

Gingerly Leah tested it. It supported her with only a twinge of protest. 'It's fine,' she answered woodenly. 'Let's go.'

Reilly handed her the stick she had dropped and started out.

Just before sunset, they stopped for the night. Leah collapsed on to the rutted track, wearily resting her head on her drawn-up knees. Reilly pushed the canteen into her hand and slipped out of his pack. Her hands were shaking too badly from exhaustion to carry the canteen to her mouth without spilling the contents. Finally Reilly had to hold the canteen to her lips.

From the backpack, he handed her a stick of jerky. 'We don't have enough water to fix one of the packaged meals.'

'I'm not hungry,' she waved it aside.

'Eat it,' he ordered.

'I'm too tired,' Leah grumbled, but she reluctantly took it from him.

'I'm going to see if I can find something for a fire.'

Tiredly she chewed on the jerky, finishing it before Reilly returned. She stretched out on the hard, uneven ground, not opening her eyes when she heard his footsteps. He threw the blanket over her, but Leah was certain her aching muscles wouldn't notice the night cold. She heard Reilly starting a fire and guessed he had found fuel of some sort. Then a horrible burning stench filled her nose.

'Whew! What's that?' she rolled over, wrinkling her nose, as she glanced at Reilly.

'There wasn't any wood, but I found some cowchips. They smell, but they burn and we need the fire to keep warm.'

Leah pulled the blanket over her head to try to shut out the odorous smoke. Eventually she was simply too tired to care. She didn't even remember the sun sinking below the horizon.

A hand gripped her shoulder. Leah reluctantly opened her eyes, her vision blurring from heavy sleep. A pair of boots were near her head, topped by the narrowed flare of dusty levis. Her gaze followed the snugly fitting denim material upwards over muscular thighs, slim hips and waist to wide shoulders, finally stopping as she met a pair of green eyes.

161

'It can't be morning,' she mumbled, but the sky was light.

'Come on, get up,' Reilly said firmly, but he didn't offer to help.

Every muscle, sinew, and nerve in her legs was cramped with stiffness. Reilly, she noticed, was beginning to show signs of fatigue, too, but there was small comfort in that.

Within a few minutes the pack was on his back and they started out again. Her stiff muscles didn't loosen, each step making her wince. Leah relied more heavily on the walking stick to keep her upright when her legs wanted to buckle.

At the second rest stop, she was afraid to sit down for fear she couldn't get up. She leaned heavily on the stick, exhausted nearly beyond the point of endurance.

'How—much farther?' It took an unbelievable amount of effort to even speak.

Reilly's hands were under her arms lowering her to the ground. 'I don't know.'

'I don't think I can get up,' Leah protested, but she was already seated. Of its own accord, her body stretched itself out on the hard ground, her muscles quivering with fatigue.

'You're doing fine,' he replied.

'Am I?' Her laugh was choked off by a lack of breath.

Her lashes fluttered wearily. When she opened them, Reilly was crouching beside her, offering her a lit cigarette to her lips.

'It's the last one,' he smiled faintly, a mere twist of his mouth. 'We'll have to share.'

He kept a hold of it as she took a long drag on the filtered end. Which was just as well, because Leah doubted she could have held on to it herself.

'I—feel like a dying man having his last cigarette,' she said, exhaling the smoke in a tired sigh.

'Don't talk. Rest.' He offered her another puff of the cigarette.

Strange, Leah thought as she felt his fingertips brush her lips, we've said more to each other in these few minutes than we did all day yesterday. Were they both too tired to be angry any more?

After the cigarette was ground into the sand beneath his boot, Reilly lifted Leah to her feet. She couldn't prevent herself from leaning weakly against him. He stiffened away from her, supporting her with his hands and not his body. She knew that not all the barriers had crumbled between them. The walking stick was shoved into her hand and she shifted her weight to it.

They set out at an ambling pace, yet each dragging step was an effort for Leah. Her lungs were bursting with exhaustion, making each breath a sob of determination that pushed her on.

Reilly stopped ahead of her. 'Look!' His low voice held an undertone of excitement.

Leah paused beside him, forcing her eyes to focus on the direction of his gaze. Flat, sage-covered land stretched endlessly in front of her eyes, the mountain corridor widening to make it larger.

'Where?' she asked hoarsely, seeing nothing to give them hope.

'Off to the right, near the foot of the mountains, there are some buildings. Ranch buildings if I'm not mistaken.' His gaze was riveted on the distant point.

All she could make out was some dark squares. She marvelled that he had noticed them at all. Reilly adjusted the shoulder-straps of his makeshift pack and sliced a glance at Leah.

'Let's go.'

Their course altered to angle across the open country towards the buildings. For a while, the knowledge that help might be found at those buildings gave Leah a fresh spurt of energy, but too soon it was spent, taking with it what remained of her strength and co-ordination. Her legs became like soft rubber. Without warning they collapsed beneath her and not even the stick could hold her up.

In a haze of total exhaustion, Leah felt Reilly's hands slip under her arms to try to lift her leaden weight.

'It's no use,' she breathed. 'I can't make it any farther.'

'Yes, you can.' His voice rang harshly in her ears.

He pulled her to her feet, drawing her arm across his shoulders and around his neck, while his other arm supported her waist. Half carrying and half dragging Leah, he started forward. She tried to make herself walk to help him, but her tired legs wouldn't obey.

164

The next thing she knew Reilly was swinging her into his arms. Her head lolled against his shoulder. She felt like a limp rag doll without a solid bone in her body, her head swimming in a mindless state of exhaustion. Distantly, Leah could sense the strain of his rippling muscles to carry her dead weight.

'Leave me, Reilly,' she pleaded.

'I'm not leaving you,' he refused unconditionally.

Waves of tiredness washed over her and she hadn't the strength to protest any more. She let herself drift away, semi-aware of the arms that held her and the walking motion that carried her across the ground.

The angry bark of a dog finally dragged her eyes open. Her head stirred against his shoulder, turning slightly so she could see ahead of them. Reilly's steps had slowed because of the large dog planted squarely in their path. Beyond him was a dusty white house with curtains at the windows and a wash hanging on the clothesline in the yard.

The screen door on the porch slammed. 'Laddie! Come here!' a woman called and the dog stopped barking and retreated to the porch steps. The woman stepped out of the shadows, shielding her eyes against the sun. A small child clung to her legs. 'Who are you? What do you want?' Her voice was friendly but vaguely unsure.

Reilly stopped several feet short of the porch and the dog. 'Our plane crashed eleven days ago in the mountains,' he explained calmly. 'My woman needs water and a place to rest. May we come in?'

'Yes, yes, of course!' the woman exclaimed. She clapped her hands at the dog. 'Laddie, go and lie down. We were notified of the search, my husband and I, but we had no idea the plane had gone down anywhere near here. Come in, come in.'

Leah didn't hear half of what the woman said. Her heart was still singing from Reilly's words, 'my woman.' Her hazel eyes lovingly searched his face, dusty and lined with weariness yet indomitably strong. Had he meant that? Or was it only a figure of speech?

'Are you hurt?' the woman rushed, holding the screen door open for Reilly, a wide-eyed little girl still clinging to her legs. 'Shall I call a doctor? Or an ambulance?'

'No, it's just exhaustion from the long walk.' Reilly stopped inside the door. 'Where can she rest?'

'There's a sofa in the living room. This way.' The woman ushered them into the living room, hovering uncertainly for a minute. 'I'll get some water.' She walked swiftly out of the room, the little girl hurrying in her shadow.

Gently Reilly lowered Leah on to the sofa, plumping pillows beneath her head. 'Comfortable?'

She nodded, smiling wanly. 'I didn't remember anything could be so soft. Reilly——' She didn't finish the sentence as the woman returned carrying a pitcher of water and glasses on a tray.

Leah drank thirstily from the glass Reilly held to her lips, then sank back against the pillows as some of the strength ebbed back into her weary limbs.

The woman disentangled the little girl from her legs, bending slightly towards her. 'Go out to the barn, Mary, and get your father. Tell him to hurry.' She turned to Reilly, who was pouring a glass of water for himself. 'Is there anything else I can get for you? Whisky? Food?'

'Black coffee, if you have some.' He straightened away from the sofa. 'And would you show me where the telephone is so I can notify the authorities?'

The little girl named Mary had shyly inched past Reilly, then dashed out of the room, the screen door banging as she ran for her father.

'The telephone is in the kitchen, and I do have some coffee on,' the woman smiled.

Reilly glanced down at Leah lying on the couch. 'You'll be okay. I'll only be gone a few minutes.'

'I'm fine,' she assured him softly, warmed by the flecks of concern that had been present in his green eyes.

As Reilly and the woman left the room, Leah relaxed against the cushions and pillows. It seemed strange to have four walls surrounding her and a ceiling instead of the open sky above her head. Tonight she'd be taking a hot bath, changing into clean clothes, and sleeping in a soft bed. She'd willingly trade it all——

The light, quick footsteps belonging to the woman entered the living room. 'Here's your coffee. It's hot and black and sweet, the way your husband ordered it. He said to drink it all,' she smiled brightly, her plain features, freckled by the desert sun, suddenly taking on a rare beauty.

Leah pushed herself into a sitting position, using the pillows to help prop herself up. A hint of pink brought colour to her cheeks as she held the mug of coffee with both hands.

'Reilly isn't my . . . husband.' Much as she wished she could say otherwise.

The woman looked surprised. 'I thought . . . that is . . .' She laughed to cover her confusion. 'I guess I just presumed you were married without thinking. I'm sorry.'

'There's no need to apologise,' Leah insisted, carefully sipping the hot coffee, some of her weakness easing as the sweet liquid travelled down her throat.

'I'm Tina Edwards,' the woman introduced herself.

'Leah Talbot,' supplied Leah.

'This must have been quite an ordeal for you.'

Ordeal. How could she explain to the woman that it hadn't been an ordeal? Despite the shock of the crash, the days she had been delirious with fever from her infected wound, Leah couldn't think of the time she had been alone with Reilly as an ordeal. It had been primitively idyllic.

'It wasn't really too bad,' she answered, choosing her words carefully. 'The worst was today and yesterday.' When Reilly had withdrawn from her, she added to herself.

'I can imagine,' the woman nodded understand-

168

ingly. 'Walking in this heat even a short distance can be exhausting.'

The screen door slammed and the little girl came racing into the living room to stand beside her mother, peering at Leah through her lashes. There were other footsteps. Then the sound of a strange man's voice speaking to Reilly.

'That's my husband, Mike. He was doctoring one of the horses in the barn,' the woman explained.

Leah swallowed more coffee, the sugar and caffeine stimulating her senses. She glanced up when Reilly entered the living room, accompanied by a shorter man wearing a straw cowboy hat and sunglasses. Intense weariness was etched around Reilly's eyes and mouth. She marvelled that he could still keep pushing himself on.

'Mr Edwards has offered to drive us into Tonopah,' said Reilly, the same tiredness in his face lacing his voice. 'Your family will be there to meet us. They're being notified that you're safe and well.'

'Are we leaving now?' she asked.

'As soon as you finish your coffee.'

Concealing a sigh of regret, Leah carried the mug to her lips. She had hoped for some time alone with Reilly, but he seemed to be avoiding any opportunity for a private discussion between them. There was little reason for her to object to his plans. Later, some time, she would speak to him and she wouldn't allow him to stop her. She swallowed the last of the coffee.

'I'm ready,' she said. When Reilly bent to lift

her into his arms, she shook her head. 'I'm a little wobbly, but I think I can walk.'

His fingers closed over her elbow to help her to her feet. She swayed unsteadily for a moment, then found her balance. But Reilly didn't release his grip on her arm, his touch impersonal and cool, as he guided her towards the door.

'Thank you, Mrs Edwards,' Leah smiled when they paused near the screen door, 'for everything.'

There was a brief exchange of goodbyes before they went out to the car. Leah sat alone in the back seat, so she could stretch out and rest, Reilly had said. She was still tired and she did rest, but her thoughts kept straying to the man seated in front of her. Although she tried, she couldn't concentrate on the welcome she would receive when they arrived.

Several miles from the house, the ranch road joined a secondary road that led them to the highway. Mike Edwards' foot was heavy on the accelerator and the utility poles whizzed by the car window in a blur. Yet it was more than an hour before they reached the outskirts of Tonopah, Nevada.

They stopped in front of the building housing the sheriff's office. Leah straightened stiffly in her seat, wincing at the soreness of her muscles. Her fingers closed over the door handle, but Reilly was already out of the car, opening the door for her. His hand firmly gripped her elbow to help her out and steady her once she was standing on the sidewalk. She resisted when he tried to lead her towards the building.

When his cool jade eyes glanced questioningly at

her, Leah spoke in a low voice so Mike Edwards couldn't overhear. 'Reilly, please, we have to talk.'

'About what?' His dark head was tipped to the side, his expression deliberately devoid of understanding.

She swallowed nervously. 'About us.'

'Leah, I don't see——' Reilly began, with an arrogant kind of patience.

'Leah!' A familiar voice interrupted him with the strident call of her name. 'Leah!'

She turned slightly in the direction of the voice, and a smile of growing joy curved her mouth as she recognised the tall and lanky, sandy-haired man half walking and half running towards her.

'Lonnie!' The bubble of happiness made her brother's name a choked sound, so Leah said it again. 'Lonnie!'

She took one step towards him. Beyond him she could see the blue Air Force uniform of her father emerging from a car along with the vivacious figure of her mother. Then Lonnie's hands were on her waist, lifting her into the air and hugging her tightly as he swung her around.

'You're all right. You're all right!' her brother kept repeating as if to convince himself while he buried his head in her sunstreaked hair.

'Yes,' Leah whispered with sobbing happiness. 'Yes, I'm all right.'

He finally let her feet touch the ground, and drew his head back to look at her, unmanly tears shimmering in his brown eyes. 'You crazy little nut!' Every word reinforced the closeness of the bond between them. 'What did you think you were doing?'

Tears flowed down her cheeks. 'I was coming to see you—to surprise you for your birthday.'

'Leah, my baby!' At the tearfully happy voice of her mother, Lonnie released her from his embrace, letting her turn to meet both their parents.

Leah was immediately engulfed in another tight embrace, her arms winding themselves around their mother and feeling the shudders of relief and happiness that coursed through her.

'My baby, my darling,' her mother whispered over and over. 'We've been so worried. They'd given you up for dead. We——'

'I'm all right, Momma.' She slid one arm around her father's waist as he stood erectly beside them, unable to express his relief and joy. She hugged them both lightly. Her father's hand tentatively stroked her hair as she buried her face against the buttons of his uniform.

'You gave us quite a scare, child,' he said tightly.

'I know, Daddy,' Leah whispered. She tossed back her head and gazed into his face, seeing the love shining in his eyes that he couldn't express in words.

'Heavens, just look at you!' Her mother brushed the tears from her face, then shakily tried to do the same for Leah. 'You're a sight, Leah Talbot! Your clothes are a mess. You must have lost ten pounds and you look as brown as an Indian.'

Leah stiffened away from her parents, glancing

frantically over her shoulder. Reilly wasn't standing beside the car where she had left him. Her heart leapt in fear. Then she saw him nearly at the building's entrance.

'Reilly!' She pulled the rest of the way free of her parents' arms, ignoring their confused frowns. Taking a quick step to follow him, she called again. 'Reilly!'

She could see the tensing of his wide shoulders as he hesitated, then stopped. He pivoted back abruptly, impatience underlining his reluctance. She knew he had hoped to slip away unnoticed during the reunion with her parents.

'Reilly, don't leave——' Her voice lilted upwards as she nearly tacked on 'me'. She tried to cover her lack of pride with, 'I want you to meet my family.'

His long strides covered the distance that separated them with an eagerness that said he wanted to get this over and be on his way. His implacable features could have been carved out of hard granite, an emotionless statue with impassive jewelled eyes of jade. He looked noble and proud, and without feeling.

Leah was almost afraid that if she touched him, she too would turn to stone. Quickly she introduced him to her parents, her heart freezing at the distantly polite smile he gave them.

'This is Reilly Smith. We shared the charter of the plane,' she explained tautly, feeling nervous and awkward. 'I wouldn't be here if it wasn't for him.' Her voice sounded brittle with its forced cheerfulness.

There was a brief exchange of courteous responses to the introductions. Then Reilly took a withdrawing step backwards. 'It was a pleasure meeting all of you,' he said politely. 'If you'll excuse me now, I have some things to attend to, and I know you'd like to be with your daughter.'

As he started to turn away, Leah caught at his arm. 'Where are you going?'

Reilly glanced at her hand on his arm, then blandly into her upturned face. 'To the sheriff's office to give him an account of the plane crash.'

'I should go with you.' She didn't want to let him out of her sight. If she did, she was afraid she would never see him again.

'I'm certain I can answer any questions myself,' he refused firmly. 'If the sheriff needs to corroborate my story, he can talk to you after you've had some time to rest. Right now you're exhausted, too tired to think straight and know what you're saying.'

Leah knew what he was implying—that she only imagined she was in love with him. Her teeth bit tightly into her lower lip to hide its tremor.

'I do know,' she insisted in a choked murmur. Before he could stop her, she slid her arms around his waist and clung to him, burying her head against his chest to hear the beat of his heart and make certain he wasn't made of stone. In a voice so low that only he could hear, she cast aside her pride. 'When will I see you again?'

His hands hesitated on her shoulders for a tantalising moment, then slid firmly down to grasp her arms and push her away from him. Her eyes were tear-bright as she met the unrelenting indifference of his.

'Go with your parents, Leah. Get some food and some sleep.' His hard mouth moved upwards at the corners in what was supposed to be a smile, but it left her chilled. 'We'll have dinner some time and laugh about our misadventure.'

His cool gaze flicked briefly to her parents, then he released her and left. She watched him striding so easily away from her and felt a pain so intense that she wanted to die. Self-consciously she turned back to her family, glancing first at Lonnie.

Her brother's brown eyes had narrowed on the man's shirt she wore, resting briefly on the thrust of her breasts against the material. The absence of a brassiere was obvious. Quiet speculation was in his eyes when they raised to meet her glance before swinging to look at their father. His calculating gaze was directed at Reilly disappearing into the building.

Leah knew what was going through their minds. They had just realised she had spent eleven days alone with a man. Now they were wondering how she had spent the eleven nights.

Lonnie's arm curved around her shoulders and he hugged her against his side. 'Let's take her back to the motel where she can clean up,' he smiled at his parents. There was a challenging glint in his eyes when he met his father's gaze. 'Then we'll eat, since Leah owes me a belated birthday dinner.'

CHAPTER TEN

A HAND brushed the hair away from her cheek, tucking it behind her ears, then running to rest gently along her cheek.

'Wake up, Leah,' a male voice coaxed softly.

Her lashes fluttered but didn't open. 'Mmmm.' Contentedly she rubbed her cheek against the masculine hand. 'Have I told you I love you?' she whispered with a blissful smile.

'Not lately,' was the mocking reply.

'I love you, Reilly Smith.' Her voice vibrated huskily with the depth of her emotion.

The hand was instantly withdrawn. 'Wake up, Leah! You're dreaming,' the voice ordered tightly.

With a start her eyes flashed open. Bewilderedly, Leah realised that she wasn't sleeping in Reilly's arms. She was in a bed, with a pillow instead of his shoulder beneath her head. And her brother Lonnie was standing beside the bed, his hands shoved deep in the pockets of his trousers, a troubled frown drawing his eyebrows together.

Hot colour flamed through her face as she realised she had mistaken her brother for Reilly and guessed the conclusion he must have jumped to at her words. She rolled on to her back, turning her head towards the window and the heavy drapes that had been drawn to shut out the sunlight.

'Is it time for dinner already?' Leah blinked, as if unaware of what she had revealed.

'Dinner?' His laugh, instead of being lightly teasing, had overtones of bitterness. 'You've been asleep for nearly thirty-six hours.'

'I have?' Her head jerked towards him in disbelief.

Leah started to sit up, then remembered she wasn't wearing anything and quickly drew the covers up under her arms before shifting into a half-sitting position. It seemed only a few hours ago that her mother had suggested she take a nap after her bath.

'Mom was going out to buy me some clothes to wear.' She nervously ran her fingers through her hair.

'They're over on the chair.' He nodded his head abruptly towards the chair. 'I'll go next door to the folks' room while you get dressed.' Lonnie paused at the door, his hand on the knob. 'Leah——' He seemed to hesitate.

'Yes?' She held her breath.

'Never mind,' he sighed with an impatient shake of his head. 'I'll meet you over there.'

Afterwards, Leah wished Lonnie had asked the question that had been uppermost in his mind. It would have eased the strange tension that suddenly sprang between them. She tried to be bright and cheerful, the way her parents expected her to be, when they breakfasted together later, but she kept

177

lapsing into moody silences, her thoughts wandering to Reilly—where he was—what he was doing—when or if she would see him.

Partly the cause was due to the subject of their conversation which continued when they returned to her parents' room. Her parents were naturally interested in receiving a first-hand account of what had happened when the plane crashed and what she had done during the eleven days she was missing.

Naturally Leah couldn't relate the story without explaining the large part Reilly had played in her survival. The more often she repeated his name, the more often she thought about him. She had only to close her eyes to see him in her mind and remember what it was like to be in his arms.

'Maybe we should take you to see a doctor this afternoon,' her father suggested.

'What for?' Leah flashed defensively, then flushed guiltily at the grim look from her brother.

Her father frowned, his eyes narrowing. 'To verify that the gash on your arm is healing properly and make certain there are no more signs of infection.'

Too late Leah remembered that only moments before telling them of the time she had been ill with fever. Absently she touched the small bandage on her left arm.

'It's fine. There's no need to see a doctor,' she murmured self-consciously. She moved away from the motel room window.

'Really, dear,' her mother laughed, unaware of the

178

tension that had enveloped her daughter. 'I can't help marvelling at the way you avoided catching pneumonia, considering how cold it gets in this part of the country at night.'

Leah flinched. Her mother had not meant it as a subtle probe into the relationship between Leah and Reilly. But Leah knew she had been carefully sidestepping any comment that might reveal what she felt. She had basically never kept anything from her family before, and her lack of openness was making her feel guilty when there was no reason.

'Actually, Mom, it was quite simple.' She lifted her chin in an unconsciously defiant pose. 'Reilly and I slept together to keep warm.' A pregnant silence followed her statement. 'I didn't mean that the way it sounded,' she inserted, nervously reaching for the pack of cigarettes sitting on the dresser. 'Reilly didn't actually make love to me, if that's what you're wondering.'

'Leah——' her mother hesitated, searching for the right words, 'we honestly weren't thinking anything like that.'

'I know, but——' Leah pressed her lips tightly together and quickly lit a cigarette.

'But——' her father picked up the unfinished part of Leah's sentence, his hands clasped behind his back as he stared out the window, 'it's what you were thinking.'

Leah stared at the glowing tip of the cigarette. 'I'm in love with him, Dad.'

'I see. And how does Mr Smith feel about you?'

She crushed the unsmoked cigarette out in the ashtray. 'I don't know. He——' she glanced at her father, 'he hasn't called, has he?'

'No,' her father answered.

'Leah, are you quite sure you know what you're saying?' her mother asked gently. 'Maybe the emotion you feel is only gratitude. Patients often fall in love with their doctor.'

'No.' Leah's sunstreaked hair swung about her shoulders as she shook her head and laughed without humour. 'It definitely isn't gratitude.'

Her father turned away from the window, his gaze piercingly intent. 'You barely know the man, Leah,' he snapped impatiently.

'I can't accept that argument, Dad,' she replied calmly. 'I spent eleven days alone with him on the desert under conditions that would bring out the true colours of any man.'

It was becoming painful to talk about Reilly. Leah didn't know how long her shell of composure would last before it cracked and all the uncertainties of whether he loved her or ever would love her would come tumbling out.

She nervously smoothed a hand over the waist of the lightweight cotton dress. 'If you don't mind, I think I'll go to my room and freshen up.'

She wasn't surprised when her parents didn't attempt to detain her. She guessed they wanted to discuss the situation in private. Naturally they were dubious that their daughter had fallen in love with a man who was a complete stranger to them.

In her own room, Leah leaned against the door she had just closed and tried to take her own stock of the situation. Her thoughts were immediately interrupted by a knock on the door.

'Who is it?' she asked impatiently, wanting to be alone.

'It's me—Lonnie. Can I come in?'

'Of course.' With a sigh, she shot back the bolt on the door and opened it. His eyes flicked thoughtfully to her tense expression as he wandered into the room. 'What did you want?' Leah asked with forced non-chalance.

'My company gave me leave of absence while you were missing. Now that you've been found, I'll be re-porting back to work in the morning,' her brother answered idly. 'Dad's made arrangements for the three of you to fly back to Vegas tomorrow. He's going on alone to Alaska from there and Mom will join him in a couple of weeks.'

Leah waited without commenting on the news. Her brother was leading up to something, but she didn't know what.

'That was quite a write-up in the paper about your Reilly Smith,' Lonnie went on in the same casual tone. 'He's quite well known in his field.'

'He's not my Reilly Smith.' She stared at the hands she had clasped in front of her, fingers twisting nervously.

'But you do want him to be?' Lonnie asked quietly for verification of her love.

'I love him, Lonnie, more than I ever thought it was possible to love a man,' Leah answered, then laughed bitterly. 'For all the good it does me.'

'Why do you say that?' He tipped his head to the side, a wayward lock of sandy brown hair falling across his forehead.

'Because he said nearly the same thing Mom and Dad just said, only in a different way.' She walked agitatedly to the dresser mirror, pausing to gaze at her brother's watchful reflection. 'He said that the time we spent together would seem like a dream that never really happened, once we got back. He meant that I would forget him when I was surrounded by the civilised world again.'

'But you haven't,' Lonnie supplied.

'No.' She turned away from the mirror. 'Lonnie, do you know where he's staying?'

'You want to go see him, is that it?' He smiled understandingly as she nodded her affirmative answer. 'I don't know, but it shouldn't be too hard to find out in a town the size of Tonopah. Let me make a few phone calls.'

When he located the motel where Reilly was registered, Leah asked him to take her there. If Reilly wouldn't make the effort to see her, then she would make one last effort to see him before she resigned herself to the fact that he didn't care about her.

'You don't need to come in with me, Lonnie,' she

said when he got out of the car to walk with her to the motel entrance.

'He wasn't in when I called. He might not be in yet. I'll go in with you to see,' her brother smiled, linking her arm in his.

'If Reilly isn't in, I'm going to wait until he comes.' Her chin lifted with determination. 'I won't leave without seeing him.'

Inside the motel, Lonnie asked her to wait for him at the entrance door while he checked at the desk. A few minutes later he was back.

'Come on.' His hand gripped her elbow as he guided her past a row of rooms.

'Is he in?' she asked anxiously.

'No.' He dangled a key in the air. 'But you can wait for him in his room.'

'How did you get that?'

'I greased the right palm.' Lonnie grinned cheekily. 'I couldn't have my sister waiting in a motel lobby for a man.' He squeezed her hand when tears misted her eyes, the tight lump in her throat making it impossible for her to voice her gratitude. His gaze shifted to the numbered doors. 'Here's his room.' He unlocked the door and opened it for her. 'Good luck, Sis, and if he doesn't listen to you, call me and I'll talk to him.'

'What would I ever do without you?' Leah murmured, hugging him tightly.

'You could make it without me.' His voice was muffled against her hair as he gave the top of her head an affectionate kiss. 'But if you love this guy as much as you say you do, I don't think you could make it without him. So fight for him, Leah, with everything you have.'

'I will,' she promised.

Then she was alone in the motel room and Lonnie's footsteps were receding.

There wasn't a clock in the room, so she had no idea how long she waited for Reilly to return. It seemed like hours and hours that she wandered aimlessly from the bed to the lone chair to the window and back to the bed. She thought of countless arguments she could make and rehearsed them over and over again.

When she heard a key inserted in the lock, Leah forgot them all. She stood frozen beside the chair as the door opened and Reilly walked in. He didn't see her immediately as he shut the door and tossed a jacket on the bed, so she had a few precious seconds to take in his tiredly drawn features.

His sunbrowned fingers had just impatiently unbuttoned the top buttons of his shirt when he saw her. He stopped shortly, his green eyes narrowing into jade slits. Leah hoped to surprise him, possibly make him reveal some small sign of gladness at seeing her again. She was disappointed.

'What are you doing here, Leah?' His mouth thinned grimly.

Her throat went dry. It all suddenly seemed hopeless. 'I came to see you. I wanted to talk.' She moistened her dry lips. 'I've been waiting for you for hours. Where have you been?'

'I had to show the sheriff the location of the crash,' Reilly breathed in deeply. 'I stayed around until they'd recovered Grady's body from the wreckage, then came back to make the arrangements with his family to have the body sent back to Las Vegas for burial. I imagine one of the sheriff's men will be taking your luggage to your motel.'

Although she spared a silent thought of sympathy for Grady's family and a flash of grief at his death, Leah knew she didn't dare let Reilly sidetrack her from the reason she had come.

'You could have brought my things to the motel,' she said. 'Why didn't you?'

He rubbed a hand tiredly over his jaw and chin. 'Because I didn't want to see you,' Reilly answered with brutal honesty. 'Look, I'm hot and tired. I need a shower and some sleep. So why don't you say whatever it is that you've come here to say and get out!'

Leah flinched. 'I love you, Reilly.'

'Dammit, Leah, we've been over that before!' he growled angrily beneath his breath.

'And you believed that once I was back with my family and the so-called real world, what I felt for you would fade like the memory of a dream.' The corners of her mouth lifted in a sad smile. 'Look around you, Reilly. There are man-made walls and ceilings, beds and chairs and running hot and cold water. Outside there's concrete instead of sage-dotted

185

desert sand and cars and trucks instead of jack-rabbits and snakes. But I'm still me and you are still you. And I still love you, more than I did before, because I found out how empty I feel not waking up in your arms.'

A tense silence enclosed them. His level gaze crossed the width of the room to hold hers. His impassive face, austerely handsome, was a granite mask carved by the sun and desert wind. Abruptly he pivoted away, an impatient stride carrying him to the dresser table.

'You don't know what you're saying,' Reilly muttered. Ice from a styrofoam container clunked into a plastic glass, joined by the melted water in the container.

Leah reached behind her and unzipped her dress. 'I told you once that if you left me, I would follow.' She slipped her arms out of the sleeves. 'I meant that, Reilly. If you don't want me as your wife, then I'll stay with you as your woman.' She stepped out of the dress as it slid to the floor.

'Will you——' Reilly turned towards her. His eyes flashed over her semi-naked state. Whatever he was going to say was never finished. 'What the hell are you doing!' The plastic glass was shoved on to the table, water sloshing over the sides. In lightning strides, he eliminated the distance between them, tearing the bedspread from the bed and throwing it around her.

Calmly Leah met his fiery gaze. 'A naked body is part of nature,' she repeated the words he had once used. 'You've seen me once. Why should I be ashamed for you to see me unclothed again?'

'The circumstances are different,' Reilly snapped, drawing the spread tightly around her like a cocoon.

'How are they different?' she challenged, swaying towards him, her lips parting in a deliberate invitation.

His fingers dug into the soft flesh of her upper arm, preventing her from leaning against his chest yet not allowing her to move away. His gaze was riveted on the shimmering moistness of her lips, his breathing suddenly not as controlled and even as it had been.

'Because I'm thinking like a white man and not an Indian,' he answered with raw huskiness.

'And you want me,' Leah whispered the definition of his statement.

Hungrily his mouth devoured hers, crushing her against the hard length of his body so that she might know how desperately he wanted her. His hands roamed possessively over her, fighting the folds of the bedspread that he had wrapped her so tightly in, but he didn't let her work free of its protective covering. Leah's appetite had to be satisfied with returning his passionate kiss.

Reilly dragged his mouth from hers, his hunger unsatisfied but controlled for the moment as the iron band of his arms held her a willing prisoner.

'You need more time, Leah.' His husky voice breathed against her sunstreaked hair.

'Time won't change how much I love you or how much I want you,' she protested achingly.

'How can I make you understand?' Reilly groaned, his mouth moving over her forehead and eyes. 'If I make you mine, Leah, I could never let you go. I love you so much that I'd make you stay with me whether you wanted to or not. I know you believe you care for me.'

'Oh, Reilly darling!' A searing happiness brought a breathless laugh from her throat. 'I'm not a patient falling in love with her doctor. I'm a woman in love with a man, and I don't ever want you to let me go.' The iron band of his arms constricted. 'If you do love me, why didn't you want to see me?' she asked tightly, still trying to believe that Reilly was telling her the truth.

'Because I knew if I kept seeing you, without giving you time to consider your feelings, I wouldn't be able to keep myself from making love to you. You have no idea what torture it is not to possess you when I love you so completely.' Reilly unlocked his arms and held her face his eyes gazing into it and reflecting it. 'Please, put your dress on,' he murmured huskily, 'so we can go talk to your parents about our wedding.'

Diamond tears misted rainbow-bright on her lashes. 'You do want to marry me!' she breathed, her heart swelling with unmeasurable bliss.

Reilly looked deeply into her eyes. 'You'll be my wife, then I'll make you my woman.' His dark head bent towards hers and she lifted her mouth for his kiss.

STRANGE
BEDFELLOW

BY
JANET DAILEY

WORLDWIDE BOOKS
LONDON • SYDNEY • TORONTO

All the characters in this book have no existence outside the imagination of the Author, and have no relation whatsoever to anyone bearing the same name or names. They are not even distantly inspired by any individual known or unknown to the Author, and all the incidents are pure invention.

First published in Great Britain in 1979
Reprinted in Great Britain in 1994
by Worldwide Books, Eton House,
18-24 Paradise Road, Richmond, Surrey TW9 1SR

© Janet Dailey 1979

ISBN 0 373 59201 9

99-9405

Printed and bound in Great Britain

CHAPTER ONE

THE air was clear and the moon over Rhode Island was new, but there was a tangle of cobwebs in her mind. Dina Chandler couldn't seem to think her way out of the confusion. She shut her ears to the voices quietly celebrating in other parts of the house and stared out the window.

A shudder passed through her. It couldn't have been from the night's chill, since the house was comfortably heated. Her blue eyes slid to her arms, crossed in front of her, hugging her middle. Perhaps it was the cold weight of the precious metal around her finger.

The door to the library opened and Dina turned. Her hair shimmered in the dim light, a paler gold than the ring on her finger. A pang of regret raced through her that her solitude had been broken, followed by a twinge of remorse that she had felt the need to be alone at this time.

Closing the door, Chet Stanton walked towards her, smiling despite the faintly puzzled gleam in his eyes.

'So this is where you've gotten to,' he murmured, an unspoken question behind the indulgent tone.

'Yes,' Dina nodded, unaware of the sigh in her

voice or how forced her smile looked.

As he came closer, her gaze made a detached inspection of him. Like hers, his colouring was fair, sandy blond hair falling rakishly across his forehead, always seeming to invite fingers to push it back in place. His eyes were a smoke-blue as opposed to the brilliant shade of hers.

At thirty-six, he was twelve years her senior, a contemporary of Blake's, but there was a boyish air about him that was an integral part of his charm. In fact, it was with Blake that Dina had first met Chet. The cobwebs spun around that thought to block it out. Slim and supple, Chet was only a few inches taller than she was in her heels.

He stopped in front of her, his intent gaze studying her expressionless face. Dina was unconscious of how totally she masked her inner turmoil. As his hands settled lightly on her shoulders, she was passive under his touch.

'What are you doing in here?' Chet cocked his head slightly to the side, his gaze still probing.

'I was thinking.'

'That's forbidden.' His hands slid around her and Dina yielded to his undemanding embrace, uncrossing her arms to spread them across his chest.

Why not? His shoulder had become a familiar resting place for her head, used often in the last two and a half years. Her eyes closed at the feather caress of his lips over her temple and cheek.

'You should be in the living room noisily celebrating with the others,' he told her in mock reproval.

Dina laughed softly in her throat. 'They're not "noisily" celebrating. They don't "noisily" do anything, whether it's rejoice or grieve.'

'Perhaps not,' he conceded. 'But even a restrained celebration should have the engaged couple in attendance, namely you and me. Not just me alone.'

'I know,' she sighed.

His shoulder wasn't as comfortable as it had seemed. Dina turned out of his unresisting embrace, nerves stretching taut again as the niggling sense of unease and confusion wouldn't leave. Her troubled gaze searched the night's darkness beyond the window panes as if expecting to find the answer there. With her back turned to him, Chet rested his hands on either side of her neck where the contracted cords were hard bands of tension.

'Relax, honey. You've let yourself get all strung up again.' His supple fingers began working their magic, gently kneading the coiled muscles in her neck and shoulders.

'I can't help it.' A frown puckered her forehead despite the pleasant manipulations of his hands. 'I simply don't know if I'm doing the right thing.'

'Of course you are.'

'Am I?' A corner of her mouth lifted in a half-smile, self-mocking and sceptical. 'I don't know how I let you talk me into this engagement.'

'Me? Talk *you* into it?' Chet laughed, his warm

breath fanning the silver-blonde strands of her hair.
'You make it sound as if I twisted your arm, and I'd
never do that. You're much too beautiful to risk
damaging.'

'Flatterer!' But Dina felt old, beyond her years
old.

'It got me you.'

'And I know I agreed willingly to this engagement,' she admitted.

'Willingly but hesitantly,' added Chet, continuing the slow and relaxing massage of her shoulders
and neck.

'I wasn't sure. And I still don't know if I'm sure.'

'I didn't rush you into a decision. I gave you all
the time you wanted because I understand why you
felt you needed it,' he reasoned. 'And there won't
be any marriage until you set the date. Our agreement is little more than a trial engagement.'

'I know.' Her voice was flat. Dina didn't find the
necessary reassurance in his words.

'Look,' Chet turned her to face him, 'I was Blake's
best friend.'

Yes, Dina thought. He had been Blake's right
arm; now he was hers. Always there, ready to support her decision, coaxing a smile when her spirits
were low and the will to go on had faded.

'So I know what kind of man your husband was,'
he continued, 'I'm not trying to take his place. As a
matter of fact, I don't want to take his place any

more than I want you to take his ring from your finger.'

His remark drew her gaze to the intertwining gold band and diamond solitaire on the third finger of her left hand. The interlocking rings had been joined by a third, a diamond flowerlet designed to complement the first pair, Chet's engagement ring to her.

He curved a finger under her chin to lift it. 'All that I'm hoping is that with a little more patience and persistence I can carve some room in your heart to care for me.'

'I do, Chet,' Dina stated. 'Without you, I don't know how I would have gotten through those months when Blake was missing—when we didn't know if he was alive or dead. And when we were notified that he'd been kil——'

The rest of her words were silenced by his firm kiss. Then he gathered her into his arms to hold her close, moulding her slenderly curved shape to his lean, muscular body.

His mouth was near her temple, moving against her silken hair as he spoke. 'That's in the past. You have to forget it.'

'I can't.' There was a negative movement of her head against his. 'I keep remembering the way I argued with Blake before he left on that South American trip,' she sighed. 'He wanted me to go to the airport with him, but I refused.' Another sigh came from her lips, tinged with anger and regret.

'Our quarrels were always over such petty things, things that seem so stupid now.'

'The strong vying with the strong.' Chet lifted his head to gaze at the rueful light in her eyes. 'I'm like Blake in the respect that I'm partial to strong-minded women.'

His teasing words provoked the smile he sought. 'I suppose I have to admit to being that, don't I?'

A fire smouldered in his look, burning away the teasing light. 'And I love you for being strong, Dina.' His hand slid to the small of her back. 'And I love you for being all woman.'

Then his mouth was seeking hers again in a kiss that was warm and passionate. She submitted to his ardour, gradually responding in kind, revelling in the gentle caress of his hands that remained short of intimate. Chet never demanded more from her than she was willing to give. His understanding restraint endeared him to her, making her heart swell with quiet happiness.

When he lifted his head, Dina nestled into the crook of his arm, resting her cheek against his shoulder, smiling with tender pleasure. That lock of hair, the colour of sun-bleached sand, was across his forehead. She gave in to the impulse to brush it back with the rest, knowing it would spring forward the instant it was done. Which it did.

'Feel better?' His fingers returned the caress by tracing the curve of her cheekbone.

'Mmm.'

'What were you thinking about when I came in?'

Her hand slid to his shirt, smoothing the collar. 'I don't know. I guess I was wishing.'

'Wishing what?'

Dina paused. She didn't know what she had been wishing. Finally she said, 'That we hadn't told the others about our engagement, that we'd kept it to ourselves for a while. I wish we weren't having this engagement party.'

'It's just family and friends. There's been no official announcement made,' Chet reminded her.

'I know.' She usually had no difficulty in expressing herself, but the uncertainty of her own thoughts made it impossible.

Something was bothering her, but she didn't know what it was. It wasn't as if she hadn't waited a proper time before deciding to marry again. It had been two and a half years since Blake disappeared and a little more than a year since the South American authorities had notified her that they had found the plane wreckage and there had been no survivors.

And it wasn't as if she didn't love Chet, not in the same tumultuous way she had loved Blake. This was a quieter and gentler emotion, and probably deeper.

'Darling,' his smile was infinitely patient, 'we couldn't keep our engagement from our family and friends. They need time, too, to get adjusted to the idea that you soon won't be Mrs Blake Chandler.'

'That's true,' Dina acknowledged. It was not an idea that could be implanted overnight.

The door to the library opened, framing an older woman dressed in black in its jamb. An indulgent smile curved her mouth as she spied the embracing pair. Dina stiffened for an instant in Chet's arms, then forced herself to relax.

'We've been wondering where the two of you had gone,' the woman chided. 'It's time you came back to the party and received some of the toasts being made.'

'We'll be there in a minute, Mother Chandler,' Dina replied to the woman who was Blake's mother, her mother-in-law.

'If you don't, I'm afraid the party will move in here, and there's hardly enough room for them all.'

'We'll be there in a minute, Mother Chandler,' Chet added his promise to Dina's. With a nod, the woman closed the door and Chet glanced at Dina. 'Do you suppose you'll be able to persuade her to wear something other than black to our wedding?'

'I doubt it.' She moved out of his arms, a faintly cynical smile curving her lips. 'Norma Chandler likes portraying the image of a tragic figure.'

Within a few weeks after Dina's marriage to Blake, Kyle Chandler, his father, had died unexpectedly of a heart attack and Norma Chandler had purchased an entire wardrobe of black. She had barely been out of mourning when they received news Blake's plane was missing. Instantly, her mother-in-law began dressing again in black, not waiting for the notification that came a year ago declaring her son to be officially considered dead.

'She approves of our marriage. You know that, don't you?' Chet asked.

'Yes, she approves,' Dina agreed, 'for the sake of the company.' And for the fact that there would only be one 'widow' Chandler instead of two, but Dina didn't say that, knowing it would sound small and unkind when her mother-in-law had been almost smothering in her love towards her.

'Mother Chandler still doesn't believe you're capable of running it after all this time,' Chet concluded from her response. He shook his head wryly.

'I couldn't do it without you,' Dina stated it as a fact, not an expression of gratitude.

'I'm with you.' He curved an arm around her waist as she started for the door to leave the room. 'So you won't have to worry about that.'

As Chet reached forward to open the door for her, Dina was reminded of that frozen instant when Norma Chandler had opened the door seconds ago and wondered if the same thought had crossed her mother-in-law's mind as it had her own, recalling the numerous times Mrs Chandler had opened the library door to find Dina sitting on Blake's lap locked in one of his crushing and possessive embraces. This time it had been Chet's arms that held her instead of Blake's. She wondered if her mother-in-law was as aware of the vast differences between the two men as she was.

In the last few months after the uncertainty of Blake's fate was settled and there had been time to reflect, Dina had tried to imagine what the last two and a half years might have been like if Blake had lived. Theirs had been such a brief, stormy marriage, carrying the portent of more years of the same, always with the possibility that one battle could have ended the union permanently.

Whereas Chet was always predictable and the time Dina spent with him was always pleasant. Under his supportive influence, she had discovered skills and potentials she hadn't known she possessed. Her intelligence had been channelled into constructive fields and expanded to encompass more knowledge instead of being sharpened for warring exchanges with Blake.

Her personality had matured in a hurry, owing to the circumstances of Blake's disappearance. She had become a very confident and self-assured woman, and she gave all the credit for the change to Chet.

Some of her misgivings vanished as she walked with Chet to rejoin the party in the main area of the house. There was no earthly reason not to enjoy the engagement party, none whatsoever.

Over the weekend, the news of their engagement had filtered into the main office of the Chandler hotel chain in Newport. Dina felt certain she had spent the bulk of the morning confirming the rumours that it was true she was engaged to Chet.

She sincerely doubted that there was anyone in the building who had not stopped at her office to extend congratulations and questioning looks.

A mountain of work covered the massive walnut desk top, letters to be answered, reports to be read and memos to be issued. With her elbows on the desk top, Dina rested her forehead on her hands, rubbing the dull throb in its centre. Her pale blonde hair had grown to the point where it could be pulled to the nape of her neck in a neat bun, the style adding a few years to her relatively youthful age.

The clothing she wore to the office was chosen, too, with an eye to detracting from her youth. Today, it was a long-sleeved blouse of cream yellow with a wine-coloured waistcoat and skirt, attractive and stylish yet professional-looking.

The intercom buzzed and Dina lifted her head, reaching over to press the button. 'Yes?'

'Harry Landers is here to see you, Mrs Chandler,' was the reply from her secretary Amy Wentworth, about the only one on the executive staff younger than Dina was.

'Send him in.'

Dina picked up her reading glasses lying on a stack of papers she had been reading and put them on. She could see to read without them, but invariably after hours of reading, the eye-strain became too much. Lately, she had taken to wearing them almost constantly at the office to avoid the headaches that accompanied the strain, and subconsciously because they added a businesslike air to her appearance.

There was a wry twist of her mouth as the doorknob to her office turned, an inner acknowledgement that she had been wrong in thinking everyone had been in to offer their congratulations. Harry Landers hadn't, and the omission was about to be changed. As the door opened, her mouth finished its curve into a polite smile of greeting.

'Good morning, Harry.'

The tall and brawny, white-haired man who entered smiled and returned the greeting. 'Good morning, Mrs Chandler.' Only Chet used her christian name at the office, and then only when they were alone. 'I just heard the news that you and Chet are getting married. Congratulations,' he offered predictably.

'Thank you,' she nodded for what seemed like the hundredth time that morning.

There was no silent, unasked question in the look he gave her. 'I'm truly glad for you, Mrs Chandler. I know there are some people here who think you're somehow being unfaithful to Blake's memory by marrying again. Personally I think it speaks well of your marriage to him.'

'You do?' Her voice was briskly cool; she did not care for discussions about her private life, although her curiosity was raising by degrees trying to follow his logic.

'Yes—I mean, obviously your marriage to Blake was very satisfactory or you wouldn't want to enter the wedded state again,' he reasoned.

'I see.' Her smile was tight, lacking warmth. 'Blake and I did have a good marriage.' Whether they did she couldn't say. It had been too brief. 'And I know Chet and I will, too.'

'When is the wedding?'

'We haven't set the date yet.'

'Be sure to send me an invitation.'

'We will.' Dina's hopes for a quiet wedding and no reception were fast dissipating under the rush of requests to attend. An elopement was beginning to look inviting.

'At least you won't have to concern yourself with the company after you're married,' Harry Landers observed with a benign smile.

'I beg your pardon?' Dina was instantly alert and on the defensive, no longer mouthing the polite words she had repeated all morning.

'After you're married, you can go back to being a simple housewife. Chet will make a good president,' he replied.

Why the accent on 'simple'? Dina wondered bitterly. 'My marriage to Chet will have no effect on the company. It will continue to be run jointly by both of us with myself as president,' she stated, not wanting to remember that the work occupying both their times had been done by Blake alone. Rigid with anger, she turned to the papers on her desk. 'I

don't see the monthly report from the Florida hotel.
Has it come in?'

'I don't believe so.' Her abrupt change of subject
warned the man he was treading on forbidden
ground. His previously open expression became
closed and officious.

'Frank Miller is the manager there, isn't he?'

'Yes.'

'Call him and find out where the report is. I want
it on my desk by four this afternoon, even if he has
to telex it,' she ordered.

'I'll see to it right away, Mrs Chandler.'

When the door closed behind him, Dina rose
from the overstuffed cushion on her swivel office
chair and walked to the window. After-quakes of resentment were still trembling through her. Almost
since Blake's disappearance, she had run the company with Chet's help, but her competency to fill
the post still wasn't recognised by some of the executive officers.

It hadn't been by design but through necessity
that she had taken over. When Blake had disappeared over South America, the company had been
like a ship without a rudder, without guidance or
direction. It had operated smoothly for a while, then
it began to flounder helplessly.

The key members of the executive staff, those
who might have been competent enough to take
over, had resigned to take posts with more solid
companies, like rats deserting a sinking ship. That

was when Dina had been forced to step in, by virtue of the Chandler name.

It hadn't been easy. The odds were stacked against her because she was young and a woman and totally ignorant of the machinations of the company, not to say limited in experience. Exerting her authority had been the most difficult. Most of the staff were old enough to be her parents and some, like Harry Landers, were old enough to be her grandparents.

Dina had learned the hard way, by trial and many errors. The worries, the fears that she had about Blake, she had to keep to herself. Very early she discovered that the men who offered her a shoulder to cry on were also insistently offering their beds.

More and more in those early days, she began turning to Chet for his unselfish and undemanding support. Not once did he make a single overture towards her, not until several months after Blake's death had been confirmed. She trusted him implicitly and he had never given her a reason to doubt him. But Harry Landers had just put a question in her mind, one Dina didn't like facing, but there seemed to be no eluding it.

Shaking her head, Dina walked back to her desk. She picked up the telephone receiver and hesitated, staring at the numbers on the dial. There was a quick knock on her office door, followed by the click of the latch as it was opened without waiting for her permission to enter. Replacing the receiver, Dina turned to the door as Chet appeared.

'You'll never guess what I just heard,' he whispered with exaggerated secrecy.

'What is it?' Dina tensed.

'Chet Stanton is going to marry Mrs Chandler.'

What she expected him to say, Dina had no idea. But at his answer, she laughed with a mixture of amusement and relief, some of her tension fleeing.

'You've heard that rumour, too, have you?' she retorted.

'Are you kidding?' he grimaced in a boyish fashion that made her heart warm to him all the more. 'I've been trying to get to my office since nine o'clock this morning and haven't made it yet. I keep getting stopped along the way.'

'As bad as that?' Dina smiled.

'The hallway is a veritable gauntlet.'

She knew the feeling. 'We should have called everybody together this morning, made the announcement, then gone to work. It would have made a more productive morning.'

'Hindsight, my love,' he chided, walking over to kiss her lightly on the cheek.

'Yes,' Dina agreed. She removed her glasses and made a show of concentrating on them as she placed them on the desk top. 'Now that everyone knows, they're all waiting for me to hand in my resignation and name you as the successor to the Chandler throne.' Without seeming to, she watched Chet's reaction closely.

'I hope you set them straight about that,' he replied without hesitation. 'We make an excellent team. And there certainly isn't any reason to break up a winning combination in the company just because we're getting married.'

'That's what I thought,' she agreed.

Taking her by the shoulders, Chet turned her to face him, tipping his head to one side in an enquiring manner. 'Have I told you this morning how beautiful you are?'

'No.' The edges of her mouth dimpled slightly as she answered him in the same serious tone that he had used. 'But you can tell me now.'

'You're very beautiful, darling.'

With the slightest pressure, he drew her yielding shape to him. As his mouth lightly took possession of hers, the intercom buzzed. Dina moved out of his arms with a rueful smile of apology.

She pressed the button. 'Yes, Amy?'

'Jacob Stone is on line one,' came the reply.

'Thank you.' Dina broke the connection and glanced at Chet with a resigned shrug of her shoulders.

'Jake Stone,' he repeated. 'That's the Chandler family attorney, isn't it?'

'Yes,' she nodded, reaching for the telephone. 'Probably some business to do with Blake's estate.'

'That's my cue for an exit.' And Chet started for the door.

'Dinner tonight at eight?' Dina questioned.

'Perfect,' he agreed with a wink.

'Call Mother Chandler and tell her I've invited you.' She picked up the telephone receiver, her finger hovering above the blinking button on line one.

'Consider it done.'

Dina watched him leave. Just for a few minutes, Harry Landers had made her suspect that Chet might be marrying her to elevate his position in the company. But his instant and casual rejection of becoming president had erased that. Her trust in him was once again complete.

She pushed the button. 'Hello, Mr Stone. Dina Chandler speaking.'

'Ah, Mrs Chandler. How are you?' came the gravelly voice in answer.

'Just fine, thank you.'

CHAPTER TWO

By the end of the week, the excitement generated by the news of their engagement had died down and work was able to settle into a routine again. The invisible pressure the news had evoked, eased as well.

Yet on Saturday morning Dina wakened with the sun, unable to go back to sleep. Finally she stopped trying, arose and dressed in slacks and white blouse with a pullover sweater. The other members of the household, Blake's mother Norma Chandler and their housekeeper Deirdre, were still asleep.

After Blake's disappearance two and a half years ago, it had seemed senseless for both Dina and his mother to keep separate households, especially when the days began to stretch into weeks and months. In the end, Dina had subleased the apartment she and Blake had in town to move to the suburbs with his mother.

She had thought it would ease her loneliness and provide an outlet for her inner fears, but it hadn't proved to be so. Dina had spent the bulk of her private time consoling Mother Chandler, as she called her mother-in-law, and received little if any consolation in return.

Still, it was a suitable arrangement, a place to

sleep and eat, with all the housekeeping and meals done by others. With most of her time and energy spent in keeping the company going, the arrangement had become a definite asset.

Now, as she tiptoed out of the house into the dawn, Dina wished for the privacy of her own home, where she could steal into the kitchen and fix an early morning breakfast without feeling she was invading someone else's turf. And Deirdre was jealously possessive about her kitchen.

Closing the door, she listened for the click of the lock. When she heard it, she turned to the steps leading to the drive and the white Porsche parked there. Inside the house, the telephone rang, loud in the silence of the pink morning.

Dina stopped and began rummaging through her oversize purse for the house key. It was seldom used since there was always someone there to let her in. Before she found it, the phone had stopped ringing. She waited several seconds to see if it would start ringing again. Someone in the house must have answered it, Dina decided, or else the party must have decided to call later in the morning.

Skimming down the steps, she hurried to the Porsche, folding the top down before climbing in and starting the engine. With doughnuts and coffee in a styrofoam container from a pastry shop, she drove through the quiet business streets.

There was a salty tang to the breeze ruffling her hair. Dina shook her head to let its cool fingers rake through the silken gold strands. Her blue eyes narrowed in decision as she turned the sports car away from the street that would take her to the office building and headed towards the solitude of an early morning ocean beach.

Sitting on a piece of driftwood, Dina watched the sun finish rising on Rhode Island Sound, the water shimmering and sparkling as the waves lapped the long strand of ocean beach. The city of Newport was located on the island of Rhode Island from which the state derived its name.

The doughnut crumbs had been tossed to the seagulls, still swooping and soaring nearby in case she had missed one. It was peaceful and quiet. The nearest person was a surf fisherman, a stick figure distantly visible. It was one of those times when she thought of many things in the intervening hours, but couldn't remember a single one when she rose to leave.

It was nine o'clock, the time she usually arrived at the office for a half day's work, minimum. But Dina couldn't think of a single item that was pressing, except the one the family attorney had called about the first of the week.

Returning to her Porsche parked in a layby near the beach, she drove to the nearest telephone booth and stopped. She rummaged through her purse for change and dialled the office number. It was answered on the second ring.

'Amy? This is Mrs Chandler.' She shut the door

of the phone booth to close out the whine of the semi-trailer going by. 'I won't be in this morning, but there's some correspondence on the dictaphone I would like typed this morning.'

'I've already started it,' her young secretary answered.

'Good. When you have it done, leave it on my desk. Then you can call it a day. All right.'

'Yes, thank you, Mrs Chandler.' Amy Wentworth was obviously delighted.

'See you Monday,' Dina said, and rang off.

Back in the white sports car, she headed for the boat marina where Blake's sailing boat was docked. She parked the car by the small shed that served as an office. A man sat in a chair out front.

Balanced was the better word, as the chair was tilted back, allowing only the two rear legs to support it. His arms were folded in front of him and a faded captain's hat was pulled over his face, permitting only a glimpse of his double chin and the greying stubble of beard to show.

Dina hopped out of the sports car, smiling at the man who hadn't changed in almost three years. 'Good morning, Capt'n Tate.'

The chair came down with a thump as a large hand pushed the hat back on top of his head. Grey eyes stared at her blankly for a minute before recognition flickered.

'How do, Miz Chandler.' He rose lumberingly to his feet, pulling his faded trousers up to cover his paunch. The end result was to accentuate it.

'It's been so long since I've seen you. How have you been?'

'Mighty fine, Miz Chandler, mighty fine.' The owner of the marina smiled and succeeded in extending the smile to his jowled cheeks. 'I s'pose you're here to get the *Starfish* cleaned out. Shore was sorry when your attorney told me you was goin' to rent it out.'

'Yes, I know.' Her smile faded slightly. Getting rid of the boat seemed to be like closing the final chapter about Blake in her life. 'But it was pointless to keep the boat tied up here, unused.'

'She's a damn fine boat,' he insisted, puffing a bit as he stepped inside the shed door and reached for a key. 'Never know, some day you might want it yourself.'

Dina laughed, a little huskily. 'You know I'm not a sailor, Capt'n Tate. I need a whole bottle of motion sickness pills just to make it out of the harbour without getting seasick!'

'Then you sleep the whole time.' He guffawed and started coughing. 'I never will forget that time Blake came carrying you off the boat sound asleep. He told me aft'wards that you didn't wake up till the next morning.'

'If you will recall, that was the last time he even suggested I go sailing with him.' She took the key he handed her, feeling a poignant rush of memories and trying to push them back.

'Do'ya want some help movin' any of that stuff?' he offered.

'No, thank you.' She couldn't imagine the two of them in the small cabin, not with Capt'n Tate's protruding belly. 'I can manage.'

'You just give me a holler if you need anything,' he nodded his grizzled head. 'You know where she's tied.'

'I do.' With a wave of her hand, Dina started down the long stretch of dock.

Masts, long, short and medium, stood in broken lines along the pier, sails furled, the hulls motionless in the quiet water. Her steps were directed by memory along the boards. Although she had rarely ever joined Blake after her first two disastrous attempts at sailing, Dina had often come to the marina to wait for his return. But Blake wouldn't be coming back any more.

The bold letters of the *Starfish* stood out clearly against the white hull. Dina paused, feeling the tightness in her throat. Then, scolding herself, she stepped aboard. The wooden deck was dull, no longer gleaming and polished as Blake had kept it.

It didn't do any good to tell herself she shouldn't have waited so long to do something about the boat. There had been so many other decisions to make and demands on her time. Plus there had been so much legal entanglement surrounding Blake's disappearance. Those had become knots on the notification of his death. Since his estate wasn't settled, the boat still couldn't be sold until the court decreed the dispensation of his property.

The *Starfish* had been laid up since his disappearance, everything aboard exactly the way he had left it after his last sail. Dina unlocked the cabin to go below. The time had come to pack away all his things. Jake Stone, the family attorney, had decided the boat should be leased, even if it couldn't be sold yet, to eliminate the maintenance costs and to keep the boat from deteriorating through lack of use.

It had occurred to Dina that she could have arranged for someone else to clear away his things and clean up the boat. That was what she had planned to do when the attorney phoned the first of the week to tell her he had received the court's permission to lease the boat. But she was here now and the task lay ahead of her.

Opening drawers and doors, she realised there was a great deal more aboard than she had supposed. The storehouse of canned goods in the cupboards would have brought a smile of delight to any gourmet, but Blake had always been very particular about his food and the way it was prepared. Sighing, Dina wondered how many of the cans were still good. What a waste it would be if she had to throw them all out.

Picking up a can, she quickly set it down. The first order was to get a general idea of what had to be done. She continued her methodical examination of the cabin's contents. The clean, if now musty, clothes brought a smile to her lips. It was funny how a person's memory of little things could dim over such a short time as a few years.

A glance at his clothes brought it all back. Blake had been very meticulous about his clothes, being always clean and well dressed. Even the several changes of denim levis kept aboard the boat were creased and pressed. A thin coating of dust couldn't hide the snow-white of his sneakers.

Both seemed something of an extreme, yet Dina couldn't remember a time when she had seen him dressed in a manner that could be described as carelessly casual. It made him sound a bit pompous, but the trait hadn't been at all abrasive.

Blake had been used to good things all his life, a beautiful home, excellent food, vintage wines and specially tailored clothes. Spoiled? With a trace of arrogance? Perhaps, Dina conceded. He had been something of a playboy when she had met him, with devastating charm when he wanted to turn it on. Brilliantly intelligent and almost dreadfully organised, he had been exciting and difficult to live with.

Not at all like Chet, she concluded again. But what was the point in comparing? What could be gained by holding up Blake's smooth sophistication to Chet's easygoing nature? With a shrug of confusion, she turned away from the clothes, shutting her mind to the unanswerable questions.

For the better part of the day, she worked aboard the boat, first packing and carrying Blake's belong-ings to the Porsche, where she stuffed them in every conceivable corner of the small sports car. Then she began cleaning away the years of dust and salt spray, airing the mattresses and cushions, and polishing the interior woodwork.

Dirty and sweaty and physically exhausted, she returned the key to the crusty marina operator. Yet the laborious job had been cathartic, leaving her with an oddly refreshed feeling. Lately all her energy had been expended mentally. The hard manual work felt good even if her muscles would be stiff and sore tomorrow.

She was humming to herself as the white Porsche rounded the corner on to the street where she lived with her mother-in-law. At the sight of the half dozen cars parked around the cul de sac of the driveway, Dina frowned and slowed the car, forced to park it some distance from the entrance.

There wasn't any dinner party she had forgotten, was there? she wondered to herself. The cars resembled those belonging to close family friends. One, the silver-grey Cadillac, was Chet's. She glanced at her watch. He had said he would stop around seven for a drink before taking her out to dinner. It was barely five o'clock.

Her mouth formed a disgruntled line. She had hoped to soak in a tubful of scented bubbles for an hour, but obviously that luxury was going to be denied her. And why hadn't Mother Chandler mentioned she would be entertaining this evening? It wasn't like her.

Puzzled, Dina raised the convertible top of her sports car and rolled up the windows. This was not the time to transport all the items from the car into the house, so she climbed out of the car, her handbag slung over her shoulder, and locked the doors.

Happy voices were talking all over each other from the living room as she entered the house. The double doors of carved oak leading into the room were closed, concealing the owners of the voices. She hesitated, then decided for a quick wash and change while her return was still unnoticed.

Only it wasn't unnoticed. As she started to cross the foyer for the stairs leading to the second floor and her bedroom, one of the double doors was surreptitiously opened. Her eyes widened as Chet slipped out, his handsome features strained and tense.

'Where have you been?' There was a hint of desperation in his low voice.

If it wasn't for the joyful tone of the voices in the other room, Dina might have guessed that some catastrophe had befallen, judging by Chet's expression.

'At the marina,' she answered.

'The marina?' he repeated in disbelief. Again there was that strangled tightness in his voice. 'My God, I've been calling all over trying to find you. I never even considered the marina. What were you doing there, for heaven's sake?'

'The *Starfish*, the boat has been leased. I was getting it cleaned up.'

'Of all the times——'

Dina broke in sharply. 'What's going on?' His attitude was too confusing when she couldn't fathom the reason.

'Look, there's something I have to tell you.' Chet moistened his lips nervously, his grey-blue gaze darting over her face as if trying to judge something from her expression. 'But I don't know how to say it.'

'What is it?' impatiently. His tension was becoming contagious.

He took her by the shoulders, his expression deadly serious as he gazed intently into her eyes. Her muscles were becoming sore and they protested at the tightness of his hold.

'It's this,' he began earnestly.

But got no further as a low, huskily-pitched male voice interrupted. 'Chet seems to think you're going to go into a state of shock when you find out I'm alive.'

The floor rocked beneath her feet. Dina managed a half turn on her treacherously unsteady footing, magnetically drawn to the voice. The whole floor seemed to give way when she saw its owner, yet she remained upright, her collapsing muscles supported by Chet.

There was a dreamlike unreality to the moment.

Almost nightmare-like, since it seemed a cruel joke for someone to stand in the doorway of the living room masquerading as Blake, mimicking his voice.

She stared wordlessly at the tall figure framed by the living room doors. There was much about the chiselled features that resembled Blake, the wide forehead, the carved cheek and jaw, the strong chin and classically straight nose.

Yet there were differences too. The sun had burned this man's face a dusky tan, making it leathery and tough, giving a hardness to features that in Blake had been suavely handsome. The eyes were the same dark brown, but they wore a hooded look, narrowed as they seemed to pierce into the very marrow of her soul.

His hair was the same deep shade of umber brown, but its waving thickness was much longer than Blake had ever worn it, giving the impression of being rumpled instead of smoothly in place. As tall as Blake, this man's build was more muscled. Not that Blake had been a weakling by any means, it was just that this man seemed more developed without appearing heavier.

The differences registered with computer swiftness, her brain working while the rest of her was reeling from the similarities. The buzzing in her head continued non-stop, facts clicking into place. But it wasn't her eyes that Dina trusted; it was Chet's peculiar behaviour before this man appeared, his innate kindness that would never have permitted a cruel joke like this to be played on her, and the something that he was going to tell her that finally led her to a conclusion.

Blake was alive. And he was standing in the doorway. She swayed forward, but her feet wouldn't move. Chet's hands tightened in support, drawing her stunned look. The confirmation was there in his carefully watchful face.

'It's true,' she breathed, neither a statement nor a question.

Chet nodded, a silent warning in his eyes. It was then that Dina felt the cold weight of his engagement ring around her finger, and the blood drained from her face. Her hands reached out to cling to Chet's arms, suddenly and desperately needing his support to remain upright.

'It seems Chet was right,' that familiar, lazy voice drawled in an arid tone. 'My return is more of a shock to you than I thought it would be,' Blake observed. The angle of his head shifted slightly to the side to direct his next words over his shoulder without releasing Dina from his level gaze. 'She needs some hot, sweet coffee, laced with a stiff shot of brandy.'

'Exactly,' Chet agreed, and curved a bracing arm around her waist. 'Let's find you a place to sit down, Dina.' Numbly she accepted his help, aware of his gaze flickering to Blake. 'Seeing you standing in the doorway was bound to have been like seeing a ghost. I told you we were all convinced you were dead.'

'Not me,' Mother Chandler denied, moving to stand beside her son. 'I always knew somehow that he was still alive somewhere out there, despite what everyone said.'

Fleetingly, Dina was aware of the blatant lie contained in her mother-in-law's assertion. The thought had barely formed when she realised there were others in the living room. She recognised the faces of close family friends, gathered to celebrate Blake's return. They had been watching the reunion between husband and wife—or rather, the lack of it.

In that paralysing second, Dina realised she had not so much as touched Blake, let alone joyously fallen into his arms. Her one swaying attempt had been accidentally checked by Chet's steadying hold. It would seem staged and faked if she did so now.

Equally startling was the discovery that she would have to fake it, because, although the man in front of her was obviously Blake Chandler, he did not seem like the same man she had married. She felt as if she was looking at a total stranger. He knew what she was thinking and feeling; she could see it in the coolness of his expression, aloof and chilling.

As she and Chet approached the doorway, Blake stepped to one side, giving them room. He smiled down at his mother, his expression revealing nothing to the others that might let them think he found her behaviour unnatural under the circumstances.

'If you were so positive I was alive, Mother, why are you wearing black?' he chided.

Colour rose in Norma Chandler's cheeks. 'For your father, Blake,' she responded, not at a loss for an explanation.

Everyone was still standing, watching, as Chet guided Dina to the empty cushions of the sofa. After she was seated, he automatically sat down beside her. Blake had followed them into the room.

Every nerve in Dina's body was aware of it, although she wasn't able to lift her gaze to him. Guilt burned inside her, gnawing away at any spontaneous reaction she might have had. It didn't help when Blake sat down in the armchair nearest her end of the couch.

The housekeeper appeared, setting a china cup and saucer on the glass-topped table in front of the sofa. 'Here's your coffee, just the way Mr Blake ordered it.'

'Thank you, Deirdre,' she murmured. She reached for the china cup filled with steaming dark liquid, but her hands were shaking like aspen leaves and she couldn't hold on to it.

Out of the corner of her eye, she caught a suggestion of movement from Blake, as if he was about to lean forward to help her. Chet's hand was already there, lifting the cup to carry it to her lips. It was purely an automatic reaction on Chet's part. He had become used to doing things for her in the last two and a half years, just as Dina had become used to having him do them.

Instinctively, she knew he hadn't told Blake of

their engagement and she doubted if anyone else
had. But Chet's solicitous concern was telling its
own story. And behind that façade of lazy interest,
he was absorbing every damning detail. Without
knowing it, Chet was making matters worse.

The hot and sweetly potent liquid Dina sipped
eased the constriction strangling her voice, and she
found the strength to raise her hesitant gaze to
Blake's.

'How——' she began self-consciously. 'I mean,
when——'

'I walked out of the jungle two weeks ago.' He
anticipated her question and answered it.

'Two weeks ago?' That was before she had agreed
to marry Chet. 'Why didn't you let ... someone
know?'

'It was difficult to convince the authorities that I
was who I claimed to be. They, too, believed I was
dead.' There was a slashing line to his mouth, a
cynical smile. 'It must have been easier for Lazarus
back in the Biblical days to return from the dead.'

'Are you positive I can't fix you a drink, Mr
Blake?' the housekeeper enquired. 'A Martini?'

'Nothing, thank you.'

Dina frowned. In the past, Blake had always
drunk two if not three Martinis before dinner. She
had not been wrong. There were more than just surface changes in him during the last two and a half
years. Unconsciously she covered her left hand with
her right, hiding not only the wedding rings Blake

had given her, but Chet's engagement ring as well.

'The instant they believed Blake's story,' his mother inserted to carry on his explanation, 'he caught the first plane out to come home.' She beamed at him like the adoring and doting mother that she was.

'You should have phoned.' Dina couldn't help saying it. Forewarned, she might have been better prepared for the new Blake Chandler.

'I did.'

Simultaneously as he spoke, Dina remembered the telephone ringing in the dawn hour as she had left the house. Seconds. She had missed by seconds of knowing about his return.

'I'd switched off my extension,' Norma Chandler said, 'and Deirdre was wearing her earplugs. Did you hear it, Dina?'

'No. No, I'd already left,' answered Dina.

'When Blake didn't get any answer here,' Chet continued the story, 'he called me.'

'Chet was as stunned as you were, Dina,' Blake smiled, but Dina suspected that she was the only one who noticed the lack of amusement in his voice. She knew her gaze wavered under the keenness of his.

'I came over right away to let you and Mrs Chandler know,' Chet finished.

'Where were you, Dina?' Sam Lavecek grumped. He was Blake's godfather and a very old friend of both Blake's father and mother. Over the years, he had become something of a Dutch uncle to Blake, later extending the relationship to Dina. 'Chet has been half out of his mind worrying about where you were all day. Played hookey from the office, did you?'

'I was at the marina,' she answered, and turned to Blake. 'The *Starfish* has been leased to a couple, and they plan to sail to Florida for the winter. I spent the day cleaning it up and moving out all of your things.'

'What a pity, boy!' Sam Lavecek sympathised, slapping the arm of his chair. 'You always did love going out on that boat. Now, the very day you come home, it's being turned over to someone else.'

'It's only a boat, Sam.' There was an enigmatic darkness to his eyes that made his true thoughts impossible to see.

To Dina, in her super-sensitive state, he seemed to be implying something else. Perhaps that he didn't object to his boat being loaned to someone else as long as it wasn't his wife. Her apprehension mounted.

'You're right!' the older man agreed with another emphatic slap of his hand on the armchair. 'It's only a boat. And what's that compared to having you back? It's a miracle! A miracle!'

The statement brought a surfeit of questions for Blake to answer about the crash and the events that followed. Dina listened to his account. Each word that came from his mouth made him seem more and more a stranger.

The small chartered plane had developed engine trouble and had crashed in the teeming jungle. When Blake had come to, the other four people aboard were dead and he was trapped in the twisted wreckage, his leg broken along with a few ribs. There had been a deep gash on his forehead still seeping blood and other cuts and bruises. Dina's gaze found the scar that had made a permanent crease in his forehead.

Blake didn't go into too much detail about how he had got out of the plane the following day, but Dina had a vivid imagination and pictured the agony he must have endured fighting his way out with his injuries, letting the wreckage become a coffin for the mangled lifeless bodies of the others. Not knowing when or if he would be rescued, Blake had been forced to set his own leg.

That was something Dina could not visualise him doing. In the past when there was anything that required professional skill or experience, Blake had always hired someone to do it. So for him to set his own broken bone, regardless of the dire circumstances, seemed completely out of character, something the man she knew would never have done.

When the emergency supply of rations from the plane had run out, Blake had foraged for his food, his diet consisting of fruits and whatever wild animals he could trap, catch or kill. And this was supposed to be the same Blake Chandler who had considered the killing of wild game a disgusting sport and who dined on gourmet cuisine.

Blake, who despised flies and mosquitoes, told of the insects that swarmed in the jungle, flying, crawling, biting, stinging, until he no longer noticed them. The heat and humidity of the jungle had rotted his shoes and clothes, forcing him to improvise articles of clothing from the skins of the animals he had killed. Blake, the meticulous dresser, always presenting such a well-groomed appearance.

As he began his tale of the more than two-year long walk out of the jungle, Dina discovered the crux of the difference. Blake had left Rhode Island a civilised man and had come back part primitive. She stared at him with seeing eyes.

Leaning back in his chair, he looked indolent and relaxed, yet Dina knew his muscles were like coiled springs, always ready to react with the swiftness of a predatory animal. His senses, his nerves were alert to everything going on around him. Nothing escaped the notice of that hooded dark gaze. From the lurking depths of those hard brown eyes, Blake seemed to be viewing them all with cynical amusement as if he found the so-called dangers and problems of their civilised world laughable when compared to the battle of survival he had fought and won.

'There's something I don't understand,' Sam Lavecek frowned when Blake had completed his basically sketchy narrative. 'Why did the authori-

ties tell us you were dead after they'd found the
wreckage? Surely they must have discovered there
was a body missing,' he added bluntly.

'I don't imagine they did,' Blake answered in a
calm, matter-of-fact tone.

'Did you bury their bodies, Blake?' his mother
asked. 'Is that why they didn't find them?'

'No, Mother, I didn't.' The cynical amusement
that Dina suspected was there, glittering through
the brown shutters of the indulgent look he gave his
mother. 'It would have taken a bulldozer to carve
out a grave in that tangled mess of brush, trees and
roots. I had no choice but to leave them in the plane.
Unfortunately the jungle is filled with scavengers.'

Dina blanched. He sounded so cold and insensitive! Blake had been a passionately vital and volatile man, quick to temper and quick to love.

What had he become? How much would the
savagery in his life in the last two and a half years
influence his future? Would his determination become ruthlessness? Would his innate leadership become tyranny? Would his compassion for others
become contempt? Would his love turn into lust?
Was he a virile man or a male animal? He was her
husband, and Dina shuddered at what the answers
to those questions might be.

Distantly she heard the housekeeper enter the
room to enquire, 'What time would you like dinner
served this evening, Mrs Chandler?'

There was hesitation before Norma Chandler replied, 'In about an hour, Deirdre. That will be all right for everyone, won't it?' and received a murmur of agreement.

From the sofa cushions beside her, Chet expanded on his agreement to remark, 'That will give you ample time to freshen up before dinner, won't it, Dina?'

She clutched at the lifeline he had unknowingly tossed her. 'Yes, it will.' She wanted desperately to be alone for a few minutes to sort through her jumbled thoughts, terribly afraid she was overreacting. Rising, she addressed her words to everyone. 'Please excuse me. I won't be long.'

CHAPTER THREE

THE brief shower had washed away the last lingering traces of unreality. Wrapping the sash to her royal blue towelling robe around her middle, Dina walked through the open doorway of the private bath to her bedroom. She moved to the clothes closet at the far corner of the room to choose what she would wear for dinner, all the while trying to assure herself that she was making mountains out of molehills where Blake was concerned.

There was a click and movement in her peripheral vision. She turned as the door opened and Blake walked in. Her mouth opened to order out the intruder, then closed. He was her husband. How could she order him out of her bedroom?

His gaze swept the room, located her, and stopped, fixing her with a stare like a predator would his prey. Her fingers clasped the folds of her robe at the throat, her palms moistening with nervous perspiration. Dina was conscious of the implied intimacy of the room and her own nakedness beneath the terrycloth material. Blood pounded in her head like a thousand jungle drums signalling danger. Vulnerable, she was wary of him.

The brand new tan suit and tie he wore gave him

a cultured look, but she wasn't taken in by the thin veneer of refinement. It didn't conceal the latent power of that muscled physique nor soften the rough edges of his sun-hardened features. Blake closed the door, not releasing her from his pinning gaze, and searing alarm halted her breath.

'I've come through hell to get back to you, Dina, yet you can't seem to walk across a room to meet me.' The accusation was made in a smooth, low tone rife with sardonic amusement.

His words prodded her into movement. Too much time had elapsed since his return for her to rush into his arms. Her steps were stiff, her back rigid as she approached him. She was cautious of him and it showed. Even if she wanted to, she doubted if she could batter down the wall of reserve she had erected. Stopping in front of him, she searched her mind for welcoming words that she could issue sincerely.

'I'm glad you came back safely,' were the ones she could offer that had the ring of truth.

Blake waited—for her kiss; the muscles in her stomach contracted sharply with the realisation. After a second's hesitation, she forced herself on tip-toe to bring her lips against his mouth in a cool kiss. His large hands spanned the back of her waist, their imprint burning through the material on to her naked flesh. His light touch didn't seem at all familiar, almost alien.

At her first attempt to end the kiss, his arms be-

came a vice, fingers raking into her silver-gold hair
to force her lips to his. Her slender curves were
pressed against the hard contours of his body. Her
heartbeat skittered madly, then accelerated in
alarm.

The hungry demand of his bruising mouth asked
more than Dina could give to a man who seemed
more of a stranger than her husband. She struggled
to free herself of his iron hold and was surprised
when Blake let her twist away.

Her breathing was rapid and uneven as she
avoided his eyes. 'I have to get dressed.' She pretended that was her reason for rejecting his embrace. 'The others are waiting downstairs.'

Those fathomless brown eyes were boring holes
into her. Dina could feel them even as she turned
away to retrace her steps to the closet and her much-
needed clothes. Her knees felt watery.

'You mean Chet is waiting,' Blake corrected with
deadly softness.

Her blood ran cold. 'Of course. Isn't Chet there
with the others?' She feigned an obtuseness to his
meaning and immediately regretted not taking advantage of the opening he had given her to tell him
about Chet.

'I've had two and a half years of forced celibacy,
Dina. How about you?' The dry contempt in his
question spun her around, blue fires of indignation
flashing in her eyes, but Blake didn't give her a
chance to defend her honour. 'How long was it

after I disappeared before Chet moved in?'

'He did not *move* in!' she denied.

With the swiftness of a swooping hawk, he seized her left hand. His savage grip almost crushed the slender bones of her fingers into a pulp, drawing a gasp of pain from her.

'Figuratively speaking!' His mouth was a thin, cruel line as he lifted her hand. 'Or don't you call it moving in when another man's ring joins the ones I put on your finger? Did you think I wouldn't see it?' he blazed. 'Did you think I wouldn't notice the looks the two of you were exchanging and the way all the others watched the three of us?' He released her hand in a violent gesture of disgust. Dina nursed the pain-numbed fingers, cradling them in her right hand. 'And neither of you had the guts to tell me!'

'Neither of us really had a chance,' she defended, her temper flaring from the flame of his. 'It isn't an announcement one wants to make in front of others. What was I supposed to say when I saw you standing in the doorway, a husband I thought was dead? "Darling, I'm so glad you're alive. Oh, by the way, I'm engaged to another man." Please credit me for having a bit more delicacy than that!'

He gave her a long, hard look. His anger was so tightly controlled that it almost frightened her. It was like looking at a capped volcano and knowing that inside it was erupting and wondering when the lid would blow.

'This is some homecoming,' Blake declared in a contemptuous breath. 'A wife who wishes I was still in the grave!'

'I don't wish that,' she denied.

'This engagement——' he began, bitter sarcasm coating his words.

'The way you say it makes it sound like something sordid,' Dina protested, 'and it isn't. Chet and I have been engaged for barely more than a week. At the time that he proposed to me, I thought you were dead and I was free to accept.'

'Now you know differently. I'm alive. You're my wife, not my widow. You're still married to me.' The way he said it, in such cold, concise tones, made it sound like a life sentence.

Dina was trembling and she didn't know from what. 'I'm aware of that, Blake.' Her voice was taut to keep out the tremors. 'But this isn't the time to discuss the situation. Your mother is waiting dinner and I still have to get dressed.'

For a few harrowing seconds, she thought he was going to argue. 'Yes,' he agreed slowly, 'this isn't the time.'

She heard the door being yanked open and flinched as it was slammed shut. If this was a new beginning for their marriage, it was off to a rotten start. They had argued before Blake had disappeared, and now war had nearly been declared on his return. Dina shuddered and walked to the closet again.

As they all took their chairs around the Danish-styled dining table, the tension in the air was almost electrical. Yet Dina seemed to be the only one who noticed it. Blake sat at the head of the table, the place of honour, with his mother at the opposite end and Chet seated on her right. Dina sat on Blake's left.

Ever since she had come down, Blake had possessively kept her at his side, as if showing everyone that she was his and effectively separating her from Chet. On the surface, he seemed all smiles, at times giving her glimpses of his former devastating charm. But there was still anger smouldering in his brown eyes whenever his gaze was directed to her.

When everyone was seated, the housekeeper came in carrying a tureen of soup. 'I fixed your favourite, Mr Blake,' she announced, a beaming smile on her square-jawed face. 'Cream of asparagus.'

'Bless you, Deirdre,' he smiled broadly. 'Now that's the way to welcome a man home!'

The sharp side of his double-edged remark sliced at Dina. She paled at the censure, but otherwise retained a firm hold on her poise.

The meal was an epicurean's delight, from the soup to the lobster thermidor to the ambrosia of fresh fruit. Blake made all the right comments and compliments, but Dina noticed he didn't seem to savour the taste of the various dishes the way she remembered he had in the past. She had the impression that dining had been reduced to the simple matter of eating. Food was food however it was prepared, and man needed food to live.

Coffee was served in the living room so Deirdre could clear away the dishes. Again Dina was kept at Blake's elbow. Chet was on the far side of the room. As she glanced his way, he looked up, smoke-blue eyes meeting the clear blue of hers. He murmured a quick excuse to the older woman who had him cornered, a Mrs Burnside, an old school friend of Norma Chandler's, and made his way towards her.

Through the cover of her lashes, Dina dared a glance at Blake and saw the faint narrowing of his gaze as Chet approached. The smile on Chet's face was strained when he stopped in front of them. Dina guessed he was trying to find a way to tell Blake of their engagement and she wished there was a way to let him know that Blake was aware of it.

'It seems like old times, Blake,' Chet began, forcing a camaraderie into his voice, 'coming over to your house for dinner and seeing you and——' His gaze slid nervously to Dina.

'Chet,' Blake interrupted calmly, 'Dina has told me about your engagement.'

The room grew so quiet Dina was certain a feather could have been heard dropping on the carpet. All eyes were focused on the trio, as if a brilliant spotlight was shining on them. She discovered, like everyone else, she was holding her breath. After the savage anger Blake had displayed upstairs, she wasn't sure what might happen next.

'I'm glad you know. I——' Chet lowered his gaze, searching for words.

Blake filled in the moment's pause. 'I want you to know I don't bear any ill feelings. You've always been a good friend and I'd like it to continue that way.' Dina started to sigh with relief. 'After all, what are friends for?'

No one except Dina seemed to pay any attention to the last caustic comment. Chet was too busy shaking the hand Blake offered in friendship. The others were murmuring among themselves about the moment they had been waiting all day to happen.

'Naturally, the engagement is broken,' Blake joked with a smile that contrasted with the sharply serious light in his eyes.

'Naturally,' Chet agreed with an answering smile.

And Dina felt a rush of anger that she could be tossed aside so readily without protest. For that matter, she hadn't even been consulted about her wishes.

Immediately she berated herself. It was what she wanted. Blake was alive and she was married to him. She didn't want to divorce him to marry Chet, so why was she fussing? A simple matter of ego, she decided.

After the confrontation over the engagement, the party became anticlimactic. There was a steady trickle of departures among the guests. One minute

Dina was wishing Mrs Burnside goodbye and the next she was alone in the foyer with Blake, his eyes watching her in that steady, measured way she found so unnerving.

'That's the last of them,' he announced.

Dina glanced around. 'Where's your mother?'

'In the living room helping Deirdre clean up.'

'I'll give them a hand.' She started to turn away.

But Blake caught her arm. 'There's no need.' He released it as quickly as he had captured it. 'They can handle it by themselves.'

Dina didn't protest. The day had been unconscionably long and she felt enervated from the physical and mental stresses it had held. What she really wanted was a long night of hard, dreamless sleep. She started for the stairs, half aware that Blake was following.

'You didn't return Chet's ring,' he reminded her in a flat tone.

Raising her left hand, she glanced at the flower-like circlet of diamonds. 'No, I ... must have forgotten.' She was too tired at this point to care about such a small detail.

When she started to lower her hand, Blake seized it and stripped the ring from her finger before she could react to stop him. He gave it a careless toss on to the polished mahogany table standing against the foyer wall.

'You can't leave valuable things lying around!' Dina instantly retrieved it, clutching it in her hand as she frowned at him, Blake who insisted there was a place for everything and everything in its place.

'Valuable to whom?' he questioned with cool arrogance.

Her fingers tightened around the ring. 'I'll keep it in my room until I can give it back to him.' She waited for him to challenge her decision. When he didn't, she walked to the stairs.

'He'll be over tomorrow,' Blake stated, speaking from directly behind her. 'You can give it to him then.'

'What time is he coming?' Dina climbed the stairs, knowing she was loath to return the ring when Blake was around, but he seemed to be leaving her little option.

'At ten for Sunday brunch.'

At the head of the stairs, Dina turned. Her bedroom was the first door on the right. She walked to it, only to have Blake's arm reach around her to open the door. She stopped abruptly as he pushed it open, her look bewildered.

'What are you doing?' she frowned.

'I'm going to bed.' An eyebrow flickered upward as he eyed her coolly. 'Where did you think I was going to sleep?'

She looked away, her gaze darting madly about. She was thrown into a trembling state of confusion by his taunting question. 'I didn't think about it,' she faltered. 'I guess I've become used to sleeping alone.'

His hand was at the small of her back, firmly directing her into the room. 'Surely you don't expect that to continue?'

'I——' Oh, god, yes, she did, Dina realised with a frozen start. 'I think it might be better ... for a while.' She stopped in the centre of the room and turned to face him as he closed the door.

'You do?' Inscrutable brown eyes met her wavering look, his leather-carved features expressionless.

'Yes, I do.'

Her nerves were leaping about as erratically as jumping beans, not helped by the palpitating beat of her heart. She watched with growing apprehension as Blake peeled off his suit jacket and tie, and began unbuttoning his shirt.

She tried to reason with him, her voice quivering. 'Blake, it's been two and a half years.'

'Tell me about it,' he inserted dryly.

Her throat tightened to make her voice small. 'I don't know you any more. You're a stranger to me.'

'That can be changed.'

'You aren't trying to understand, Blake.' Dina fought to keep control of herself. 'I can't just hop into bed with——'

'Your husband?' he finished the sentence, and gave her a searing look. 'Who else would you choose?'

The shirt was coming off, exposing a naked chest and shoulder tanned the same dusky shade as his face. The result heightened Dina's impression of a primitive male, powerful and dangerous, sinewy muscles rippling in the aritficial light.

Her senses catapulted in alarm as she felt the force of his earthy, pagan attraction. In an attempt to break the black magic of its spell, she turned away, walking stiffly to her dresser to place Chet's ring in her jewel case.

'No one. That isn't what I meant.' She remained at the dresser, her hands flattened on its top, knuckles showing white. He came up behind her and she lifted her gaze. In the dressing-table mirror, her wary eyes saw his reflection join with hers. 'You've become hard, Blake, a cynic,' she accused. 'I can imagine what you've gone through——'

'Can you?' There was a faint curl of his lip. 'Can you imagine how many nights I held on to my sanity by clinging to the vision of a blue-eyed woman with cornsilk hair?' His fingers twined themselves through the loose strands of her pale gold hair and Dina closed her eyes at the savage note in his voice. 'Roughly nine hundred and twenty-two nights. And when I finally see her again, she's clinging to the arm of my best friend. Is it any wonder that I'm hard, bitter, when I've been waiting all this time for her lips to kiss away the gnawing memory of those hours? Did you even miss me, Dina?' With a handful of hair as leverage, he twisted her around to face him. 'Did you grieve?'

Her eyes smarted with tears she refused to shed

at the tugging pain in her scalp. 'When you first disappeared, Blake, I was nearly beside myself with fear. But your mother was even more distraught— losing her husband, then possibly you. I had to spend most of my time comforting her. Then the company started to fall apart at the seams and Chet insisted I had to take over or it would fail. So I was plunged head first into another world. During the day I was too busy to think about myself and at night, there was your mother depending on me to be her strength. The only moments I had alone were here in this room. And I took sleeping pills so I would get enough rest to be able to get through another day. To be truthful, Blake, I didn't have time to grieve.'

He was unmoved by her words, his dark eyes flat and cold. 'But you had time for Chet,' he accused with icy calm.

Dina winced as the point of his arrow found its target. 'It began very innocently. He was your closest friend, so it was natural that he kept in touch with your mother and me. Later, there was the company connection. He was always there, bolstering me, encouraging me, and offering me a shoulder to lean on the odd moments that I needed it without mauling me in return,' she explained, refusing to sound guilty. 'It grew from there after you were reported killed. I needed him.'

'And I need you—now.' He drew her inside the

steel circle of his arms, flattening her against his chest.

The hard feel of his naked flesh beneath her hands rocked her senses. The warmth of his breath wafted over her averted face, the musky scent of him enveloping her. She pushed at his arms, straining to break out of his hold.

'You haven't listened to a word I've said!' she stormed angrily, inwardly battling against his physical arousal of her senses. 'You've changed. I've changed. We need time to adjust!'

'Adjust to what?' Blake snapped. 'The differences between a man and a woman? Those are differences we could discover and compensate for very quickly.' The zipper of her dress was released.

'Stop it!' She struggled to keep him from sliding the dress off her shoulders. 'You're making me feel like an animal!'

'You are. We both are animals, species homo sapiens.' The words were issued in a cold, insensitive tone. 'Put on this earth to sleep, eat, and breed, to live and die. I learned in the jungle that that's the essence of our existence.'

Hysterical laughter gurgled in her throat. 'Oh, my god,' Dina choked on the sound. 'That sounds like "You Tarzan, me Jane"!'

'Eliminate the trappings of society and the pretty words and that's what it comes down to in the end.'

'No, our minds are more fully developed. We have feelings, emotions,' she protested. 'We——'

The dress was stripped away despite her efforts.

'Shut up!' he growled the order against her mouth and smothered the sounds when she refused to obey.

Leaning and twisting backwards, Dina tried to escape the domination of his kiss, but his hands used the attempt to mould her lower body more fully to his length, her hip bones crushed by oak-solid thighs. The silk of her slip was a second skin, concealing and revealing while calloused fingers moved roughly about in exploration.

Cruelly, Blake ravaged the softness of her lips. Dina thought her neck would snap under its driving force. Beneath her straining hands, she felt the flexing of his muscles, smooth like hammered steel, latent in their sensuality. He was devouring her strength by degrees, slowly and steadily wearing her down. Doubling her fingers, she began hammering at him with her fists, puny blows that made little dent.

The effort seemed to dredge the reserves of her strength. Within seconds, a blackness swam in front of her eyes and a dizzying weakness spread through her limbs. Her fingers dug into his shoulders, clinging to him to keep from falling into the yawning abyss that seemed to be opening in front of her.

As her resistance ebbed into nothingness so did the brutality of his assault. The terrible, bruising pressure of his mouth eased, permitting Dina to straighten her neck. Gradually she began to surface from the waves of semi-consciousness, enough to become aware of his loosened hold.

With a determined effort, she broke out of his arms. Gasping in air in panicked breaths, she backed away from him, her knees quivering. Blake swayed towards her, then stopped. A second later she realised why, as her retreat was stopped short by a wall. A cornered animal, she stared at the man who held her at bay. A stranger who was her husband.

She lifted her head, summoning all her pride to beg, 'Don't do this, Blake.'

Slow, silent strides carried him to her and she didn't attempt to flee. There was no mercy in his eyes and she would not submit to the ignominy of cowering. Her resistance became passive as he undressed, her eyes tightly closed.

'Are you choosing to portray the martyred wife submitting to the bestiality of her husband?' Blake taunted. 'This display of frigidity is a farce. My memory wasn't damaged. I remember, too well, what a passionate lover you are.'

Dina paled as she remembered too. A flicker of the old searing fire licked through her veins as he drew her to him and her bare curves came in contact with his nude body. The tiny flame couldn't catch hold, not when the hands fanning it were calloused and rough instead of the smooth, manicured hands that had once brought it to a full blaze.

'Don't destroy our marriage,' she whispered, try-

ing not to see the curling, sunbleached hairs forming a pale cloud against the burnished bronze of his
chest. 'I want to love you again, Blake.'

With a muffled imprecation, he buried his face
in her hair. 'Damn you! Why didn't you say that
when I came home?' he muttered thickly in a rasping sound that suggested pain. 'Why did you have
to wait until now?'

'Would it have mattered?' Dina caught back a
sob.

'It might have then.' Effortlessly he swung her
off her feet and into his arms, his jaw set in a ruthless line. 'I couldn't care less now. You're mine and
I mean to have you.'

The overhead light was switched off, throwing
the room into darkness. As if guided by animal instinct, Blake carried her to the bed. Without
bothering to pull down the covers, he laid her on
the bed and towered beside it.

'Blake.' There was an unspoken plea in the way
she spoke his name, a last attempt to make him
understand her unwillingness.

'No,' he answered, and the mattress sagged under
his weight. 'Don't ask me to wait.' His low voice
commanded near her ear, his breath stirring her
hair. 'It's been too long.'

And we both have changed, Dina thought, stif-
fening at the moist touch of his mouth along her
neck. Can't you see the differences, Blake? Physical looks as well as mental attitudes? Haven't you

noticed I'm wearing my hair longer? As his hand slid over her ribs to cup her breast, she remembered when its roundness had filled it. Now, with maturity, it overflowed.

But Blake seemed intent on discovering the ripeness of her female form, ignoring comparisons. His caressing hands roamed over her with intimate familiarity and she felt her body responding, reluctantly at first. A series of long, drugging kisses soon made her mind blank to all but the demands of her flesh.

Her senses took over, reigning supreme. She gloried in the taste of his lips probing the sensual hollows of her mouth and the brush of the soft, curling hairs on his chest hardening her nipples into erotic pebbles.

The rapidly increasing throb of her pulse was in tempo with the pagan beat of his, building to a climax. And the heady male scent of him, heightened by perspiration and his rising body heat, served to stimulate all her senses until she was filled with nothing but him.

For a time she glimpsed heights she had thought she would never see again. Blake sought out all the places that brought her the most pleasure, waiting until she moaned his name in final surrender.

CHAPTER FOUR

DINA lay in bed, the covers pulled up to her neck, but she knew the blankets couldn't warm the chill. Her passion spent, she felt cold and empty inside as she stared upwards into the darkness of the room. A tear was frozen on an eyelash.

Physically her desires had been satisfied by Blake's skilled knowledge, but she had not been lifted to the rapturous heights of a spiritual union. That only happened when there was love involved. Tonight it had been merely a mutual satisfaction of sexual desires. And that special something that had been missing eliminated the warm afterglow Dina had previously known.

Blake was beside her, their bodies not touching. An arm was flung on the pillow above his head. She could hear the steady sound of his breathing, but doubted that he was asleep. Her sideways glance sought his carved profile in the dim light. There seemed to be a grim line to his mouth as if he was experiencing the same reaction.

As if feeling her look and hearing her question, he said in a low, flat voice, 'There's one argument you didn't make, Dina. If you had, it might have prevented this disillusionment.'

'What is it?' she asked in a tight, throbbing voice, longing to know what it was so she could keep this from happening again.

'The real thing can't match two and a half years of expectations.'

No, she agreed silently, not when there are no words of love exchanged, no mating of their hearts nor coming together of their souls. It was an act of lust, born out of anger and frustration.

'Passion never can, Blake,' she murmured.

He tossed aside the blanket draped across his waist and swung his feet to the floor. Her head turned on the pillow to stare at him in the darkness.

'Where are you going?' she asked softly. Something told her that if Blake would hold her in his arms, the aching void inside her might close.

There was a faint sheen to his sun-browned skin in the shadowy light. She could make out the breadth of his shoulders and the back muscles tapering to his waist. His steps were soundless, silent animal strides.

'Another unfortunate discovery I've made since returning to civilisation is that the mattresses are too soft,' he spoke in a low voice, a biting, cynical tone. 'I'm used to firm beds. That's what comes from spending too many nights sleeping in trees and on hard ground.'

She lost him in the darkness, and propped herself up on an elbow, keeping the covers tightly around her. 'Where are you going?'

'To find a spare blanket and a hard floor.' There was the click of the door being opened. 'You have part of your wish, Dina,' he added caustically. 'The bed is yours. You can sleep alone.'

As the door closed, a convulsive shudder ran through her. She turned her face into the pillow, curling her body into a tight ball of pain. With eyes squeezed shut, she lay there, aching for the forgetfulness of sleep.

A hand gently, but persistently, shook her shoulder. 'Mrs Blake? Wake up, please.' Dina stirred, lashes fluttering as she tried to figure out whether or not she was imagining the voice. 'Wake up, Mrs Blake!'

But she wasn't imagining the hand on her arm. Her head throbbed dully as she opened her eyes and rolled over, dragging the covers with her. Her sleepy gaze focused on the agitated expression of the housekeeper hovering above her.

Dina became conscious of several things at once, the rumpled pillow beside her where Blake had lain so briefly, her own naked state beneath the covers, and the clothes scattered about the room— hers and Blake's. My God, the room is a mess, she thought.

'What is it, Deirdre?' she questioned, trying to maintain a measure of composure despite the surge of embarrassment.

The older woman bit her lip as if uncertain how

to reply. 'It's Mr Blake.'

The anxious look on the housekeeper's face brought an instant reaction as Dina propped herself up on her elbows, concern chasing away the remnants of sleep. 'Blake? What's wrong? Has something happened to him?'

'No, it's ... it's just that he's sleeping downstairs —on the floor in the library.' A dull red was creeping up her neck into her cheeks. 'And he isn't wearing an ... any pyjamas.'

Dina swallowed back a smile, her relief lost in amusement. Poor Deirdre Schneider, she thought, never married in her life nor seriously close to it and probably shocked to her prim core when she found Blake sleeping in the library in his altogether.

'I see,' she nodded, and tried to keep her face straight.

'Mr Stanton will be arriving in just more than an hour.' The woman's gaze was trying desperately to avoid seeing the bareness of Dina's shoulders. 'I thought you should be the one to ... to wake up Mr Blake.'

'I will,' said Dina, and started to rise, then decided against adding to the housekeeper's embarrassment. 'Would you hand me my robe at the foot of the bed, Deirdre?'

After handing the robe to her, the housekeeper turned discreetly away while Dina slipped into it. 'Mrs Chandler had a few things sent over yesterday for Mr Blake,' she informed Dina. 'There are pyjamas and a robe. I put them in the empty closet.'

'I'll take them to him,' Dina finished tying the sash of her robe. 'And, Deirdre, tomorrow I think you'd better make arrangements with Mrs Chandler to purchase a bed with a very firm mattress, one that's as hard as a rock.'

'I will,' Deirdre promised as if taking an oath. 'Sorry to have awakened you, Mrs Blake.'

'That's quite all right, Deirdre,' Dina smiled.

With a brief self-conscious nod, the housekeeper left the room. Dina put on her slippers and walked to the small closet Deirdre had indicated. It was used mostly for storage. Amidst the few boxes and garment bags hung three shirts and a brown suit. On the two inside door hooks were the pyjamas and matching dressing robe in a muted shade of cranberry silk. Leaving the pyjamas, Dina took the robe.

Downstairs, her hand hesitated on the knob of the library door. Tension hammered in her temples, her stomach twisted into knots. Steeling herself to ignore the attack of nervousness, she opened the door quietly and walked in. Her gaze was directed first to the floor and its open area around the fireplace.

'Deirdre sent in the reserves, I see,' Blake's male voice mocked from the side of the room.

Dina turned in its direction and saw him standing near the solid wall of shelves filled with books. A dark green blanket was wrapped around his waist, his naked torso gleamed in that deep shade of tan. Fingers had combed his thick brown hair into a semblance of order, a suggestion of unruliness remaining. Dina's pulse fluctuated in alarm, her head lifted as if scenting danger. He looked like a primitive native, proud, noble and savage.

'Did you hear her come in?' She realised it was a foolish question after she had asked it. Those long months in the jungle had to have sharpened his senses, making them more acute.

'Yes, but I decided it was wiser to pretend I was still asleep rather than shock her sensibilities,' he admitted with cynical derision. 'I thought she would scamper up the stairs to inform you or my mother of my lewd behaviour.'

Behind his veiled look, Dina felt the dark intensity of his gaze scanning her face, searching for something, but she didn't know what. It made her uncomfortable and she wished she had dressed before coming down.

'I brought you a robe.' She held it out to him, aware of the faint trembling that wasn't yet visible.

'No doubt at Deirdre's suggestion. She must have been more shocked than I thought.' But Blake made no move towards it, forcing Dina to walk to him.

'Deirdre isn't accustomed to finding naked men sleeping on the library floor,' she defended the housekeeper's reaction, discovering a similar one in herself as Blake reached down to unwrap the blanket from around his waist. Self-consciously she averted her eyes, her colour mounting as if it was a stranger undressing in front of her instead of her husband.

There was a rustle of silk, then, 'It's safe to look now,' Blake taunted, his mouth quirking in ungentle mockery.

She flashed him an angry look for drawing attention to her sudden burst of modesty and turned away. The vein in her neck pulsed with a nervousness that she wasn't able to control. His hand touched her shoulder and she flinched from the searing contact.

'For God's sake, Dina, I'm not going to rape you!' he cursed beneath his breath. 'Dammit, can't I even touch my wife?'

Her blue eyes were wide and wary as she looked over her shoulder at his fiercely burning gaze. 'I don't feel like your wife, Blake,' she said tightly. 'I don't feel as if I'm married to you.'

Immediately the fires were banked in his eyes, that freezing control that was so unlike him coming into play. 'You are married to me,' he stated, and walked by her to the door. Opening it, he called, 'Deirdre! Bring some coffee into the library for my wife and myself.' With emphasis on 'wife'.

'Chet is coming and I still have to dress,' Dina

reminded him, objecting to more minutes alone with him.

'He isn't due for an hour,' Blake dismissed her protest and walked to the leather-covered sofa, pausing beside its end table to lift the lid of the ceramic cigarette box. 'Cigarette?' He flicked a questioning glance in her direction.

'No, I don't smoke. Remember?' she said with a faintly taunting arch to her voice.

'You might have acquired the habit during my absence,' he shrugged.

'I didn't.'

Brisk footsteps in the foyer signalled the housekeeper's approach. Seconds later she entered the library with a coffee service and two china cups on the tray she carried. A pink tint was still rouging her cheeks as Deirdre steadfastly avoided looking directly at Blake.

'Where would you like the tray?' she asked Dina.

'The table by the sofa will be fine.'

Blake carried the ceramic table lighter to the cigarette in his mouth and snapped the flame to its tip. Smoke spiralled upwards and he squinted his eyes against it. Despite his show of disinterest, Dina knew he was aware of the housekeeper's every movement. After setting the tray on the table at the opposite end of the sofa from where Blake stood, Deirdre straightened erectly.

'Will there be anything else?' Again her query was directed to Dina.

It was Blake who answered. 'That will be all,' exhaling a thin trail of smoke. 'And close the door on your way out, Deirdre.'

'Yes, sir.' Two red flags dotted her cheeks.

As Deirdre made a hasty exit, firmly closing the door, Blake walked to the tray. Lifting the coffee pot, he filled the two cups and offered one to Dina.

'Black, as I remember, with no sugar,' he said in a tone that baited.

'Yes, thank you.' Dina refused to bite as she took the cup and saucer from his hand.

Scalding steam rose from the brown liquid and Blake let his cup sit. He studied the glowing tip of his cigarette and the gossamer-thin white smoke rising upwards. A wry smile crooked his mouth.

'I'd forgotten how good a cigarette can taste first thing in the morning,' he mused.

Dina felt as edgy as a cat with its tail caught in a trap. She couldn't help retorting. 'I thought you hadn't forgotten anything.'

'Not the important things, I haven't,' Blake replied, levelly meeting her irritated glance.

With a broken sigh, she wandered to the library window overlooking the expansive front lawn of the house and the cul-de-sac of its drive. She was caught by the memory of the last time she had stared out the window in troubled silence. Oddly it seemed an eternity ago instead of the short time that it was.

'What are you thinking about?' Blake was close,

only a scant few feet behind her.

'I was merely remembering the last time I stood at this window.' She sipped at the hot coffee.

'When was that?' He seemed only idly curious.

Dina felt his gaze roaming her shapely length as surely as if he touched her, and stiffened to answer bluntly, 'The night of my engagement party to Chet.'

'Forget about him.' The command was crisp and impatient as Dina guessed it would be.

'It isn't that easy to turn back the clock,' she muttered tightly.

The cup nearly slipped from her fingers as she felt the rasping brush of his fingers against her hair. Her throat constricted, shutting off her voice and her breath.

'Have I told you I like your hair this length?' His low voice was a husky caress running down her spine.

He lifted aside the molten gold of her hair, pushing it away from her neck. The warmth of his breath against her skin warned her an instant before she glimpsed the waving darkness of his hair in her side vision.

His unerring mouth sought and found the ultra-sensitive and vulnerable spot at the base of her neck. Her heart felt as though it had been knocked sideways and Blake took full advantage of her Achilles' heel. She felt boneless, her head tipped down and to the side to give him freer access.

The cup rattled in its saucer, but she managed to hold on to it. His arms wound around her waist to mould her back to his muscular length. For a magic second, she was transported back to another time. Then a roughened hand slid under the overlapping fold of her robe to encircle the swell of her breast, a calloused finger teasing its nipple, and the arms felt suddenly strange.

'Blake, no!' Weakly she tugged at his wrist, no match for his strength.

She gasped as his sensual mouth moved upwards to her ear, and desire licked through her veins at the darting probe of his tongue. An all-pervading weakness went through her limbs. It was a dizzying sensation, wild drums pounding in her ears.

'Do you remember the way we used to make love in the mornings?' Blake murmured against her temple.

'Yes,' she moaned, the memory all too vivid.

The cup disappeared from her hand, carried away by a fluid movement of Blake. It took only the slightest pressure to turn her around. She was drawn to his side, a muscular, silk-covered thigh insinuating itself between her legs as she was arched against him. She lifted her head, subconsciously braced for the punishment of his rough kisses. Her fingers curled into his shoulders for support.

There was the tantalising touch of his lips against hers. 'After last night, I thought I had you out of my system,' he said against them, 'but I want you more than before.'

A half-sob came from her throat at the absence of any mention of love. In the next second, she didn't care, as his mouth closed over hers with sweet pressure. There was no plundering demand, only a persuasive exhorting to respond.

Her lips parted willingly, succumbing to the rapturous mastery of his exploration. The dream world of sensation seemed almost enough. She slid her fingers through the springing thickness of his hair, the scent of him earthy and clean.

As if tired of bending his head to reach her lips, Blake tightened his arm around her waist to lift her straight up, bringing her eye level. Another indication of his increased strength, that he should carry her weight so effortlessly. At the moment, Dina was oblivious to the example of his change.

His mouth blazed a moist trail downward to explore the pulsing vein in her neck. 'Did Chet ever make you feel like this?' he challenged.

And Dina caught her breath sharply in pain. Was that all this had been? An attempt to exorcise the memory of Chet's kisses from her mind? Had it been motivated by nothing more than that? She pushed out of his hold, staring at him with wounded pride.

'Did he?' Blake repeated, a faintly ragged edge to his breathing.

'You'll never know,' she answered in a choked voice. 'Maybe he made me feel better.'

He took a threatening step towards her, his features dark with rage. There was nowhere for Dina to retreat. She had to stand her ground, despite its indefensibility. Just then there was a knock at the door. Blake halted, casting an angry glance at the door.

'Who is it?' he demanded.

The door opened and Chet walked in. 'I'm a bit early, but Deirdre said you were in here having coffee. She's going to bring me a cup.' He stopped as if sensing the heaviness in the atmosphere. 'I didn't think you'd mind if I joined you.' But it was something of a question.

'Of course not.' Dina was quick to use him as a buffer.

'Come in Chet,' Blake continued the invitation. 'Speak of the devil, Dina and I were just talking about you.'

'Something good, I hope,' Chet joked stiffly.

'Yes.' Blake's dark gaze swung to Dina, a considering grimness in their depths. 'Yes, it was.' But he didn't explain what it had been.

She started breathing again, her hand sliding up to her throat. She became conscious of her partially clothed state and used it as an excuse to leave.

'If you two don't mind, I'll leave you to have coffee alone,' she said.

'I hope you aren't going on my account,' Chet frowned.

'No,' Dina assured him quickly, avoiding Blake's

mocking look. 'I was going upstairs anyway to dress before Deirdre served brunch. I'll be down shortly.'

As Dina left, she met Deirdre bringing the extra cup for Chet. The housekeeper's composure was under admirable control now and she was her usual calm-faced self.

Once she was dressed, Dina slipped Chet's ring into the pocket of her dirndl skirt. At some point during the day, she hoped to have the chance to return it to him while they were alone. But it was late afternoon before the opportunity presented itself.

The press had learned of Blake's return and the house was in a state of siege for the greater part of the day. Either the doorbell or the telephone seemed to be ringing constantly. Blake had to grant interviews to obtain any peace, but his answers were concise, without elaboration, downplaying his ordeal. As his wife, Dina was forced to be at his side, while Chet adopted the role of press secretary and spokesman for the Chandler company.

Finally, at four o'clock, the siege seemed to be over and a blessed quietness began to settle over the house. Norma Chandler, who had insisted that coffee and sweets be served to all those who had come, was busy helping Deirdre clear away the mess.

The ringing of the telephone signalled a last interview for Blake, one conducted over the phone. Dina had started helping the other two women clean up. When she noticed Chet slip away to the library, she excused herself, knowing she might not have another chance to speak to him alone.

As she stepped inside the library, she saw him pouring whisky from a crystal decanter over ice cubes in a squat glass. The engagement ring seemed to be burning a circle in her pocket.

'Would you pour me a sherry, Chet?' She quietly closed the door, shutting out Blake's voice coming from the living room.

Chet's sandy blond head lifted, his surprised look vanishing into a smile when he saw her. 'Of course.' He reached for another glass and a different decanter. Pouring, he remarked, 'It's been quite a hectic day.'

'Yes, it has.' Dina walked over to take the sherry glass from his hand.

Ice clinked as Chet lifted his glass to take a quick swallow of whisky. 'A reporter that I know from one of the local papers called and got me out of bed this morning. He'd gotten wind that there was a shake-up in the Chandler hotel chain and he wanted to know what it was. I pleaded ignorance. But that's why I rushed over here so early, to warn Blake that the onslaught was coming. I knew it was only a matter of time before they found out.'

'Yes,' she nodded in agreement, glad there had been no announcement of their engagement in the newspapers or they would have turned Blake's return into a circus.

'Blake really knows how to handle himself with the press,' Chet stated with undisguised admiration.

'Yes, he does.' Dina sipped at her drink.

'And it will make good publicity for the hotels,' he added.

'Yes.' She was beginning to feel like a puppet whose string was being pulled to nod agreement to everything Chet said when it really wasn't what she wanted to talk about at all.

'I imagine somebody in the company let it slip about Blake.' He stared thoughtfully at the amber brown liquid in his glass. 'I called around to all the major officers yesterday to let them know he was back. That's probably how the word got out.'

'Probably,' Dina agreed, and promptly took the initiative to lead into her own subject. 'Chet, I've been wanting to see you today, alone,' she reached in her pocket to take out the circlet of diamonds, 'to return this to you.'

He took it from her outstretched hand, looking boyishly uncomfortable. His thumb rubbed it between his fingers as he stared at it, not meeting the sapphire brightness of her gaze.

'I don't want you to get the idea that I was deserting you yesterday.' His voice was uncertain, almost apologetic. 'But I know how you felt about Blake and I didn't want to stand in the way of your happiness.'

With the explanation given for the way he had so readily abandoned their engagement, Chet lifted his head to gaze at her earnestly, a troubled shade of clouded blue in his eyes. Affection rushed through Dina at his unselfishness, sacrificing his wants for hers.

'I understand, Chet.'

Relief glimmered in his smile. 'You must really be glad to have him back.'

'I——' She started to repeat the positive assertion she had been making all day, ready to recite the words automatically, but she stopped herself. Among other things, Chet was her best friend as well as Blake's. With him, she could speak her mind. 'He's changed, Chet.'

He hesitated for a second before answering, as if her response had caught him off guard and he wanted to word his reply carefully.

'Considering all Blake has been through, it's bound to have left a mark on him,' he offered.

'I know, but——' she sighed, agitated and frustrated because she couldn't find the words to explain exactly what she meant.

'Hey, come on now,' Chet cajoled, setting his glass down and grasping her gently by the shoulders, his head bent down to peer into her apprehensive face. 'When two people care as much about each other as you and Blake do, they're bound to work out their differences. It just can't happen overnight,' he reasoned. 'Now come on. What do you say let's have a little smile? You know it's true that nothing is ever as bad as it seems.'

Mountains and molehills. Reluctantly almost, her lips curved at his coaxing words. His steadying influence was having its effect on her again.

'That's my girl!' he grinned.

'Oh, Chet,' Dina declared with a laughing sigh, and wrapped her arms lightly around him, taking care not to spill her drink. She hugged him fondly. 'What would I do without you?' She drew her head back to gaze at him.

'I hope neither of us has to find out,' he remarked, and affectionately kissed the tip of her nose.

The knob turned and the library door was pushed open by Blake. At the sight of Dina in Chet's arms, he froze and the same paralysis gripped her. She paled as she saw his lips thin into an angry line.

But the violence of his emotion wasn't detectable in his voice as he remarked casually, 'Is this a private party or can anyone join?'

His question broke the chains holding Dina motionless. She withdrew her arms from around Chet to hold her sherry glass in both hands. Chet turned to greet him, insensitive to the heightening tension in the air.

'Now that you're here, Blake, we can drink a toast to the last of the newspaper reporters,' he announced in a celebrating tone, not displaying any self-consciousness about the scene Blake had interrupted.

'For a while anyway,' Blake agreed, his gaze swinging to Dina. 'What are you drinking?'

'Sherry.' There would be no explosion now, Dina realised. Blake would wait until they were alone.

'I'll have the same.'

It was late that evening before Chet left. Each dragging minute in the interim honed Dina's nerves to a razor-thin edge. When he had left, she could no longer stand the suspense of the prolonged confrontation with Blake.

With the revving of Chet's car coming from the drive, Dina paused in the foyer to challenge Blake. 'Aren't you going to say it?'

He didn't pretend an ignorance of her question, his gaze hard and unrelenting. 'Stay away from Chet.'

All the blame for the innocent encounter was placed on her and she reacted with indignant outrage. 'And what about Chet?'

'I know Chet well enough to be assured he isn't going to trespass, unless encouraged, on my territory.'

'So I'm supposed to avoid him, is that it?' she flashed.

'Whatever relationship you had with him in my absence is finished,' Blake declared in a frigid tone. 'From now on, he's simply an acquaintance of mine. That's all he is to you.'

'That's impossible!' She derided his suggestion that she could dismiss Chet from her life with a snap of her fingers. 'I can't forget all he's meant to me that easily.'

A pair of iron clamps dug into the soft flesh of her arms and she was jerked to him, the breath knocked out of her by the hard contact with the solid wall of his chest. Her lips were crushed by the angry fire of his kiss, searing his brand of possession on her and burning away any memory of another's mouth.

Dina was released from his punishing embrace with equal force. Shaken and unnerved, she retreated a step. With the back of her hand, she tried to rub away the fiery imprint of his mouth.

'You——' she began with impotent rage.

'Don't push me, Dina!' Blake warned.

They glared at each other in thundering silence. Dina had no idea how long the battle of wills would have continued if his mother hadn't entered the foyer seconds later. Each donned a mask to conceal their personal conflict from her eyes.

'Deirdre just told me you'd asked her to bring some blankets to the library, Blake.' Norma Chandler was wearing a frown. 'You aren't going to sleep there again tonight, are you?'

'Yes, I am, Mother,' he responded decisively.

'But it's so uncivilised,' she protested.

'Perhaps,' Blake conceded, for an instant meeting Dina's look. 'It's also infinitely preferable to not sleeping.'

'I suppose so.' his mother sighed her reluctant agreement. 'Good night, dear.'

'Good night, Mother,' he returned, and coldly arched an eyebrow at Dina. 'Good night.'

CHAPTER FIVE

THE library door stood open when Dina came down the stairs the next morning. She smoothed a nervous hand over her cream linen skirt and walked to the dining room where breakfast coffee and juice were already on the table. But there was no sign of Blake. Dina helped herself to juice and coffee and sat down.

'Isn't Blake having breakfast this morning?' she questioned the housekeeper when she appeared.

'No, ma'am,' Deirdre replied. 'He's already left. He said he was meeting Jake Stone for breakfast and going to the office from there. Didn't he tell you?'

'Yes, I believe he did,' Dina lied, and forced a smile. 'I must have forgotten.'

'Mrs Chandler was most upset about it,' the woman remarked with a knowing nod.

Dina frowned. 'Because Blake is meeting the attorney?'

'No, because he's going into the office. Mrs Chandler thought he should wait a few days. I mean, he just came back and all, and right away he's going to work,' Deirdre explained.

'He's probably anxious to see how everything is.' There was a smug feeling of satisfaction that he would find the entire operation running smoothly and knowing that a great deal of the credit was hers.

'What will you have this morning, Mrs Blake? Shall I fix you an omelette?'

'I think I'll just have juice and coffee, Deirdre, thank you.' She wanted to be at the office when Blake arrived and to be able to see his face when he realised how capably she had managed in his absence.

'As you wish,' the housekeeper sniffed in disapproval.

The morning traffic seemed heavier than usual and Dina chafed at the delay it caused. Still she arrived at the office building well within her usual time. As she stepped out of the elevator on to the floor the company occupied, she was relieved that Chet had already notified the various executive personnel of Blake's return and that she was spared that task. She would have time to go over her notes on the departmental meeting this afternoon and have much of the Monday morning routine handled before Blake arrived.

She breezed down the corridor to her office, keeping her pace brisk while she nodded greetings and returned good mornings to the various employees along the way. She didn't want to stop and chat with anyone and use up her precious time. She felt very buoyant as she entered the office of her private secretary.

'Good morning, Amy,' she said cheerfully.

'Good morning, Mrs Chandler,' the young woman beamed back a smile. 'You're in good spirits this morning.'

'Yes, I am,' Dina agreed. Her secretary was going through the morning mail and she walked to her desk to see if there was anything of importance she should know about before Blake arrived.

'Your good spirits wouldn't have anything to do with Mr Chandler coming back, would it?' Amy Wentworth enquired with a knowing twinkle. Dina wasn't obliged to make a comment as her secretary continued. 'All of us here are so happy he's back safely.'

'So am I, Amy,' Dina nodded, and glanced over the girl's shoulder for a glimpse at the mail. 'Anything special in the mail this morning?'

'Not so far,' her secretary replied, returning her attention to the stack of letters.

'Any calls?'

'Only one. Mr Van Patten called.'

'Did he leave a message?' Dina questioned, her quick perusal of the mail completed.

'Oh, no,' Amy hastened to explain, 'Mr Chandler took the call.'

'Mr Chandler?' she repeated. 'Do you mean Blake is already here?'

'Yes, he's in the office.' Amy motioned towards Dina's private office. 'I'm sure he won't mind if you go right on in, Mrs Chandler.'

For several seconds, Dina was too stunned to

speak. It was *her* office, her pride protested. And *her* secretary was grandly giving her permission to enter it. Blake had moved in and managed to convey the impression that she had moved out.

Her blue eyes darkened in bitter rage. Turning on her heel, she walked to the private office. She didn't bother to knock, simply pushing the door open and walking in. Blake was seated behind the massive walnut desk—*her* desk! He glanced up when she entered. The arrogantly enquiring lift of his eyebrow lit the fuse of her temper.

'What are you doing here?' she demanded.

'I was about to ask you the same question,' countered Blake with infuriating calm.

'It happens to be *my* office and that's *my* secretary outside!' Dina retorted. Her flashing eyes saw the papers in his hands and she recognised the notes as those she had been going to go over for the departmental meeting this afternoon. 'And those are *my* notes!'

He leaned back in the swivel chair, viewing her tirade with little emotion. 'I was under the impression that all of this,' he waved his hand in an encompassing gesture, 'belonged to the company.'

'I happen to be in charge of the company,' she reminded him.

'You *were* in charge of the company,' Blake corrected. 'I'm taking over now.'

She was trembling violently now, her anger almost uncontrollable. She fought to keep her voice low and not reveal how thoroughly he had aroused her.

'You're taking over,' she repeated. 'Just like that!' She snapped her fingers.

'Your job is done,' Blake shrugged, and fingered the papers on the desk. 'And excellently, from all that I've seen this morning.'

It was the compliment she had sought, but not delivered the way she had intended it to be. Therefore it brought no satisfaction; the thunder was stolen from her glory.

'And what am I supposed to do?' she demanded.

'Go home. Go back to being my wife.' His sun-roughened features wore a frown, as if not understanding why she was so upset.

'And do what?' challenged Dina. 'Twiddle my thumbs all day until you come home? Deirdre does all the cooking and the cleaning. It's your mother's house, Blake. There's nothing for me to do there.'

'Then start looking for an apartment for us. Or better yet, a house of our own,' he suggested. 'That's what you wanted before, a place of our own that you could decorate the way you wanted it.'

A part of her wanted it still, but it wasn't the motivating force in her life. 'That was before, Blake,' she argued. 'I've changed. If we did have a house and the decorating was all done the way I wanted it, what would I do then? Sit around and admire my handiwork? No, I enjoy my work here. It's demanding and fulfilling.'

He was sitting in the chair, watching her with narrowed eyes. 'What you're saying is you enjoy the power that goes along with it.'

'I enjoy the power,' Dina admitted without hesitation, a hint of defiance in the tightness of her voice. 'I enjoy the challenge and the responsibility, too. Men don't have a monopoly on those feelings.'

'What are you suggesting, Dina? That we reverse our roles and I become the house-husband? That I find the house, do all the decorating, cleaning and entertaining?'

'No, I'm not suggesting that.' Confusion was tearing at her. She didn't know what the solution was.

'Perhaps you'd like me to take another flight to South America and this time not bother to come back?'

'No, I wouldn't—and stop twisting my words!'

Hot tears flooded her eyes, all the emotional turmoil inside her becoming too much to control. She turned sharply away, blinking frantically at the tears, trying to force them back before Blake saw them.

There was a warning squeak of the swivel chair as Blake rose and approached her. Her lungs were bursting, but she was afraid to take a breath for fear it would sound like a sob.

'Is this the way you handle a business disagreement?' he lashed out in impatient accusation.

Aware that he towered beside her, Dina kept her face averted so he wouldn't see the watery blue of her eyes. 'I don't know what you mean,' she lied.

His thumb and fingers clamped on her chin and twisted it around so he could see her face. 'Do you usually indulge in a female display of tears when you don't get your own way?'

The wall of tears was so solid that Dina could barely see his face. 'No,' she retorted, pushing at the hand that held her chin. 'Do you always attack on a personal level whenever someone doesn't agree with you wholeheartedly?'

She heard his long impatient sigh, then his fingers curved to the back of her neck, forcing her head against his chest. An arm encircled her to draw her close. His embrace was strong and warm, but Dina made herself remain indifferent to Blake's attempt to comfort her. She felt the pressure of his chin resting atop her head.

'Would you mind telling me what the hell I'm supposed to do about this?' Blake muttered.

She wiped at the tears with shaking fingers and sniffed, 'I don't know.'

'Here.' He reached inside his suit jacket to hand her his handkerchief. There was a light rap on the door and Blake stiffened. 'Who is it?' he snapped, but the door was already opening.

Self-consciously Dina tried to twist out of his arms, but they tightened around her as if closing ranks to protect her. She submitted to their hold, her back to the door.

'Sorry,' she heard Chet apologise with a trace of

chagrin. 'I guess I've gotten used to walking in un-
announced.'

He must have made a move to leave because
Blake said, 'It's all right. Come on in, Chet.' Un-
hurriedly he withdrew his arms from around Dina.
'You'll have to excuse Dina. She still gets emotional
once in a while about my return,' he explained
away her tears and the handkerchief she was using
to busily wipe away their traces.

'That's understandable,' said Chet. 'I came in to
let you know everyone's here. They're waiting in
the meeting room.'

His statement lifted Dina's head with a start.
'Meeting?' She picked up on the word and frowned.
'There isn't any meeting scheduled on my agenda
this morning.'

'I called it,' Blake announced smoothly, his bland
gaze meeting her sharp look. Then he shifted his attention to Chet in a dismissing fashion. 'Tell them
I'll be there in a few minutes.'

'I will.' And Chet left.

At the click of the closing door, Dina turned
roundly on Blake, her anger returning. 'You weren't
going to tell me about the meeting, were you?' she
accused.

Blake walked to the desk and began shuffling
through the papers on top of it. 'Initially, no. I
didn't see the need to tell you.'

'You didn't see the need?' Dina sputtered at his
arrogantly dismissive statement.

'To be truthful, Dina,' he turned to look at her, his bluntly chiselled features seeming to be carved out of teakwood, 'it didn't occur to me that you would come in to the office today.'

'Why ever not?' She stared at him in confusion and disbelief.

'I assumed you would be glad, if not grateful, to relinquish charge of the company to me. I thought you saw yourself as a stopgap president and would relish being free of the burdens of responsibility. I thought you would be happy to resume the role of a homemaker.'

'You obviously don't know me very well,' Dina retorted.

'So I'm beginning to discover,' Blake responded grimly.

'What now?' she challenged.

'No man likes to compete with his wife for a job, and I have no intention of doing so with you,' he stated.

'Why not?' Dina argued. 'If I'm equally competent——'

'But you're not,' Blake interrupted, his eyes turning into dark chips of ironstone.

'I am.' Surely she had proven that.

He ignored the assertion. 'In the first place, our age difference alone gives me fourteen more years of experience in the business than you. Secondly, my father put me to work as a bus boy when I was fifteen. Later I was a porter, a desk clerk, a cook, a manager. Compared to mine, your qualifications are negligible.'

His logic deflated her balloon of pride. He made her seem like a fool, a child protesting because a toy was taken away. Dina had learned how to disguise her feelings and she used the skill to her advantage.

'You're probably quite right,' she said stiffly. 'I'd forgotten how much of a figurehead I was. Chet did the actual running of the company.'

'Don't be ridiculous!' Blake dismissed the statement with a contemptuous jeer. 'Chet is incapable of making an important decision.'

Her eyes widened at the accusation. 'How can you say that? He's been so loyal to you all these years, your best friend.'

The lashing flick of his gaze laughed at her reference to Chet's loyalty, reminding her of Chet's engagement to her, but he made no mention of it when he spoke. 'Just because he's been my friend it doesn't mean I'm blind to his faults.'

Although puzzled, Dina didn't pursue the topic. It was dangerous ground, likely to turn the conversation to a more personal level. At the moment, she wanted to keep it on business.

'None of that really matters. It still all comes down to the same basic thing—I'm out and you're in.'

Blake raked a hand through his hair, rumpling it into attractive disorder. 'What am I supposed to do, Dina?' he demanded impatiently.

'That's up to you,' she shrugged, feigning cold indifference while every part of her rebelled at the emptiness entering her life. 'If you don't object to me borrowing *your* secretary, a letter formally tendering my resignation will be on *your* desk when you return from your meeting.'

'No, I don't object.' But Blake bristled at her cutting sarcasm. As she turned on her heel to leave, he covered the distance between them with long strides, grabbing at her elbow to spin her around. 'What do you expect me to do?' His eyes were a blaze of anger.

'I don't know——'

He cut across her words. 'Do you want me to offer you a position in the administration? Is that it?'

Excited hope leaped into her expression. After Blake had put it into words, she realised that that was exactly what she wanted—to still have a part in running the company, to be involved in its operation. 'Dammit, I can't do it, Dina!' Blake snapped.

Crushed, she demanded in a thin voice, 'Why?'

'I can't go around sweeping people out of office so you can take their place. Disregarding the fact that it smacks of nepotism, it implies that I don't approve of the people you hired to fill key positions. The logical deduction from that would be that I believed you'd done an inadequate job of running the company in my absence.' His expression was hard and grim. 'It's going to be several years before

I can make any changes without them reflecting badly on you.'

'That settles it, then, doesn't it?' Her chin quivered, belying the challenge in her voice.

His teeth were gritted, a muscle leaping along his jaw. 'If you weren't my wife——' he began, about to offer another explanation of why his hands were tied in this matter.

'That's easily remedied, Blake,' Dina flashed, and pulled her arm free before his grip could tighten. She didn't expect it to last long, but he made no attempt to recapture her.

'That's where you're wrong.' He clipped out the words with biting precision.

Inwardly quailing under his piercing look, Dina turned away rather than admit his power to intimidate. 'It's immaterial anyway,' she said with a small degree of composure. 'My resignation will be on your desk within an hour.' She walked to the door.

'Dina.' The stern command of his voice stopped her from leaving.

She didn't remove her hand from the doorknob nor turn to face him. 'What?'

'Maybe I can keep you on in an advisory capacity.' The stiffness of his words took away from the conciliatory gesture.

'I don't want any favours! And certainly not from the great Blake Chandler!' Dina flared, and yanked open the door.

It closed on a savage rush of expletives. When

Dina turned away from the door, she looked into the curious and widened gaze of the secretary, Amy Wentworth. Dina silently acknowledged that the walls of the private office were thick, but she doubted if they were thick enough to deaden the sound of voices raised in argument. She wondered how much of the after-effect of her quarrel with Blake was apparent in her face. She strained to appear composed and in command of herself as she walked to Amy's desk.

'Put aside whatever you're doing, Amy,' she ordered, trying to ignore the widening look she received.

'But——' The young secretary glanced hesitantly towards the inner office Dina had just left, as if uncertain whether she was to obey Dina or Blake.

Dina didn't give her a chance to put her thoughts into words. 'I want you to type a letter of resignation—for me. You know the standard form of these things. Just keep it simple and direct. Effective immediately.'

'Yes, Mrs Chandler,' Amy murmured, and immediately removed the dust cover from her electric typewriter.

The connecting office door was pulled open and Dina glanced over her shoulder to see Blake stride through. She could tell he had himself under rigid control, but it was like seeing a predatory animal under chained restraints. The minute the shackles were removed, he would pounce on his prey and tear it apart. And she was his prey.

Yet, even knowing she was being stalked, she was mesmerised by the dangerous look in his gaze. She waited motionless as he walked towards her, the force of his dark vitality vibrating over her nerve ends, making them tingle in sharp awareness.

'Dina, I——' Blake never got the rest of his sentence out.

Chet entered the room through the door to the outer corridor. 'Oh, I see you're on your way,' he concluded at the sight of Blake. 'I was just coming to see how much longer you'd be.' His gaze switched its attention to Dina and became a troubled blue at the white lines of stress in her face.

'Yes, I'm on my way,' Blake agreed crisply, and looked back at Dina. 'I want you to attend the meeting, Dina.' The veiled harshness in his gaze dared her to defy him.

But Dina felt safe in the company of others. 'No. It's better for everyone to realise that you're in charge now and not confuse them by having a former head of the company present.' She saw his mouth thin at her response and turned away in a gesture of dismissal.

'Dina has a good point,' Chet offered in agreement, but a darting look from Blake made him vacillate. 'Of course, unless you think it's wiser to——'

'Let's go,' Blake snapped.

In a silent storm, he swept from the room, draw-

ing Chet into his wake and leaving Dina feeling
drained and colourless. Her nerves seemed to be
delicate filaments, capable of snapping at the slightest pressure. When the letter of resignation was
typed, her hand trembled as she affixed her signa-
ture to it.

'Put it on Mr Chandler's desk,' she ordered, and
returned it to Amy.

'It was nice working for you, Mrs Chandler,' the
young secretary offered as Dina turned to go, the
words spoken in all sincerity.

'Thank you, Amy,' Dina smiled mistily, then hurried from the room.

Leaving the building, she walked to her car. She
knew there was no way she could return to the house
and listen to Mother Chandler's happy conversation
about Blake's return. With the top down on the
white sports car, she removed the scarf from her
hair and tucked it in the glove compartment.

With no destination in mind, she climbed into
the car and drove, the wind whipping at her hair,
glittering like liquid sunlight in the morning air.
Around and through the back streets, the main
streets, the side streets of the city of Newport she
went.

Half the time, she was too blinded by tears to
know where she was. She didn't notice the row of
palatial mansions on Bellevue Avenue nor the
crowds gathered on the wharf for the trials of the
America's Cup races.

She didn't know who she was, what she was or why she was. Since Blake's return, she was no longer *Dina* Chandler. She was once again Mrs *Blake* Chandler, lost in the potency of her husband's identity. She was no longer a businesswoman, nor did she feel like a housewife, since she had no home and a stranger for a husband. As to the reason why, she was in total confusion.

It was sheer luck that she glanced at the dashboard and noticed the gasoline gauge was hovering at the empty mark. Practicality forced her out of the bewildering whirlpool of questions. They stayed away until she was parked in a gas station and waiting in the building while her tank was being filled.

Then they returned with pounding force and Dina reeled under the power of them. Her restlessly searching gaze accidentally spied the telephone inside the building. She walked blindly to the phone and, from long habit, dialled the number of the one person who had already seen her through so much emotional turmoil.

The impersonal voice of an operator answered and Dina requested in an unsteady voice, 'Chet Stanton, please.'

'Who is calling, please?'

Dina hesitated a fraction of a second before answering, 'A friend.'

There was a moment when Dina thought the operator was going to demand a more specific answer than that, then she heard the call being put through. 'Chet Stanton speaking,' his familiar voice came on the line.

'Chet, this is Dina,' she rushed.

'Oh.' He sounded surprised and guarded. 'Hello.'

She guessed at the cause for the way he responded. 'Are you alone?'

'No.'

Which meant that Blake must be in his office. Dina wasn't certain how she knew it was Blake and not someone else, but she was positive of it.

'Chet, I have to talk to you. I have to see you,' she declared in a burst of despair. Glancing at her wristwatch, she didn't give him a chance to reply. 'Can you meet me for lunch?'

She heard the deep breath he took before he answered, 'I'm sorry, I'm afraid I've already made plans for lunch.'

'I have to see you,' she repeated. 'What about later?'

'It's been a long time since I've seen you.' Chet began to enter into the spirit of the thing, however uncertainly. 'Why don't we get together for a drink? Say, around five-thirty?'

It was so long to wait, she thought desperately, and realised it was the best he could offer. 'Very well,' she agreed, and named the first cocktail lounge that came to mind.

'I'll meet you there,' Chet promised.

'And, Chet,' Dina hesitated, 'please don't say anything to Blake about meeting me. I don't want him to know. He wouldn't understand.'

There was a long pause before he finally said, 'No, I won't. See you then.'

After hanging up the receiver, Dina turned and saw the gas station attendant eyeing her curiously, yet with a measure of concern. She opened the pocketbook slung over her shoulder and started to pay for the gasoline.

'Are you all right, miss?' he questioned.

She glimpsed her faded reflection in the large plate glass window of the station and understood his reason for asking. Her hair was windblown in riotous disorder. Tears had streaked the mascara from her lashes to make smutty lines around her eyes. She looked like a lost and wayward urchin despite the expensive clothes she wore.

'I'm fine,' she lied.

In the car, she took a tissue from her bag and wiped the dark smudges from beneath her eyes. A brush put her tangled mass of silky gold hair into a semblance of order before it was covered by the scarf she had discarded.

'You have to get hold of yourself,' she scolded her reflection in the rear view mirror.

Turning the key in the ignition, she started the powerful motor of the little car and drove away, wondering what she was going to do with herself for the rest of the day.

CHAPTER SIX

TYPICALLY, the lounge was dimly lit. Overhead lighting was practically non-existent and the miniature mock lanterns with their small candle flames flickering inside the glass chimneys provided little more. The dark wood panelling of the walls offered no relief, nor did the heavily-beamed, low ceiling.

Tucked away in an obscure corner of the lounge, the table where Dina sat gave her a total view of the room and the entrance door. A drink was in front of her, untouched, the ice melting. Five more minutes, her watch indicated, but it already seemed an interminable wait.

An hour earlier she had phoned Mother Chandler to tell her she would be late without explaining why or where she was. Blake would be angry, she realised. 'Let him,' was her inward response. The consequences of her meeting with Chet she would think about later.

Brilliant sunlight flashed into the room as the door was opened. Dina glanced up, holding her breath that this time it might be Chet. But the tall figure that entered the lounge paralysed her lungs. Her heart stopped beating, then skyrocketed in alarm.

Just inside the lounge, Blake paused, letting his eyes adjust to the gloom. There was nowhere Dina could run without drawing his attention. She tried to make herself small, hoping he wouldn't see her in this dim corner of the room. Dina felt rather than saw his gaze fasten on her seconds before his purposeful strides carried him to her table.

When he stopped beside her, Dina couldn't look up. Her teeth were so tightly clenched they hurt. She curled her hands around the drink she hadn't touched since it had been set before her. Despite the simmering resentment she felt, there was a sense of inevitability, too. Blake didn't speak, waiting for Dina to acknowledge him first.

'Imagine meeting you here,' she offered in a bitter tone of mock surprise, not letting her gaze lift from the glass cupped in her hands. 'Small world, isn't it?'

'It's quite a coincidence,' he agreed.

There was a bright glitter in her blue eyes when she finally looked at him. His craggy features were in the shadows, making his expression impossible to see. The disturbing male vitality of his presence began to make itself felt despite her attempt to ignore it.

'How did you know I was here?' she demanded, knowing there was only one answer he could give.

And Blake gave it. 'Chet told me.'

'Why?' The broken word came out unknowingly,

directed at the absent friend who had betrayed her trust.

'Because I asked him.'

'He promised he wouldn't tell you!' Her voice was choked, overcome by the discovery that she was lost and completely alone in her confusion.

'So I gathered,' Blake offered dryly.

Dina averted her gaze to breathe shakily, 'Why did he have to tell you?'

'I am your husband, Dina, despite the way you try to forget it. That gives me the right to at least know where you are.'

His voice was as smooth as polished steel, outwardly calm and firm. Her gaze noticed his large hands clenched into fists at his side, revealing the control he was exercising over his anger. He was filled with a white rage that his wife should arrange to meet another man. Dina was frightened, but it was fear that prompted the bravado to challenge him.

'You were in Chet's office when I called, weren't you?' she accused.

'Yes, and I could tell by the guilty look on his face that he was talking to you. After that, it didn't take much to find out what was going on.'

'Who did you think I would turn to? I needed him.' Dina changed it to present tense. 'I need Chet.'

Like the sudden uncoiling of a spring, Blake leaned down, spreading his hands across the table top, arms rigid. In the flickering candlelight, his features resembled a carved teakwood mask of some pagan god, harsh and ruthless and dangerously compelling.

'When are you going to get it through that blind little brain of yours that you've never needed him?' he demanded.

Her heart was pounding out a message of fear. 'I don't know you,' she breathed in panic. 'You're a stranger. You frighten me, Blake.'

'That makes two of us, because I'm scared as hell of myself!' He straightened abruptly, issuing an impatient, 'Let's get out of here before I do something I'll regret.'

Throwing caution away, Dina protested, 'I don't want to go anywhere with you.'

'I'm aware of that!' His hand clamped a hold on her arm to haul her to her feet, overpowering her weak resistance. Once upright, his fingers remained clamped around her arm to keep her pressed to his side. 'Is the drink paid for?' Blake reminded her of the untouched contents in the glass on the table

As always when she came in physical contact with him, she seemed to lose the ability for coherent thought. His muscled length was like living steel and the softness of her shape had to yield. Everything was suddenly reduced to an elemental level. Not until Blake had put the question to her a second time did Dina take in what he had asked.

She managed a trembling, 'No, it isn't.'

Releasing her, Blake took a money clip from his pocket and peeled off a bill, tossing it on the table. Then the steel band of his arm circled her waist to guide her out of the lounge, oblivious to the curious stares.

In towering silence, he walked her to the white Porsche, its top still down. He opened the door and pushed her behind the wheel, then slamming the door shut, he leaned on the frame, an unrelenting grimness to his mouth.

'My car is going to be glued to your bumper, following you every inch of the way. So don't take any detours on the route home, Dina,' he warned.

Before Dina could make any kind of retort, he walked to his car parked in the next row of the lot. Starting the car, she gunned the motor as if she was accelerating for a race, a puny gesture of impotent defiance.

True to his word, his car was a large shadow behind hers every block of the way, an ominous presence she couldn't shake even if she had tried, which she didn't. Stopping in the driveway of his mother's house, their house, Dina hurried from her car, anxious to get inside where the other inhabitants could offer her a degree of safety from him.

Halfway to the door, Blake caught up with her, a hand firmly clasping her elbow to slow her down. 'This little episode isn't over yet,' he stated in a low undertone. 'We'll talk about it later.'

Dina swallowed the impulse to challenge him. It

was better to keep silent with safety so near. Together they entered the house, both concealing the state of war between them.

Mother Chandler appeared in the living room doorway, wearing an attractive black chiffon dress. Her elegantly coiffed silver hair was freshly styled, thanks to an afternoon's appointment at her favourite salon. She smiled brightly at the pair of them, unaware of the tension crackling between them.

'You're both home—how wonderful!' she exclaimed, assuming her cultured tone. 'I was about to suggest to Deirdre that perhaps she should delay dinner for an hour. I'm so glad it won't be necessary. I know how much you detest overcooked meat, Blake.'

'You always did like your beef very rare, didn't you, Blake?' Dina followed up on the comment, her gaze glittering with diamond sharpness to his face. 'I always considered your desire for raw flesh as a barbaric tendency.'

'It seems you were right, doesn't it?' he countered.

Mother Chandler seemed impervious to the barbed exchange as she waved them imperiously into the living room. 'Come along. Let's have a sherry and you can tell me about your first day back at the office, Blake.' She rattled on, covering their tight-lipped silence.

It was an ordeal getting through dinner and making the necessary small talk to hide that there was anything wrong. It was even worse after dinner when the three of them sat around with their coffee in the living room. Each tick of the clock was like the swing of a pendulum, bringing the moment nearer when Blake's threatened discussion would take place.

The telephone rang and the housekeeper answered it in the other room. She appeared in the living room seconds later to announce, 'It's for you, Mr Blake. A Mr Carl Landstrom.'

'I'll take it in the library, Deirdre,' he responded.

Dina waited several seconds after the library door had closed before turning to Mother Chandler. 'It's a business call.' Carl Landstrom was head of the accounting department and Dina knew that his innate courtesy would not make him call after office hours unless it was something important. 'Blake is probably going to be on the phone for a while,' she explained, a fact she was going to use to make her escape and avoid his private talk. 'Would you explain to him that I'm very tired and have gone on to bed?'

'Of course, dear.' The older woman smiled, then sighed with rich contentment. 'It's good to have him back, isn't it?'

It was a rhetorical question that didn't require a reply, and Dina didn't offer one as she bent to kiss the relatively smooth cheek of her mother-in-law. 'Goodnight, Mother Chandler.'

'Goodnight.'

Upstairs, Dina undressed and took a quick shower. Towelling herself dry, she wrapped the terrycloth robe around her and removed the shower cap from her head, shaking her hair loose. She wanted to be in bed with the lights off before Blake was off the telephone. With luck he wouldn't bother to disturb her. She knew she was merely postponing the discussion, but for the moment that was enough.

Her nightgown was lying neatly at the foot of the bed as she entered the bedroom that adjoined the private bath, her hairbrush in hand. A few brisk strokes to unsnarl the curling dampness at the ends of her hair was all that she needed to do for the night, she decided, and sat on the edge of the bed to do it.

The mattress didn't give beneath her weight. It seemed as solid as the seat of a wooden chair. Dina was motionless as she assembled the knowledge and realised the new mattress and box springs she had ordered for Blake had arrived and hers had been removed.

She sprang from the bed as if discovering a bed of hot coals beneath it. No, her heart cried, she couldn't sleep with him, not after that last humiliating experience, not with his anger simmering so close to the surface because of today.

The door opened and Blake walked in, and the one thing in the forefront of her mind burst out in panic. 'I'm not going to sleep with you!' she cried.

A brow flicked upwards. 'At the moment, sleep is

the furthest thing from my mind.'

'Why are you here?' She was too numbed to think beyond the previous moment.

'To finish our discussion.' Blake walked to the chair against the wall and motioned towards the matching one. 'Sit down.'

'No,' Dina refused, too agitated to stay in one place even though he sat down with seemingly re-laxed composure while she paced restlessly.

'I want to know why you were meeting Chet.' His hooded gaze watched her intently, like an animal watching its trapped prey expend its nervous energy before moving in for the kill.

'It was perfectly innocent,' she began in self-defence, then abruptly changed her tactics. 'It's really none of your business.'

'If it was as perfectly innocent as you claim,' Blake said, deliberately using her words, 'then there's no reason not to tell me.'

'What you can't seem to understand, or refuse to understand, is that I need Chet,' she flashed. 'I need his comfort and understanding, his gentleness. I cer-tainly don't receive that from you!'

'If you'd open your eyes once, you'd see you're not receiving it from him either,' Blake retorted.

'Don't I?' Her sarcastic response was riddled with disbelief.

'Chet doesn't comfort. He merely mouths the words you want to hear. He's incapable of original thought.'

'I should hate to have you for a friend, Blake,' she declared tightly, 'if this is the way you regard them when they aren't around, cutting them into little pieces.'

'I've known Chet a great deal longer than you have. He can't survive unless he's basking in the reflected glory of someone else. When I disappeared, he transferred his allegiance to you, because you represented strength. He's a parasite, Dina, for all his charm,' Blake continued his cold dissection. 'He never comforted you or gave you strength. He lived on your strength. He persuaded you to take charge of the company because he knew he was incapable of leading a child, let alone a major corporation.'

'You don't know what you're saying,' Dina breathed, walking away from his harsh explanation.

'The next time you're with him, take a good look at him, Dina,' he ordered. 'And I hope you have the perception to see that you've been supporting him through all this, not the other way around.'

'No!' She shook her head in vigorous denial.

'I should have stayed away for a couple more months. Maybe by then, the rose-coloured spectacles would have come off and you would have found out how heavily he leans on you.'

Pausing in her restless pacing, Dina pressed her hands over her ears to shut out his hateful words. 'How can you say those things about Chet and still call him your friend?'

'I know his flaws. He's my friend in spite of them,'

Blake responded evenly. 'Yet you were going to marry him without acknowledging that he had any.'

'Yes. Yes, I was going to marry him!' Dina cried, pulling her hands away from her ears and turning to confront him.

'Only when I came back, he dropped you so fast it made your head swim. Admit it.' Blake sat unmoving in the chair.

'He wanted me to be happy,' she defended.

'No,' he denied. 'My return meant you were on the way out of power and I was in. Chet was securing his position. There was nothing chivalrous in his reason for breaking the engagement. He wasn't sacrificing anything, only insuring it.'

'So why did you hound him into admitting he was meeting me today?' challenged Dina.

'I didn't hound him. He was almost relieved to tell me.'

'You have an answer for everything, don't you?' She refused to admit that anything Blake was saying made any sense. She fought to keep that feeling of antagonism; without it, she was defenceless against him. 'It's been like this ever since you came back,' she uttered the thought aloud.

'I knew when everyone discovered I was alive, it was going to be a shock, but I thought it would be a pleasant shock,' Blake sighed with wry humour. 'In your case, I was wrong. It was a plain shock and you haven't recovered from it yet.'

Dina heard the underlying bitterness in his tone

and felt guilt. She tried to explain. 'How did you think I would feel? I'd become my own person. Suddenly you were back and trying to absorb me again in your personality, swallow me up whole.'

'How did you think I would react when you've challenged me every minute since I've returned?' His retaliation was instant, his temper ignited by her defensive anger, but he immediately brought it under control. 'It seems we've stumbled on to the heart of our problem. Let's see if we can't have a civilised discussion and work it out.'

'Civilised!' Dina laughed bitterly. 'You don't know the meaning of the word. You spent too much time in the jungle. You aren't even civilised about the way you make love!'

Black fires blazed in his eyes. The muscles along his jaw went white from his effort to keep control. 'And you go for the jugular vein every time!' he snarled, straightening from the chair in one fluid move.

Dina's heart leapt into her throat. She'd aroused a beast she couldn't control. She took a step backward, then turned and darted for the door. But Blake intercepted her, spinning her around, his arms circling her, crushing her to his length.

His touch sizzled through her like an electric shock, immobilising her. She offered not an ounce of resistance as his mouth covered hers in a long, punishing kiss. She seemed without life or breath, except what he gave her in anger.

Anger needs fuel to keep it burning, and Dina gave him none. Gradually the brutal pressure eased and his head lifted a fraction of an inch. She opened her eyes and gazed breathlessly into the brilliant darkness of his. The warm moistness of his breath was caressing her parted lips.

His hand stroked the spun gold of her hair, brushing it away from her cheek. 'Why do you always bring out the worst in me?' he questioned huskily.

'Because I won't let you dominate me the way you do everyone else,' Dina whispered. She could feel the involuntary trembling of his muscled body and the beginnings of the same passionate tremors in her own.

'Does it give you a feeling of power,' he kissed her cheek, 'to know that,' his mouth teased the curling tips of her lashes, 'you can make me lose control?' He returned to tantalise the curving outline of her lips. 'You are the only one who could ever make me forget reason.'

'Am I?' Dina breathed sceptically, because he seemed in complete control at the moment and she was the one losing her grip.

'I had a lot of time to think while I was trying to fight my way out of that tropical hell. I kept remembering all our violent quarrels that got started over the damnedest things. I kept telling myself that if I ever made it back, they were going to be a thing of the past. Yet within hours after I saw you, we were at each other's throats.'

'I know,' she nodded.

As if believing her movement was an attempt to escape his lips, Blake captured her chin to hold her head still. With languorous slowness, his mouth took possession of hers. The kiss was like a slow-burning flame that kept growing hotter and hotter.

Its heat melted Dina against his length, so hard and muscular and very male. Her throbbing pulse sounded loudly in her ears as the flames coursed through her body.

Before she succumbed completely to the weakness of her physical desire, she twisted away from his mouth. She knew what he wanted, and what she wanted, but she had to deny it.

'It won't work, Blake.' Her throat worked convulsively, hating the words even as she said them. 'Not after the last time.'

'The last time . . .' He pursued her lips, his mouth hovering a feather's width from them, and she trembled weakly, lacking the strength to turn away. 'I hated you for becoming engaged to Chet, even believing I was dead. And I hated myself for not having the control to stop when you asked me not to make love to you. This time it's different.'

'It's no good.' But the hands that had slipped inside her robe and were caressing her skin with such arousing thoroughness felt very good.

For an instant, Dina didn't think Blake was going to pay any attention to her protest and she wasn't sure that she wanted him to take note of it. Then she felt the tensing of his muscles as he slowly became motionless.

He continued to hold her in his arms as if considering whether to concede to her wishes or to overpower her resistance, something he could easily accomplish in her present, half-willing state.

A split second later, he was setting her away from him, as if removing himself from temptation. 'If that's what you want, I'll wait,' he conceded grimly.

'I——' In a way, it wasn't what she wanted and Dina almost said so, but checked herself. 'I need time.'

'You've got it,' Blake agreed, his control superb, an impenetrable mask concealing his emotions. 'Only don't make me wait too long before you come to a decision.'

'I won't.' Dina wasn't even certain what decision there was to make. What were her choices?

His raking look made her aware of the towelling robe hanging loosely open, exposing the cleavage of her breasts. She drew the folds together to conceal the naked form Blake knew so well. He turned away, running his fingers through the wayward thickness of his dark hair.

'Go to bed, Dina,' he said with a hint of weariness. 'I have some calls to make.'

Her gaze swung to the bed and the quilted spread that concealed the rock-hard mattress. 'The new box springs and mattress that I had Deirdre order for you came today, and she put it in here. I'll ...

I'll sleep in the guest room.'

'No.' Blake slashed her a look over his shoulder. 'You will sleep with me, if you do nothing else.'

Dina didn't make the obvious protest regarding the intimacy of such an arrangement nor its frustrations, but offered instead, 'That bed is like lying on granite.'

There was a wryly mocking twist of his mouth. 'To use an old cliché, Dina, you've made your bed, now you have to lie in it.'

'I won't,' she declared with a stubborn tilt of her chin.

'Am I asking too much to want my wife to sleep beside me?' He gave her a long, level look that Dina couldn't hold.

Averting her head, she closed her eyes to murmur a soft, 'No, it isn't too much.'

The next sound she heard was the opening of the door. She turned as Blake left the room. She stared at the closed door that shut her inside, wondering if she hadn't made a mistake by giving in to his request.

Walking over to the bed, she pressed a hand on the quilt to test its firmness. Under her full weight, it gave barely an inch. It was going to be quite a difference from the soft mattress she usually slept on, but then her bed partner was a completely different man from the urbane man she had married. Dina wondered which she would get used to first—the hard bed or the hard man?

Nightgowned, with the robe lying at the foot of the bed, she crawled beneath the covers. The unyielding mattress wouldn't mould to her shape, so she had to attempt to adjust her curves to it, without much success. Sleep naturally became elusive as she kept shifting positions on the hard surface trying to find one that was comfortable.

Almost two hours later she was still awake, but she closed her eyes to feign sleep when she heard Blake open the door. It was difficult to regulate her breathing as she listened to his quiet preparations. Keeping to the far side of the bed, she stayed motionless when he climbed in to lie beside her, not touching but close enough for her to feel his body heat.

Blake shifted a few times, then settled into one position. Within a few minutes, she heard him breathing deeply in sleep. Sighing, she guessed she was still hours away from it.

CHAPTER SEVEN

A HAND was making rubbing strokes along her upper arm, pleasantly soothing caresses. Then fingers tightened to shake her gently.

'Come on, Dina, wake up!' a voice ordered.

'Mmm.' The negative sound vibrated from her throat as she snuggled deeper into her pillow.

Only it wasn't a pillow. There was a steady thud beneath her head and the pillow that wasn't a pillow moved up and down in a regular rhythm. No, it wasn't a pillow. She was nestled in the crook of Blake's arm, her head resting on his chest. She could feel the curling sun-bleached hairs on his chest tickling her cheek and nose.

Some time in the night, she had forsaken the hardness of the mattress to cuddle up to the warm hardness of his length. Her eyelids snapped open at the familiarity sleep had induced. Dina would have moved away from him, but the arm around her tightened to hold her there for another few seconds.

A calloused finger tipped her chin upward, forcing her to look at him, and her heart skipped a beat at the lazy warmth in the craggy male face.

'I'd forgotten what it was like to sleep with an octopus,' Blake murmured. 'Arms and legs all over the place!'

Crimsoning, Dina rolled out of his arms, an action he didn't attempt to prevent. The movement immediately caused a wince of pain. Every bone and fibre in her body was an aching reminder of the night she had spent in the rock-hard bed.

'How can you stand to sleep in this bed?' she groaned. 'It's awful!'

'You'll get used to it.' When Blake spoke, Dina realised he had slid out of bed with barely a sound while she had been discovering her aches and pains. Her gaze swung to him as he stepped into the bottoms of his silk pyjamas and pulled them on. Feeling her eyes watching him, Blake glanced around. There was a laughing glint in his dark eyes as he said, 'It's a concession to Deirdre this morning and her Victorian modesty.'

Dina smiled. Even that hurt. 'What time is it?'

'Seven,' he answered somewhat absently, and rubbed the stubble of beard on his chin.

'That late?'

Her pains deserted her for an instant and she started to rise, intent only on the thought that she would be late getting to the office unless she hurried. Then she remembered she no longer had any reason to go to the office and sank back to the mattress, tiredness and irritation sweeping over her.

'Why did you wake me up?' she demanded crossly. 'It took me long enough to get to sleep. Why didn't you just let me keep right on sleeping?'

'You'd be late to work,' was Blake's even response.

'Have you forgotten?' Bitterness coated her tongue. 'I've been replaced. I'm a lady of leisure now.'

'Are you?' He gave her a bland look. 'Your boss doesn't think so.'

'What boss? You?' Dina breathed out with a scornful laugh. 'You're only my husband.'

'Does that mean you're turning it down?'

'What? Will you quit talking in riddles?'

'Maybe if you hadn't been so proud and stubborn yesterday morning and attended the meeting like I asked you to, you'd know what I'm talking about.'

She pressed a hand against her forehead, tension and sleeplessness pounding between her eyes. 'I didn't attend the meeting, so perhaps you could explain.'

'We're starting a whole new advertising campaign to upgrade the image of the Chandler Hotel chain,' he explained. 'We can't possibly compete with the bigger chains on a nationwide basis, especially when the bulk of our locations are in resort areas, not necessarily heavily populated ones. We're going to use that fact to our advantage. From now on, when people think of resort hotels, it's going to be synonymous with Chandler Hotels.'

'It's a sound idea,' Dina conceded. 'But what does that have to do with me?'

'You're going to be in charge of the campaign.'

'What?' Blake's calm announcement brought her upright, wary disbelief and scepticism in the look she gave him. 'Is this some kind of a cruel joke?'

There was an arrogant arch to one dark eyebrow. 'Hardly.' He walked around the bed to where she stood. 'I put the proposal to the rest of the staff yesterday, along with the recommendation that you handle it.'

'Is this a token gesture? Something for me to do to keep me quiet?' She couldn't accept that there wasn't an ulterior motive behind the offer. It might mean admitting something else.

'I admit that my picking you as my choice to head the campaign was influenced by the tantrum you threw in the office yesterday morning when you discovered I was taking over.' His gaze was steady, not yielding an inch in guilt. 'But you can be sure, Dina, that I wouldn't have suggested your name to the others if I didn't believe you could handle the job. You can put whatever interpretation you like on that.'

Dina believed him. His candour was too forthright to be doubted, especially when he acknowledged the argument they had had earlier. It surprised her that he had relented to this extent, putting her in charge of something that could ultimately be so important to the company. True, she would be working *for* him, but she would be making decisions on her own, too.

'Why didn't you tell me about this last night?' she frowned. 'Your decision had already been made. You just said a moment ago that you told the staff yesterday. Why did you wait until now to tell me?'

Blake studied her thoughtfully. 'I was going to tell you last night after we'd had our talk, but circumstances altered my decision and I decided to wait.'

'What circumstances?' Dina persisted, not following his reasoning.

'To be perfectly honest, I thought if you knew about it last night you might have been prompted to make love to me out of gratitude,' Blake replied without a flicker of emotion appearing on his impassive expression.

There was an explosion of red before her eyes. 'You thought I'd be so grateful that I'd——' Anger robbed her of her speech.

'It was a possibility.'

Dina was so blind with indignant rage that she couldn't see straight, but it didn't affect her aim as her opened palm connected with the hard contour of his cheek. As the white mark turned scarlet, Blake walked into the bathroom. Trembling with the violence of her aroused temper, Dina watched him go.

When her anger dissipated, she was left with a niggling question. Would she have been persuaded to surrender to him if she had known about the job last night? Hindsight could not provide the answer.

At the breakfast table, their conversation was frigidly civil.

'Please pass the juice.'

'May I have the marmalade?'

That fragile mood of shy affection they had woken up to that morning was gone, broken by the doubting of each other's motives.

When both had finished breakfast, Blake set his cup down. 'You may ride to the office with me this morning,' he announced.

'I would prefer to take my own car.'

'It's impractical for both of us to drive.'

'If you had to work late, I would be without a way home,' Dina protested.

'*If* that should arise, you may have the car and *I'll* take a taxi home,' he stated, his demeanour cold and arrogant.

Dina was infuriatingly aware that Blake would have an argument for every excuse she could offer. 'Very well, I'll ride with you,' she gave in with ill grace.

The morning crush of Newport traffic seemed heavier than normal, the distance to the office further, the time passing slower, and the polar atmosphere between them colder than ever.

Feeling like a puppy dog on a leash, Dina followed Blake from the parking lot to his office. There she sat down, adopting a business air to listen to specific suggestions that had been offered by Blake and the staff for the campaign. It was a far-reaching plan, extending to redecorating some hotels to meet with their new resort image.

At that one, Dina couldn't help commenting caustically, 'I'm surprised I'm not limited to that task. Decorating is woman's work, isn't it?'

The thrust of his frigid gaze pierced her like a cold knife. 'Do you want to discuss this programme intelligently? Or do you want to bring our personal difficulties into it? Because if you do, I'll find someone else for the job.'

Her pride wanted to tell him to find that person, but common sense insisted she would ultimately be the loser if she did. The project promised to be a challenge, and Dina had come to enjoy that. Her pride was a bitter thing to swallow, but she managed to get it down.

'Sorry. That remark just slipped out,' she shrugged. 'Go on.'

There was a second's pause as Blake weighed her words before continuing. When he had concluded, he gave her a copy of the notes from the staff meeting and a tentative budget.

Dina glanced over them, then asked, 'Where am I to work?'

'I'll take you to your new office.'

She followed him out of the office and walked beside him down the long corridor until they came to the end. Blake opened the last door.

'Here it is.'

The metal desk, chair and shelves seemed to fill up the room. Three offices this size could have fit into Blake's office, Dina realised. And that wasn't all. It was cut off from the other staff offices, at the end of the hall, isolated. She could die in there and nobody would know, she thought to herself.

Blake saw the fire smouldering in her blue eyes. 'This is the only office that was available on such short notice,' he explained.

'Is it?' she retorted grimly.

'Yes,' he clipped out the word, challengingly, 'unless you think I should have moved one of the executive staff out of his office to make room for you.'

Dina knew that would have been illogical and chaotic with records being shifted and their exact location possibly unknown for several days. Still she resented the size and location of her new office, regardless of how much she accepted the practicality of its choice. But she didn't complain. She didn't have to, since Blake knew how she felt.

She looked at the bare desk top and said, 'There's no telephone?'

'Arrangements have already been made to have one installed today.'

'Fine.' She walked briskly into the room, aware of Blake still standing in the doorway.

'If you have any questions——' he began in a cool tone.

Dina interrupted, 'I doubt if I will.' The banked fires of her anger glittered in the clear blue of her eyes.

His gaze narrowed, his expression hardening. 'You can be replaced, Dina.'

'Permanently?' she drawled in a taunting kitten-purr voice.

For an instant, she thought he might do away with her violently, but instead, he exhibited that iron control and pivoted to walk away. There was a tearing in her heart as he left. Dina wondered if she was deliberately antagonising him or merely reacting to his attempted domination of her.

Pushing the unanswerable question aside, she set to work, taking an inventory of the supplies on hand versus what she would need. After obtaining the missing items from the supply room, she began making a list of information she would require before drawing a plan of action for the advertising campaign.

At the sound of footsteps approaching the end of the hallway, she glanced up from her growing list. She had left the door to her office open to lessen the claustrophobic sensation, and she watched the opening, curious as to who would be coming and for what reason.

Chet appeared, pausing in the doorway, a twinkle in his grey-blue eyes, an arm behind his back. 'Hello there,' he smiled.

'Are you lost or slumming?' Dina questioned with a wry curve to her lips.

He chuckled and admitted, 'I was beginning to think I was going to have to stop and ask directions before I found you.'

'It's certain I'm not going to be bothered with

people stopping by to chat on their way someplace else. This is the end of the line,' she declared with a rueful glance around the tiny office. 'Which brings me to the next obvious question.'

'What am I doing here?' Chet asked it for her. 'When I heard you were exiled to the far reaches of the office building, I decided you might like a cup of hot coffee.' The arm that had been behind his back moved to the front to reveal the two styrofoam cups of coffee he was juggling in one hand. 'At least, I hope it's hot. After that long walk, it might be cold.'

'Hot or lukewarm, it sounds terrific.' Dina straightened away from the desk to relax against the rigid back of her straight chair. 'I shall love you forever for thinking of it.'

She had tossed out the remark without considering what she was saying, but she was reminded of it as a discomfited look flashed across Chet's face.

'I guess that brings me to the second reason why I'm here.' He lowered his head as he walked into the room, not quite able to meet her gaze.

'You mean about not meeting me yesterday and sending Blake in your place,' Dina guessed, accurately as it turned out.

'Yes, well,' Chet set the two cups on the desk top, 'I'm sorry about that. I know you didn't want me to tell Blake and I wouldn't have either, except that he was in my office when you called and he guessed who I was talking to.'

'So he said,' she murmured, not really wanting to

talk about it in view of the discussion she had with Blake last night regarding Chet.

'Blake didn't lay down the law and forbid me to go or anything like that, Dina.'

'He didn't?' she breathed sceptically.

'No. He asked if you sounded upset,' Chet explained. 'When I said that you did, he admitted that the two of you were having a few differences, and he thought it was best that I didn't become involved in it. He didn't want me to be put in the position of having to take sides when both of you are my friends.'

Friends? Dina thought. Just a few days ago, Chet had been her fiancé, not her friend. But he looked so pathetically sorry for having let her down yesterday that she simply couldn't heap more guilt on his bowed head.

Instead she gave him the easy way out. 'Blake was right, it isn't fair to put you in the middle of our disagreements. If I hadn't been so upset I would have realised it. Anyway, it doesn't matter now,' she shrugged. 'It all worked out for the best.' That was a white lie, since it almost had, until their blow-up this morning.

'I knew it would.' The smile he gave her was tinged with relief. 'Although I wasn't surprised to hear Blake admit that the two of you had gotten off to a rocky start.' He removed the plastic lid from the styrofoam cup and handed the cup to her.

'Why do you say that?' she asked.

'The two of you were always testing each other to see which was the stronger. It looks like you still are.'

'Which one of us is the stronger? In your opinion,' Dina qualified her question.

'Oh, I don't know.' His laughter was accompanied by a dubious shake of his head. 'A feeling of loyalty to my own sex makes me want to say Blake, but I have a hunch I would be underestimating you.'

In other words, Dina realised, Chet was not taking sides. He was going to wait until there was a clearcut winner. In the meantime, he was keeping his options open, buttering up to both of them.

The minute the last thought occurred to her Dina knew it had been influenced by Blake's comment that Chet was always beside the one in power, but she immediately squashed the thought as small and not deserving of someone as loyal as Chet.

'You're a born diplomat, Chet.' She lifted the coffee cup in a toast. 'No wonder you're such an asset to this company.'

'I try to be,' he admitted modestly, and touched the styrofoam side of his cup to hers. 'Here's to the new campaign.'

The coffee was only medium hot and Dina took a big sip of it. Chet's reference to the new project made her glance at the papers, notes and lists spread over her desk.

'It's going to be quite a formidable project.' She took a deep breath, aware of the magnitude of the image change for the Chandler Hotel chain. 'But I can feel it's right and that it will be very successful.'

'That's the third reason I'm here.'

Her startled gaze flew to his face, her blue eyes rounded and bright with question. 'Why?'

Had she made Blake so angry that he was already taking her off the campaign? Oh, why hadn't she held her tongue? she thought, angered by the way she had kept pushing him.

'Blake wants me to work with you on it,' Chet announced.

Her relief that Blake hadn't replaced her didn't last long. 'Doesn't he think I'm capable of handling it by myself?' Her temper flared at the implied doubt of her ability.

'You wouldn't be here if he didn't believe you could,' he placated. 'But after all, you said it yourself. It's going to be a formidable project and you're going to need some help. I've been nominated to be your help. Besides, Blake knows how well we worked together as a team while he was gone.'

Dina counted to ten, forcing herself to see the logic of Chet's explanation. But she wasn't sure that she liked the idea. There was still the possibility that Blake had appointed Chet as her watchdog and he would go running to Blake the instant she made a miscue.

She was doing it again, she realised with a desperate kind of anger. She was not only questioning Blake's motives, but making accusations against

Chet's character as well. Damn Blake, she thought, for putting doubts about Chet in her mind.

Chet took a long swig of his coffee, then set it aside. 'Where shall we begin?'

'I've been making some lists.' Dina readjusted her attention to the project at hand.

But the aspersions Blake had made against Chet's character haunted her over the next two weeks. Again and again, she cursed in silent protest at the seeds of doubt Blake had planted in her mind. The cold war between herself and Blake neither accelerated in those two weeks, nor was there even a hint of a thaw.

A knock at the opened door brought her out of her gloomy reverie. She had been staring out the dusty pane of the solitary window in her small office. She turned, slipping her reading glasses to a perch on top of her head.

'Hello, Chet.' She stiffened at the sight of him and tried to relax but she had become too self-conscious lately in his company, not feeling the same freedom and trust she had once found with him.

'I've finally got all the interior and exterior photographs of the hotels that you wanted.' He indicated the stack of folders he was carrying with both hands. 'I thought we should go over them together. Are you too busy to do it now?'

'No, bring them in.' Dina began moving the papers from her desk. 'Just give me a second to make some room.'

Before the actual advertising campaign could begin, there was a lot of groundwork to be done. The most time-consuming one was the physical appearance of the hotels.

'I've already looked through them,' Chet told her.

'Good,' Dina nodded, and began to scan them herself.

The line of her mouth kept growing grimmer and grimmer. By the time she reached the bottom of the stack of photographs, she realised she had underestimated the amount of time and money it would take to superficially re-do the hotels.

'It's worse than I thought,' she sighed.

'Yes, I know,' Chet agreed, matching her expression.

'Let's take the hotels one by one and make notes.' she sighed. 'The one thing we want to keep in mind is that each hotel should be different, its decor indigenous to its location. We don't want a vacationer to think that if he's been in one Chandler Hotel, he's been in them all.'

'That's right.'

'Okay, let's start out with the one in Florida.' Dina gazed at the photographs. 'I think it has to be the most challenging. I didn't realise it looked so sterile.' She flipped her glasses into place on her nose and reached for her notepad. 'Here we'll take advantage of the tropical environment. Heavy on wicker furniture, light and airy colours, no carpeting, cool tile floors, and lots of potted palms and greenery. Something like the decor in our Hawaiian hotel would be good, but without the Polynesian accent.'

'What about the exterior?'

Dina thought of the budget and winced. 'I hope we can get by with some landscaping. I don't want to do a major face-lift unless there's no other way.'

Down the list of hotels and their photographs they went. The one in Maine would be done with a nautical flavour. The one in Mexico would have a lazy siesta look, complete with mock overhead fans turning leisurely from the ceiling. The founding hotel in Newport already had an elegant yachting atmosphere which would now be stressed. The themes varied with each hotel, depending on its location.

When the last photograph had been examined and set aside, Dina looked at her copious collection of notes and sighed at the dollar signs they meant. She remembered her spiteful comment to Blake about the interior decorating to be done, remarking that it was woman's work. Well, there was a mountain of it here, one that she doubted Blake would have the patience to tackle.

'Now what?' Chet questioned.

'Now,' Dina breathed in deeply, 'now we need to have these notes transferred into sketches.'

'Do you want me to start contacting some decorating firms?'

'I suppose so. With the scope of the work that

needs to be done, I'm just wondering how we should handle it.' She nibbled thoughtfully at her lower lip. 'Something, either major or minor, has to be done at each of the hotels.'

'In the past, we've always used firms within the area of the hotels, in the same city when we could,' Chet reminded her.

'Yes, I know.' Dina slid the pencil through the platinum gold hair above her ear. 'I checked the records last week to get an idea of the possible costs and noticed that in the past we'd always used local firms. Before it had proved to be both economical and good business to trade with a company in the same area as one of our hotels.'

'Since virtually all the hotels are involved, it might not be practical because of all the travelling that would have to be done,' he observed. 'That cost could eat into whatever savings we might realise by using a local decorator.'

'I'm afraid you're right,' she agreed with a rueful nod. 'We might be better off with a major firm capable of doing all the work. In the long run, it might prove to be the more economical choice.'

'I tell you what,' Chet leaned forward, his blue-grey eyes bright with suggestion, 'first let's get these notes typed up. Then why don't I contact two major companies to give us estimates on the work? To get a comparison, I can pick a half dozen hotels or so that are fairly close to here and obtain bids from local firms. I can use the hotel in Maine, the one

here in Newport, naturally, the one in the Poconos—
I can check the list.'

'That might work,' she agreed, turning the idea
over in her mind and liking it. It had been a half-
formed thought in her own mind, but when Chet
had spoken it aloud, it had solidified. 'Excellent
suggestion, Chet.'

'I'll get started on it right away.' He began gathering up the notes and the photographs from her desk.
'We don't want to waste time.'

'Before you go, there's something else I've been
thinking about that I wanted to talk over with you
to get your opinion,' Dina said to detain him.

'What's that?' Chet sat back down.

'To keep this continuity of every hotel being individual, I think we should carry it into the restaurants,' she explained.

'But we're doing that,' he frowned. 'There are
going to be decor changes in the restaurants and
lounges, too. We just went over them.'

'No, I was thinking of extending the idea to the
food.'

'Do you mean changing the menus?'

'Not completely. We would have to keep the
standard items like steaks, etcetera, but adding some
regional specialities as well. We do it already along
the coast with the seafood.'

'I see what you're saying,' Chet nodded. 'In the
Poconos, for instance, we could add some Pennsyl-
vania Dutch foods. We could even carry it down to

little touches, like serving genuine Johnnycake made out of white cornmeal with the dinner rolls here in Newport.'

'Exactly.' Dina nodded.

'I'll contact the restaurant managers of all the hotels. Those that aren't already doing this can send us a list of three or four speciality dishes they can add to their menus,' he suggested.

'Yes, do that. We can initiate this change right away by simply adding a flyer to the menus until new ones can be printed.'

'Consider it done, Dina.' He started to rise, then paused. 'Is that all?'

'For this time anyway,' she laughed.

'I'll be talking to you. And I'll have my secretary send you a copy of these notes,' he promised, and gathered the stack of notes and photographs into his arms.

As Chet walked out of the office, the smile left Dina's expression replaced by a wary frown. She stared at the open doorway, feeling those uneasy suspicions rearing their ugly heads. Then with a firm shake of her head, she dismissed them and turned back to the papers she had been working on.

CHAPTER EIGHT

BENT over her desk, Dina was concentrating on the proposals from the selected advertising agencies. Absently she stroked the eraser tip of her pencil through her hair. So intent on the papers, she didn't hear the footsteps in the hallway or notice the tall figure darkening her open doorway.

'Are you planning to work late?'

The sound of Blake's voice jerked her head up. He stood there, so lithely powerful, so magnetically attractive, The darkness of his tan seemed to have faded little, its bronze hue accentuated by the white turtleneck sweater. Through half-closed lids, he looked at her, creating the impression of lazy and friendly interest, yet his expression seemed masked.

As always when he caught her unaware, her pulse accelerated. An odd tightness gripped her throat, leaving her with a breathless sensation. For an instant, the room seemed to spin crazily.

It was at moments like these that Dina wanted to let the powerful attraction she felt simply carry her away. But that was too easy and too dangerous. It wouldn't solve any of the differences that had grown in the years they were apart.

His question registered in a delayed reaction. She

managed to tear her gaze away from his ever-watch-
ful eyes to glance at her wristwatch, surprised to
see it was a few minutes before six o'clock.

Then she noticed the silence in the rest of the
building. There were no muffled voices coming in
from the hallway, no clackety-clack of typewriters.
Nearly everyone had left for the day, except herself and Blake.

'I hadn't realised it was so late,' she offered in
answer to his question. 'I just have to clear these
things away and I'll be ready to leave.'

As she stacked the proposals one on top of the
other, preparatory to slipping them into their folder,
Blake wandered into the room. He suddenly seemed
to fill every square inch of it. Within herself, Dina
was conscious of the sensuous disturbance his presence caused.

'How is the campaign progressing?' he enquired,
his gaze flicking to the papers in her hand.

Dina had to search for the chilling antagonism
that would keep him at a disance. 'Hasn't Chet been
keeping you informed?'

'No. Was he supposed to?' There was a baiting
quality to the blandness of his voice.

'I presumed he would,' she retorted, opening a
desk drawer to put the folder away.

'If you didn't tell him to keep me up to date,
Chet won't,' said Blake, hooking a leg over the desk
corner to sit on its edge. 'He only does what he's
told.'

The desk drawer was slammed shut. 'Will you stop that!' Dina glared at him.

'Stop what?' Blake returned with seeming ignorance.

'Stop making remarks like that about Chet!' The antagonism was there. She no longer had to search for it.

Blake made an indifferent shrug. 'Whatever you say.'

Impatiently, she swept the remaining papers and pens into the middle drawer of her desk, leaving the top neat and orderly. Setting her bag on top, she pushed her chair up to the desk. Her sweater was lying on the back of the chair near where Blake stood.

'Hand me my sweater, please.' Frigid politeness crept into her voice.

Glancing around, Blake slipped it off the chair back and held it out to her as she walked around the desk to the front. 'How are you and Chet getting along?'

'The same as always—very well.' Dina gave him a cool look and started to reach for the sweater. 'Did you expect it to be different?' It was spoken as a challenge, faintly haughty. A light flashed in her mind and she forgot about the sweater. 'You did expect it to change, didn't you?' she accused.

'I don't know what you're talking about.'

'That's why you told Chet to give me a hand. I thought it was because you didn't think I could handle the job, but that wasn't it at all, was it?' Her anger was growing with each dawning thought.

Completely in control, Blake refused to react. 'You tell me.'

'You planted all those doubts in my mind about Chet, then made me work with him, hoping I would become poisoned against him. That's what this was all about, wasn't it?' Dina was incensed at the way Blake had attempted to manipulate her thinking.

'I admit that after our little talk about Chet, I hoped the blinkers would come off and you would see him as he really is.' There wasn't a trace of regret in his expression or his voice that his motive had been uncovered.

'That is the lowest, dirtiest thing I've ever heard!' she hissed.

Trembling with rage, she was completely unaware of her hand lashing out to strike him until it was caught in a vice grip short of its target. She gasped in pain as he twisted her arm to force her closer. He had straightened from the desk to stand before her, the sweater cast aside on the desk top.

'The last time you slapped me, I let you get away with it because I might have deserved it, but not this time,' Blake told her flatly. 'Not when I'm telling the truth.'

'But it isn't the truth!' Dina flared, undaunted by his implied threat. 'Not one word you've said against Chet is true. It's all lies. None of it is true!'

That darkly piercing look was back in his eyes as they scanned her upturned face. 'You know it's true, don't you?' he breathed in a low satisfied voice. 'You've started to see it for yourself—that's why you're so angry.'

'No, it isn't true,' she denied. 'I haven't seen it.'

'You have. Why don't you admit it?' Blake insisted with grim patience.

'No.' Dina continued to resist and strained to break free of his hold. 'And I'm not going to stay here and listen to you tear Chet down anymore.'

He increased the pressure of his grip and issued a taut denial. 'I am not trying to make him appear less of a man. I'm trying to make you see him the way he is and not the way you've imagined him to be in your mind. Why can't you understand that what I'm saying is not a personal attack on him?'

Suddenly, unexpectedly, she did understand and she believed him. The discovery took the heat out of her anger. Dina stopped fighting him and stood quietly.

'All right,' she admitted.

'All right what?' Blake lowered his gaze to her mouth, watching her lips as they formed the answering words.

'I have noticed a few things,' Dina admitted further.

'Such as?'

'The way he takes a suggestion and elaborates on

it until you're almost convinced the idea was his in the first place.'

'He's done that?'

'Yes. Today, when I mentioned an idea I had about adding regional dishes to the restaurant menus.' She wished Blake would stop watching her talk. It was unsettling, heightening her senses. 'He's already contacting the restaurant managers to see about starting it.'

'Chet is very good at organising and carrying out a suggestion,' Blake agreed. 'What else?'

'I don't know. A lot of little things.' The compliment Blake had given Chet prompted Dina to mention another conversation that had bothered her. 'When I didn't take a stand today about having a local or a major decorating firm redo the hotels, Chet didn't either. He suggested getting comparison bids from both and avoided offering a concrete opinion. In the last two weeks, I honestly can't remember Chet making a decision or offering a proposal of his own.'

Looking back, she realised that his proposal of marriage had been an outgrowth of a conversation about whether she would marry again or not. When she had conceded the possibility, Chet had asked if it would be someone like Blake she would choose. Her negative answer had then led to Chet suggesting himself, after first sounding out his footing.

That was hardly the mark of the strong, dependable man she had believed him to be. His reliability was limited to the times when someone else told him what to do.

Lost in her thoughts, Dina was unaware of the silence that had fallen between them until Blake spoke. 'I have another equally selfish reason for wanting Chet to work with you on this project.' His fingers were lightly stroking the inside of her wrist, a caressing motion that was disturbing.

A tingling warmth spread up her arm, her nerves fluttering in awareness of how close she stood to him. 'What is it?' There was a breathless catch to her voice. She looked into his eyes, nearly overcome by the sensation that she could willingly drown in the dark pools.

'Because I know that eventually this project is going to entail a good deal of travelling and I wanted to make certain it wasn't my wife who went on these trips.'

'I see.' She couldn't think of anything else to say.

'You might as well know this, Dina,' he said. 'You and I are never going to be separated for any reason.'

The ruthlessly determined note underlying his statement shivered through her. There was a sense of being trapped, a feeling that his wishes were inescapable. Whatever Blake wanted, he got. But not from her, her pride protested, not unless it was her own decision to agree.

With a degree of reluctance, she withdrew from his touch, turning to the desk to pick up her sweater and handbag. 'I'm ready to leave now,' she said, aware of the conflicting magnetic currents between them, alternately pulling and repelling.

Blake didn't make a move to leave. He just stood there looking at her, making her feel more uncomfortable and unsure of her own wants and needs.

'Sooner or later, you're going to have to make a decision,' he told her.

'I know. Sooner or later,' she echoed softly.

'Why are you waiting? What's holding you back?' he questioned. 'It isn't Chet any more, so what's left?'

'I don't know.' Dina shook her head uncertainly.

Needing to move, she started for the door. With that animal silence she was beginning to associate with Blake, he came up behind her, his hands sliding over her shoulders. The mere touch of him stopped her in her tracks.

'Decide now,' Blake ordered in a low murmur.

The silvery gold length of her hair was secured in a bun low on the back of her head. She felt the warm stirring of his breath on the exposed skin of her neck, sensitive and vulnerable. The sensuous pressure of his lips exploring that special pleasure point sent a delicious tremor through her.

His hands slid down to her forearms, crossing them in front of her as he moulded her shoulders, waist and hips to the hard contours of his length. Dina felt as pliable as putty, willing to be shaped into anything he wanted. Primitive passions scorched through her veins.

She struggled out of the emotional upheaval going on within her to protest, 'Blake, I can't!'

'You want to.' His mouth moved to her ear, his teeth nibbling at its lobe. 'You know you do.'

'I don't know anything,' she breathed raggedly.

'Then feel,' Blake instructed.

That was the problem. She felt too much and it blocked out her thinking processes. She didn't want to make a decision in the heat of an embrace. And certainly not in this inferno that was consuming her now.

'Blake, no!' She swallowed and pushed his hands from around her waist.

She took a step away from his tempting embrace and stopped, shaking and weak with desire. Her head was lowered, her chin tucked into her throat. She felt his gaze boring into her shoulders.

'Blake, no!' he mimicked her words with biting inflection. 'That's always your answer. How much longer are you going to keep giving it?'

'Until I'm absolutely sure that I know what I'm doing,' Dina answered.

'And how long will that be?' Blake was striving for control. It was evident in the clipped patience of his tone.

'I don't know,' she breathed. 'I just know it's easy to surrender to passion now and not so easy to face tomorrow.'

'Then you're a hell of a lot stronger than I am, Dina,' he snapped, 'because I don't give a damn about tomorrow!' He slipped a hand under her elbow. Her first thought was that he intended to ignore her uncertainties and kiss her into submission, something that would not be too difficult to do. Instead his hand pushed her forward. 'Let's go,' he muttered.

His long, ground-eating strides made it impossible for Dina to keep up with him without half-running. The rigid set of his jaw kept her from drawing attention to herself or her plight. He didn't slow down until he reached the parking lot, where she struggled to catch her breath as they walked to the car.

Without looking directly at her, Blake unlocked the passenger door and held it open for her, slamming it shut when she was safely inside. Walking around the car, he unlocked his own door and slid behind the wheel. He put the key in the ignition, but didn't start the car.

Resting his hands on the steering wheel, he stared straight ahead for several long seconds, a forbiddingly hard line to his mouth. Dina grew increasingly uneasy at the silence and felt pinned when his dark glaze finally swung to her. It wasn't a pleasant sensation.

'The first day I was back, you claimed we needed time to get to know each other again,' Blake said, 'that we had to become adjusted to each other again. You felt we should talk.'

'I'm surprised you remember,' she remarked, and

could have bitten off her tongue for issuing such caustic words.

'Believe me, I remember everything you've said,' he returned with dry weariness, his attention shifting to the windshield in front of him. Dina shifted uncomfortably in her seat, but remained silent. 'The point is, Dina, that we aren't getting to know each other again. We aren't talking. The only place we spend any time together alone is in the bedroom. And we both know there isn't any communication taking place there, physical or otherwise.'

'So what are you suggesting? That we should communicate on a physical level and work on from there?' Dina questioned stiffly, her pulse quickening in a reaction that did not reject the idea.

'No, that isn't what I'm suggesting,' there was a cynical twist to his mouth, 'although I know you've become convinced that my instincts have become purely primitive.'

A slight flush warmed her cheeks. 'Then what are you suggesting?'

'That we spend more time together, as you wanted.'

'That's a bit difficult with both of us working.'

'Neither of us work in the weekend,' Blake reminded her.

'You're forgetting we live in your mother's house.' And Mother Chandler had still not got over her son's miraculous return and hovered about him every possible moment she could.

'No, I'm not,' Blake denied calmly. 'The key word is alone—no friends, no relation, just you and I. I realise that can't be accomplished in my mother's home. That's why I've decided we'll spend the weekend at Block Island so we can have the time alone together that you claim we need.'

'Block Island,' Dina repeated the name of the resort island located roughly fourteen miles off the Rhode Island coast.

'That's what I said. Any objections?' He turned his head to look at her, a challenging glitter in his dark eyes.

'None.' How could there be when he had cornered her with her own words?

'There is one thing more, Dina.' Blake continued to study her, aware of her reluctant agreement— although why it was reluctant, Dina didn't know.

'What's that?' She was almost afraid to ask.

'I want this clearly understood before we go. If you haven't made up your mind about us by Sunday night, I'm not waiting any longer.' At the sight of her paling complexion, he smiled without humour. 'And I don't care whether you consider that a threat or a promise.'

'You can't put a deadline like that,' she protested

'Can't I?' Blake had already turned away to start the car, ignoring her now that he had stated his intentions.

'All you're doing is turning this weekend into a farce,' Dina retorted.

'Call it what you like,' Blake said indifferently. 'Just be sure to pack a suitcase and bring it to the office with you Friday morning. We'll catch the ferry to Block Island after work.'

As the ferry left the protected waters of Narragansett Bay for the open waters of the Atlantic, heading for the porkchop-shaped island off shore, Dina stared sightlessly at the Brenton Reef Light Tower. She and Blake had barely exchanged five words with each other since leaving the office and the silence was growing thicker.

She knew the reason why her lips were so tightly closed. Blake's Sunday night ultimatum had made her feel as if he was pointing a gun to her head. So how could she look forward to the weekend ahead of them? He had already foreordained the outcome, so what was the purpose? She should have refused to come. Why hadn't she?

Sighing, she glanced at Blake standing a few yards away talking to another fellow passenger. Their attention was on the low hanging clouds overhead, dull grey. There was nothing menacing about them, but they added to the gloom Dina felt.

The two were obviously discussing the weather, because Dina overheard the man remark, 'I hope you're right that it's going to be sunny and clear at the island. I don't know anything about ocean currents and how they affect the weather. All I know is that I want to get a weekend of fishing in.'

Blake's prediction of good weather on Block Island was true. They were within sight of their destination when the clouds began to thin, permitting glimpses of blue sky and a sinking yellow sun. When the ferry docked at the Old Harbor landing, there were only patches of clouds in the sky.

But the silence between Dina and Blake didn't break. Despite that, she felt her spirits lift as they drove off the ferry on to the island, named after Adrian Block, the first European to explore it. The island's atmosphere was refreshing and Dina understood why it had been a fashionable health spa in the Gay Nineties.

She became absorbed in the scenery as Blake drove across the island to the picturesque resort village of New Harbor stretched along the banks of the Great Salt Pond. It had once been an inland lake, but a man-made channel now linked it to the ocean, providing a spacious haven for both pleasure craft and commercial fishing boats.

Much of previous tension returned when Blake parked in front of a hotel. It seemed different somehow to share a hotel room. Just why, Dina couldn't say, since they'd been sharing a bedroom almost ever since Blake had returned. She felt self-conscious walking beside him into the lobby.

As he walked to the desk to register, she lingered near a rack of postcards, pretending an interest in their colourful pictures. There was a curling sensation in her stomach when she saw the porter take

heir bags. Blake walked towards her and she im-
nediately picked a card from the rack, ostensibly to
tudy it more closely.

'Were you planning to send a postcard to some-
ne?' The cynically amused query didn't help her
luttering stomach.

'No.' She quickly returned it to the rack. 'I was
ust looking at the picture.'

'Tomorrow we'll take a look at the real thing.'

Dina had to glance at the postcard. She had been
o conscious of Blake she hadn't noticed what the
ubject of the card had been. Now she saw it was
a lighthouse.

'It looks interesting,' she offered, just to be saying something.

'Yes,' Blake agreed dryly as if aware that she
aadn't previously known what it was. 'Shall we go
to our rooms?'

'Rooms?' In the plural, her eyes asked.

'Yes, two,' he answered. Dina was surprised by the
gentle, almost tender expression of patience that
crossed his usually hard features. 'We have adjoining bedrooms. I intend to give this weekend every
chance of proving whatever it is that you feel needs
proving, Dina.'

There didn't seem to be any response she could
make. Strangely this seemed more of a concession
than all the nights when Blake had shared her bed
without forcing an intimacy. Perhaps because he
was granting her the privacy to think without his

presence to disturb or influence her.

When he handed her one of the keys in his hand she managed a quiet, 'Thank you.'

'When a man is desperate, he'll try anything,' Blake returned cryptically, but Dina thought she caught a glimmer of humour in his dark eyes. It made him seem more human.

They walked to their rooms in silence, but it was no longer as strained as it had been. Blake hesitated outside his door, catching her eye for an instant before he turned the key in his lock and walked in.

Entering her room, Dina noticed her suitcase lying on the luggage rack and walked over to it intending to unpack. Instead, she paused at the interior door that connected the two bedrooms. Blake was on the other side of it. Unconsciously she reached for the doorknob. It was locked and refused to turn. Regret conflicted with relief as she walked back to her suitcase and unpacked.

An hour later, she had showered and was dressed in a wheat-coloured shirtwaister dress that was elegantly casual. Blake hadn't said whether he would meet her at the restaurant for dinner or go down with her. She debated whether she should wait in the room or go to the restaurant, then deciding to wait, she sat down on the bed.

Instantly a smile curved her lips. The mattress was blissfully soft, sinking beneath her weight like feather down. It was going to be a wonderful change from Blake's rock-firm mattress at the house.

Just then there was a knock at her door and Dina rose to answer it, the smile still lingering on her lips. Blake stood outside, his eyes warming to a dark brown at her expression.

'You look pleased about something.' he commented.

'My bed,' Dina explained, a pair of dimples etching grooves in her cheeks. 'It's soft.'

His chuckle of understanding was soft, almost silent, a disarming sight and sound. Her heart skipped a beat, then refused to return to an even tempo.

'Shall we go to dinner?'

It was more of a statement than a question as Blake held out his hand for hers. Self-consciously she let her fingers be engulfed in his hand, but he continued to block the doorway, not permitting her to step out. His hold on her hand shifted, raising the inside of her wrist to his mouth.

'Have I told you how very beautiful you are?' he murmured.

'Blake, please,' Dina protested, her lashes fluttering down at the heady touch of his warm lips against the sensitive area of her wrist.

'It's simply a compliment,' he interrupted with a wry quirk as he brought her hand away. 'All you have to do is say "thank you." '

'Thank you,' she repeated in a tight little voice, more disturbed than she cared to acknowledge by the effect he had on her.

'That's better,' Blake moved to the side, leading

her out of the room and reaching behind her to close the hotel room door.

Fresh seafood was the natural selection to make from the menu. Once that decision had been made, Dina sat in the chair opposite from Blake. Inside she was a bundle of twisted nerves, but she forced herself to be still.

Without the steady chatter of Mother Chandler to lead a table conversation, she couldn't think of anything to say. It seemed an indication of how far she and Blake had grown apart. Her tongue was tied into knots.

'I'm going to have to make a trip to the bookstore soon,' Blake commented with seeming idleness. 'I have a lot of reading to catch up on.'

'Yes, I suppose you do.' Dina wanted to cry at how stilted her response had been.

But Blake either didn't notice it or deliberately ignored it. 'It sounds a little crazy; I know, but reading was one of the things I really missed. More than good meals and clean clothes. I never considered it a necessity before.'

'I doubt if I have either,' she admitted, forgetting her self-consciousness at his provocatively profound comment.

'Any new titles you'd like to recommend?'

Dina hesitated, then suggested, 'Roots.'

Before she realised what was happening, she found herself becoming engrossed in a discussion of new books that had been published in Blake's abence and titles they had both read in the past. From reading, their conversation drifted to movies and Broadway shows. It seemed a natural progression to tell him about things she had done while he was gone, decisions she had been forced to make, such as subletting their apartment and sorting their furnishings.

When Blake later signalled their waiter for the check, Dina was astounded to discover that it was after ten o'clock and there had not been one awkward moment between them, not a single remark that had been in any way argumentative. She hadn't thought it was possible. She wondered if Blake had noticed it, but was afraid to ask. She didn't want to risk breaking whatever kind of temporary truce they had established.

They both seemed to be in a mutually reflective mood as they retraced their way to their rooms. Dina was conscious of his hand lightly resting on the back of her waist, a faintly possessive air to his guiding touch, but she didn't object to it in the least.

'Do you know what this reminds me of?' Blake questioned when they paused in front of her door.

'What?' Dina looked up, curious and thoughtful.

'All those times I used to walk you to the door of your sorority house and kiss you goodnight in a dark corner of the building.' He glanced around the hallway. 'Of course, here, there aren't any dark corners.' His gaze returned to her face. 'But I am going to kiss you goodnight.'

His head bent and Dina lifted hers to meet him halfway. The kiss was searingly light and questing, both seeking answers to unknown questions. Each seemed to realise that it would take only the slightest provocation to deepen the embrace to one of passion. Yet neither made it, merely testing the temperature of the water without becoming submerged in it.

With obvious reluctance, they both withdrew from the embrace, gazing silently at each other. Blake took a step back, a closed look stealing over his face.

'Do you have your key?' he asked.

'Yes.' Dina unfastened her clutch purse and took it out.

He hesitated a fraction of a second. 'Goodnight, Dina.' He moved towards his own door.

'Goodnight, Blake,' she murmured, and entered her hotel room alone.

CHAPTER NINE

Dina didn't sleep well that night. The irony of it was that it was because the mattress was too soft. She was wakened from her fitful dozing by a knock on the door and stumbled groggily across the room to answer it.

'Who is it?' She leaned tiredly against the door, her hand resting on the locked night latch.

'Blake,' was the answer. 'Are you ready for breakfast?'

Dina groaned. It couldn't possibly be morning already.

'Are you all right?' His tone was low and piercing.

'Fine,' she mumbled, adding silently, 'I just need some sleep.'

The doorknob rattled as he attempted to open it. 'Unlock the door, Dina,' he ordered.

She was too tired to think of a reason to refuse and too tired to argue if she had. Slipping off the night chain, she unlocked the latch and stepped aside as Blake pushed the door open. Concern was written all over his expression, but she didn't notice.

'I don't want breakfast.' Dina was already turning to make her way back to the bed. 'You go ahead without me.'

Blake's arm went around her to turn her back. He pushed the tangle of cornsilk hair behind her ear and held it there, his hand cupping the side of her head and tipping it up. His strength was a glorious thing and Dina willingly let him support her weight, too weary for standing on her own.

'What's the matter, Dina? You look exhausted.' Blake was frowning.

'I am,' she sighed. 'My beautifully soft bed was too soft. I barely slept all night.'

He laughed softly. 'Why didn't you take a pillow and blanket off the bed and sleep on the floor? Or was that too uncivilised for you?' he mocked in a gently teasing voice.

'I suppose that's what you did?' Dina lifted her tired lashes to glance at him. He looked disgustingly refreshed and rested.

'Yes,' he nodded.

'And probably slept like a baby,' she added enviously.

'I didn't sleep all that well,' Blake denied.

'Why not?' Dina slid her arms around his hard, warm body and rested her head against his shoulder, closing her eyes.

'I haven't liked sleeping alone since I met you.'

His provocative statement sailed over her sleepy head. Dina was only aware of how very right it seemed in his arms, so comfortable and so warm. She snuggled closer.

'Why don't you just hold me for a while and let

me sleep?' she suggested in a sleepy murmur.

'I don't think so.' The arm that had been around her withdrew to press a hand against her ribcage just below her breast to push her away. 'If I hold you much longer, I won't be thinking about sleep,' Blake stated, a half-smile curving one corner of his mouth. 'Why don't you shower and dress? I'll go get some coffee to help you wake up before we go to breakfast.'

Dina didn't have a chance to agree or disagree. One minute she was in his arms and the next he was walking to the door, leaving her swaying there unsteadily. The closing of the door goaded her into movement. She looked longingly at the bed, but knew it was no use. Even if she could go back to sleep, Blake would be back shortly to waken her. Following his suggestion, she walked to the bathroom.

It was shortly after mid-morning by the time Blake and Dina finished their breakfast and started out on a leisurely tour of the island, dotted with fresh-water ponds. It was not the first visit for either of them, but it had been several years since their last.

There was little noticeable change on the island with the possible exception that a few more trees had been planted by property owners. The young saplings looked forlorn in a landscape that was remarkably devoid of trees. Early settlers had long ago cut down the native ones for lumber to build their homes. Reafforestation was a new and slow process.

Stone fences criss-crossed the rolling terrain. The rocks had been deposited on the island by glaciers from the Ice Age and stacked, probably long ago by slave labour, to erect property boundaries of early farms. They were a picturesque touch on the island, called by an early Italian navigator, God's Little Isle.

On the south-eastern shore, Blake parked the car on Mohegan Bluffs. The picture-postcard lighthouse sat on the point of the bluffs, the rustic house and tower looking out to sea. Its navigational beacon was one of the most powerful on the New England coastline.

The salty breeze off the ocean was cool. Dina zipped the coral windbreaker up to her neck while Blake locked the car. Screeching seagulls soared overhead as they walked together past the lighthouse to the steep path leading down the headland to the beach.

A fisherman stood knee-deep in the surf, casting a fly line into the white-caps. He nodded a friendly acknowledgement to them as they strolled by. Blake's arm was around Dina's shoulders, keeping her close to his side. She stepped over a piece of driftwood and turned her gaze up to his face. His features were relaxed with a look of contentment about them.

'Why are we getting along so well?' she mused, more to herself than to him.

'Maybe it's because we've stopped looking at each other,' Blake suggested.

'What?' A bewildered frown creased her forehead, confusion darkening the blue of her eyes.

'It does sound a bit strange, doesn't it?' A faint smile touched his mouth when he glanced at her, then he directed his gaze ahead of them, a contemplative look about his expression. 'What I think I mean is that we've stopped trying to see the flaws in each other, the differences. We've started looking outward together.'

'Do you suppose that's it?' Dina, too, shifted her gaze to the beach in front of them.

'Why bother to analyse the reason?' he countered. 'Why not just enjoy it?'

'That's true.' She scuffed a canvas toe against a stone. 'Except that I like to know the why of things.'

'So I remember,' Blake murmured dryly. 'Like the time I gave you your engagement ring and you wanted to know what made me decide to propose to you.

Dina laughed. 'And you said it was because I would make such a beautiful ornament in your home.' The laughter died as she gave him a guarded look. 'Is that really the way you regard women? As ornaments?'

There was a hint of exasperation in his impatient glance. 'You should know me better than that, Dina.'

She was silent for several paces. 'That's the problem, I guess, I'm not certain any more how well I know you. You always seemed so cultured. Now,' she lifted her hand in a searching gesture, 'you are ... so earthy.'

'I suppose I learned that the basics of life are more important. The rest is just window-dressing. Fundamentally I don't believe I've changed.'

'Perhaps I was so busy looking for the window-dressing that I didn't recognise you,' she wondered aloud.

'Perhaps,' Blake conceded. He flashed her a quick smile. 'How did we get started on such a serious discussion?'

His lightning switch from a pensive mood to one that was lightly teasing was infectious. Dina responded immediately, 'I don't know. You started it.'

'No, I didn't. You did,' he corrected in the same light vein, 'when you questioned why we weren't arguing.'

'You didn't have to answer me, so therefore it's all your fault,' she shrugged.

'Logic like that could only come from a woman,' Blake declared with an amused shake of his head.

'Are you making disparaging remarks against my sex again?' she demanded in mock anger.

'I'm just stating facts,' he insisted.

Dina gave him a sideways push with her shoulder. Knocked off balance, his arm slipped from around her, and he had to take a step to one side to recover. Their aimless pace had taken them closer to the water's edge than either had realised, and when Blake took that step, his foot landed in salt water, shoe, sock and trouser cuff. Dina gasped in a laugh at the one wet foot.

'So you think it's funny, do you?' He took a playfully threatening step towards her.

Unconsciously she began to retreat. 'Honestly, Blake, I'm sorry.' She was trying hard not to laugh, but it bubbled in her voice. 'I didn't know. I didn't mean to push you in the water, honestly.'

Blake continued to approach her. 'Let's see if it's so funny when you get wet.'

'Blake, no!' Dina kept backing up, swallowing the laughter as she negatively shook the silver-gold mane of her hair.

The wicked glint in his eye warned her that words would not appease him. Turning, she ran, sprinting for the rock bluff a safer distance from the lapping ocean waves. Blake chased her, his long strides eating up her short lead. Any moment he would overtake her, Dina knew, and she spared a laughing glance over her shoulder.

A piece of driftwood in her path tripped her and sent her sprawling headlong on to the beach. Her outstretched arms broke most of her fall. Unharmed, she rolled on to her back, out of breath, but still trying to laugh, as Blake dropped to his knees beside her.

'Are you all right?' he asked, half smiling and half concerned.

'Fine,' she managed to gasp.

Sitting on his heels, Blake watched silently as she caught her breath. But as her breathing slowed, her heartbeat increased. An exciting tension was leaping between them, quivering over her nerve ends in lightning stimulation.

Blake moved forward as if to assist her to her feet, but as he moved closer, arms bracing him above her, her lips parted, glistening moistly. Dina lifted her hands to his chest as if to resist him, but instead they slid around his neck, pulling him down.

Fire ignited at the hard pressure of his mouth, hungry and demanding. It spread through her veins, her bones melting under the intense heat. The weight of his body crushed her to the rocky sand, exquisite pain. No part of her was immune to the fire Blake was arousing so thoroughly.

Reeling under the torrid assault of his desire, she knew she had lost control. She made no attempt to regain it, willing to let his lips dominate hers for as long as he chose. With each breath, she drew in the intoxicating scent of him, warm and magic, a fuel for the fire that consumed her.

Never had Dina felt so alive. Every corner of her heart was filled with love, overflowing and spilling out like a volcano. Any differences were burned away by the fiery embrace that transcended physical limits.

'Hey, mister?' A child's voice sounded when previously she had only been able to hear the pagan rhythms of their matching heartbeats. 'Hey, mister!' This time, the voice was more insistent and Blake dragged his mouth from hers to roll on to his side. 'Have you seen my puppy?'

A young boy of six stood beside them, knees dirty, a baseball cap on his light brown head, staring at them innocently. Dina could feel Blake gathering the control to answer him.

'No, son, I haven't.' His reply was tight and brief to conceal the raggedness of his breathing.

'He's white and black with a red collar,' the boy explained.

'Sorry, we haven't seen him, Blake repeated patiently.

'If you do, would you bring him back to me?'

'Sure.'

'Thanks.' And he trotted off, disappearing around a jutting promontory on the beach.

Blake stared in the direction the boy had taken. 'A few more seconds and it could have been embarrassing,' he remarked grimly. 'Come on.' Rolling to his feet, he caught at Dina's hand to pull her along with him.

'Where are we going?' There was a faint pink to her cheeks.

'Back to the hotel.'

'Why?'

'You're forgetting,' he accused, flashing her a look that still had the smouldering light of desire, 'I have a wet shoe, sock and pants leg.'

Slightly subdued, Dina offered, 'I'm sorry about that.'

'I'm not.' His finger touched her lips, tracing their outline, warm and still throbbing from his possession of them. 'If that's what I get for a wet foot, I can't help wondering what would happen if I'd been drenched from head to toe.' She breathed in sharply, wanting to tell him he didn't have to wait to find out, but she simply couldn't say the words. Blake didn't wait for her to speak, removing his fingers from her lips to encircle her hand. 'Let's go, shall we?'

Dina nodded in silent agreement.

The magic moment lay between them on their return trip to the hotel, the irrevocable change it had made unspoken. But it was there in the looks they exchanged, in the things they didn't say and in the way they avoided physical contact with each other. They each seemed to know how combustible a touch could be and were not ready to start a false fire.

Yet neither of them was willing to acknowledge the change in the relationship. At the same time, they couldn't go back to the cold hostility that had preceded the visit to the island. They each played a waiting game.

After a late lunch in the hotel restaurant, they entered the lobby. Blake stopped short and turned to Dina. 'We're checking out and going home,' he announced.

'It's only Saturday,' she protested.

'Yes, I know,' he agreed with a hint of impatience. 'But I'm not looking forward to spending another night here.'

Dina hesitated, uncertain of his meaning. Finally she acknowledged, 'The beds aren't very comfortable.'

His mouth twisted wryly. 'Yes, they're too soft.'

'Do we have time to catch the ferry?'

'If you don't waste too much time packing, we do,' he told her.

'I won't,' she promised.

'I'll check out while you get started,' said Blake.

During the ferry crossing, neither mentioned their abrupt change of plans that had them returning early. They talked around it as if unwilling to delve too deeply into the reason. When the ferry docked in Newport, they stopped talking altogether, both absorbed in their own thoughts.

It was several seconds before Dina noticed that Blake had missed a corner. 'You were supposed to turn at that last block,' she reminded him.

'We aren't going back to the house right away,' he said.

Dina waited for him to tell her their destination. When he didn't, she asked, 'Where are we going?'

'There's something I want to show you,' was all he answered.

After several more blocks, he turned on to a tree-shaded street, branches arching overhead, nearly touching. He slowed the car down, seeming to read the house numbers as he drove down the street. Dina's curiosity grew with each second of his continued silence. Finally he turned into a driveway and stopped the car, switching off the engine.

Dina glanced at the large white house, surrounded by a green lawn with lots of trees and flowering shrubs. She didn't recognise the place.

'Who lives here?' she asked.

Blake was already opening his car door and stepping outside. 'You'll see.'

She flashed him a blue look of irritation as he came around to open her door. He was carrying all this mystery business just a little too far. But she said nothing and walked ahead of him along the winding sidewalk to the front door.

There was jingle of metal behind her and she turned. Blake was taking a set of keys from his pocket. Selecting one, he stepped ahead of her and inserted it in the front door lock. Suspicion glittered in her eyes.

Pushing the door open, he motioned to her. 'Go on in.'

Her gaze swerved to the opened door as she moved forward to cross the threshold. On her right, carved oak posts ran from floor to ceiling to partition the mock entry way from the spacious living room beyond. Although the room was sparsely furnished, the items that were there Dina recognised as furniture stored from their apartment.

'What is this supposed to mean?' Unable to look at him, she thought she already knew the answer, and his high-handedness made her tremble with anger.

'Do you like it?' Blake ignored her question to ask one of his own.

'Am I to presume you bought this house without consulting me?' she accused in a low, shaking voice, barely able to control her ire.

'As I recall, you were too busy to be bothered with looking for a place for us to live or furnishing it,' he reminded her in an expressionless tone. 'But to answer your question, no, I haven't signed any documents to purchase this house.'

'If that's true, what is all our furniture doing here?' Her hand waved jerkily to the sofa and chairs.

'I obtained permission from the owner to have it brought in to see how it would fit in the rooms and to give the decorator an idea of what still has to be done.'

Dina turned on him roundly, her eyes flashing fire. 'In other words, you're presenting me with an accomplished fact! It doesn't matter what I want! You've decided on this house and if I don't like it, that's just too bad, isn't it?'

'Your opinion does matter.' A muscle was twitching along his jaw, the only outward sign that he felt the lashing flick of her words. 'That's why I brought you here.'

There was a sceptical lift of her chin, disbelief

glittering in her eyes despite his smooth denial. 'Why now? Why not before? All this furniture wasn't just brought here and arranged overnight.'

'No, it wasn't,' Blake agreed.

'Then why now?' Dina repeated her demand.

'Because I had the impression you were ready to start looking for a place we might share together.'

His narrowed gaze was piercing, impaling her on its point until she wanted to squirm under his sharp scrutiny. She averted her attention to the room, unable to admit that it might have been more than an impression.

'Was I wrong, Dina?' Blake questioned.

She didn't want to answer that question, not yet, not until she had more time to think about it. She didn't want to be manipulated into a commitment.

'Since I'm here, you might as well show me through the rest of house,' she said with forced diffidence.

Blake hesitated, as if to pursue the answer to his question, then gestured with his hand. 'The dining room and kitchen are this way,' he directed.

As Dina toured the house, she realised it was everything they had ever talked about in a home of their own. Spacious without being too large, ample room for entertaining, a study for Blake where he could work undisturbed in the evenings, a large patio in back, and plenty of closets.

'Since you're working, I thought we could arrange to have a maid to come in to do the housework,'

Blake explained as they walked down the hallway from the master bedroom to the main living area of the house.

'Yes,' Dina agreed absently. At the open doorway of one of the two empty rooms, she paused to look inside again. The spare bedrooms were smaller than the master bedroom, but still adequately large.

'There is one thing I haven't asked you.' Blake stopped beside her.

'What's that?' She turned to meet his gaze.

'I haven't asked how you felt about having children?'

Slightly flustered, Dina looked back to the empty room, visualising it not as a guest bedroom, but as a children's room. 'We've talked about it before.' They had discussed having two children, possibly three, she remembered.

'That was several years ago,' Blake pointed out, 'before you became a career woman.'

'Working women raise children,' she hedged, avoiding a direct answer and speaking in generalities instead.

'And there are some working women who prefer not to have children,' he added. 'I'm asking what you prefer, Dina.'

He seemed to silently demand that she look at him. Reluctantly she let gaze swing back to him, but she was unable to look any higher than his mouth. There were no soft curves to it; it was strong and firm and very masculine. Dina had the impulse to raise her fingertips to it and trace the strength of its outline.

'I would like to have children, yes.' Her reply was soft, almost inaudible.

'Do you have any objections to me being their father?' There was a husky quality to his voice.

The movement of his mouth when he spoke broke the spell and Dina looked away, her heart pulsing erratically. She didn't make a response. She couldn't seem to speak. Something was blocking her voice.

'Do you?' Blake repeated. When she remained silent, his fingers turned her chin to force her to look at him. 'Was I mistaken this morning on the beach?' His steady gaze didn't waver as he looked deeply into her eyes, seemingly into her very soul. 'Did you give me your answer, or was it a fleeting surrender to passion?'

'I don't know.' Dina wanted to look away, but she couldn't. Her mind was reeling from his touch, incapable of coherent thought. 'I ... I can't think.'

'Just this once, don't think,' Blake requested. 'Tell me what you're feeling.'

His hands slipped to her shoulders, tightening for a fraction of a second as if he wanted to shake the answer out of her, but they relaxed to simply hold her. Dina stared into the bluntly chiselled features, leather-tanned, and those compelling dark eyes. This was Blake, a man, her husband, and not quite the stranger she had thought him to be.

She swayed towards him and he gathered her into

his arms, prepared to meet her more than halfway. Her lips parted under the plundering force of his mouth, taking the prize she so readily surrendered to him. As if it had never been away, her soft shape moulded itself to the hard contours of his length.

His roaming hands caressed and shaped her ever closer to his solidly muscled flesh. Their combined body heat melted them together, fusing them with the glorious fire of their love. His driving male need made Dina aware of the empty aching in the pit of her stomach that only he could satisfy.

Soon, the torrid embrace was not enough. It was unable to meet the insatiable needs of their desires. Bending slightly, Blake curved an arm under her knees to lift her bodily and carry her to the master bedroom and the bare mattress of their old marriage bed.

As he laid her on the bed, the twining arms around his neck pulled him down to join her. Nothing existed for either of them, but each other, not the past and not the future, only the moment, eternally suspended in time.

The initial storm of their passion was quickly spent. When Blake came to her a second time, their love-making was slow and languorous. Each touch, each kiss, each intimate caress was enjoyed and prolonged, savoured and cherished.

The beauty of it brought tears to Dina's eyes, jewel-bright and awesomely happy. Blake kissed them away, gently, adoringly. Never had it been like this between them, as near to perfection as mere mortals can get.

Blake curved her to his side, locking his arms around her. Dina sighed in rapturous contentment and snuggled closer, not wanting to move, never wanting to move. Here was where she belonged, where she would always belong.

CHAPTER TEN

BLAKE stroked her hair, absently trailing his fingers through the silken ends, watching the fairness of its colour glisten in the light. Her eyes were closed in supreme contentment.

'Would you say it now, Dina?' His huskily caressing voice rumbled from deep within his chest.

'Say what?' she questioned in equal softness, not sure words could express anything close to what she was feeling.

'Welcome home, darling,' he supplied the words.

Tipping back her head, she looked up to his face, love bringing a dazzling brilliance to the blue of her eyes. 'Welcome home, darling,' she repeated the words in a voice that trembled with the depth of her meaning.

A strangled moan of torment ending came from his throat as he lifted her the few inches necessary to plant a hard, possessive kiss on her lips. Then his trembling fingers moved over her lips as if to apologise for hurting them.

'I've been waiting so long to hear that.' There was a sad, almost wistful curve to his strong mouth. 'Now, it doesn't seem nearly as important.'

'A thousand times I've wondered if it might not

have been different if I'd known you were alive before I saw you at the house,' Dina whispered, her heart aching at the time together they had lost. 'I thought it was someone's twisted idea of a joke.'

'I should have made more of an effort to get hold of you or have the authorities reach you before I came back,' Blake assented. 'I knew it would be a shock. Chet tried to convince me to let him break the news to you, but I didn't listen, not even when my own mother was so stunned that she didn't believe it was me. I was expecting too much not to think you would react the same way. In the end, I went to my mother, but I tried to make you come to me.'

'It wasn't just shock,' she explained. 'It was guilt, because I'd become engaged to Chet. And there you were, my husband. I wanted to run to you, but I couldn't. Then suddenly, you seemed so different— a stranger, someone I didn't know. It was window-dressing,' Dina sighed.

'Subconsciously, I didn't want to admit there'd been any changes in either of us,' he murmured with a rueful smile. 'I wanted everything to be the way it was, as if I'd never been gone.'

'Still, everything might have been different if I hadn't been engaged to Chet.' Dina turned to rest her head again on his bronzed chest and listen to the strong rhythm of his heartbeat.

'It might have made us less wary of each other, but we still would have had to adjust to our growth as human beings. It would have been painful under any circumstances,' he insisted.

'Yes, but Chet——' Dina started to argue.

Blake interrupted, 'He was never a threat to our relationship. Even if I hadn't come back, I'm convinced you would never have married him. You might have drifted along with the engagement for a year, but you're much too intelligent not to eventually have seen that it wouldn't work.'

She relaxed, suddenly knowing he was right, and the last little doubt vanished. Smiling, she slid her hand over the flat of his muscular stomach, as smooth and hard as polished bronze.

'Weren't you just a little bit jealous of Chet?' The question was half teasing and half serious.

'No, I was never jealous of him,' he chuckled, and tugged at a lock of hair.

'Never?' Dina was almost disappointed.

'Never,' Blake repeated in an absolutely positive tone. 'There were times, though, when I was envious.'

'Why?'

'Because you were so natural with him, so warm and friendly, trusting him, relying on him, and turning to him when you were confused. I wanted it to be me,' he explained. 'A man's instinct to protect is as strong as the maternal instinct in a woman. That's why I was envious of Chet, because you wouldn't look to me for security.'

'I feel very secure now.' Dina hugged up to him.

'I love you, Blake. I've never stopped loving you.'

'That's what I really wanted to hear.' His arms tightened around her, crushing her ribs. 'Welcome home was just a substitute for I love you.'

'I love you,' she repeated. 'You don't have to prompt me into saying that. I shall keep saying it until you get sick of it.'

'Never, my love,' he shook his head.

There was a long silence as they revelled inwardly at the rediscovery of their love and the eloquently simple words that expressed so much.

'I hate to bring up something so mundane,' Dina whispered, 'but where are we going to sleep tonight?'

'I don't even want to go to sleep,' said Blake.

'Aren't you tired?' Her sleepless night on the soft mattress was beginning to catch up with her, aided by the dreamy contentment of his embrace.

'Exhausted,' he admitted with a smile in his voice. 'But I'm afraid if I go to sleep, I'll wake up and find none of this has happened. Or worse, that I'm still in the jungle.'

'If you are, I'm going to be there with you,' she declared, and poked a finger in his chest. 'You Tarzan, me Jane.' Blake chuckled and kissed her hair. 'Seriously, Blake, are we going back to the house tonight?'

'Not if the storage boxes in the garage have any blankets in them. Do they?' he questioned.

'Did you take everything out that I had in storage?'

'Every single solitary thing,' he confirmed.

'Then there are blankets in the boxes in the garage,' she promised. 'As a matter of fact, there's everything there needed to set up housekeeping.'

'Is that what you'd like to do?' Blake asked. 'Stay here tonight?'

'I thought you'd already decided we were?'

'I'm asking if that's what you want to do,' he explained patiently.

'I must remember that and mark it on the calendar,' Dina murmured. 'Blake asked me what I wanted to do instead of telling me what I was going to do.'

'All right, troublemaker,' he laughed. 'You know what I'm really asking.'

'You want to know whether I like the house?' Dina guessed, propping herself up on an elbow beside him.

'Do you?'

'Yes. As a matter of fact, I love it,' she smiled. 'It's everything we ever said we wanted in a house.'

'Good. That's what I thought, too. Monday morning I'll have the agent draw the papers for us to sign. In the meantime, I don't think he'll mind if we start unpacking the boxes in the garage.'

'What if he sells it to someone else?'

'He won't. I put earnest money down to hold it

until you saw it and, I hoped, approved of my choice.'

'Where you so positive I'd like it?'

'As positive as I was that you'd love me again,' Blake answered.

'Conceited!' Dina teased. 'It would serve you right if I hadn't liked it.'

'But you do, and now you can take over the decorating of it.'

'It might end up looking like a hotel,' she warned.

'It better not,' he laughed, and pulled her into his arms.

There was a scattering of snowflakes outside her office window, falling from pearl-grey clouds. A serenely joyful light was in Dina's eyes as she smiled at the telephone receiver she held to her ear.

'Thank you. I'll tell him,' she promised. 'Merry Christmas.'

Hanging up, she let her attention return to the papers on her desk while absently humming a song of the winter holiday two weeks away. The inter-office line buzzed and she picked up the telephone again.

She had barely identified herself when Blake ordered crisply, 'I want you in my office immediately.'

'What's it about?'

'We'll discuss it when you get here.'

An eyebrow arched at his sharpness. 'Very well,'

Dina agreed calmly. 'Give me about fifteen minutes.'

'I said now,' he snapped.

'You're forgetting it takes that long to walk from my little cubbyhole to your office,' she reminded him dryly.

'Now, Dina!' And the connection was broken.

Breathing in deeply, she stared at the dead phone before finally replacing it on its cradle. She took a few precious seconds to put her desk into some kind of order, then walked into the corridor, closing her office door as she left.

Her statement of fifteen minutes was an exaggeration. Eight minutes later, Amy Wentworth glanced up from her typewriter and motioned her into Blake's office with a greeting wave of her hand. Dina knocked once on the connecting door and opened it to walk in.

Blake sat behind his desk, leaning back in his chair when Dina entered. The bluntly male features still retained much of his tropical tan, but they were drawn into coldly harsh lines to match the temperature outdoors. Anger glittered in his dark eyes and Dina had no idea why.

'You wanted to see me, Blake?' She walked to his desk, smiling warmly at her husband, but it didn't thaw his expression. 'Am I being called on the carpet about something?'

'You're damned right you are!' He reached forward to shove a paper across his desk towards her, his glittering and watchful gaze never leaving her face for an instant. 'What's this all about?'

Dina reached for the paper and glanced over it. 'This is the revised budget request,' she frowned as she recognised it. 'Where did you get it?'

'From Chet,' Blake snapped.

Her mouth became a straight line of grim exasperation. 'He wasn't supposed to give it to you. I wanted to go over it with you when I submitted it.'

'He didn't give to me, I took it. And you can go over it with me now,' he ordered. 'This is the—what—third or fourth budget revision?'

'The third.' Dina was determined not to match his biting tone. 'And if you'd told me why you wanted to speak to me, I could have brought some supporting papers.'

'I'm not interested in supporting papers, I want an explanation. What's the cause for the increase this time? And don't tell me it's inflation.'

'It's a combination of things,' she began. 'We had to change advertising agencies for the campaign because the original firm wasn't able to produce due to some internal problem. That meant an increase in the cost.'

'You should have checked more thoroughly into the first company,' he rebuked.

'Their difficulties occurred after we'd signed a contract with them,' she replied sharply to his criticism.

There was disbelief in his look, but he didn't

pursue that aspect. 'What else?'

'We had to revise the cost figures on revamping the hotels. The——'

'I knew it,' he declared through clenched teeth. 'The redecorating costs for the hotels have escalated every time you've submitted a budget. Are you redecorating them or rebuilding?'

The slow-burning fuse of her temper was lit. 'There are times when I'm not so positive myself,' she simmered. 'Have you seen that hotel in Florida? It looks like a hospital. We've tried landscaping, painting, but it needs a whole new façade.'

'Why don't you just arrange to tear it down and build a new one? he flashed.

'That's the best suggestion I've heard yet!' she retorted. 'Why don't you bring that up to the expansion department?

'At the rate you're going, it might be the most economical decision!' With controlled violence, Blake pushed out of his chair, standing behind the desk to glance at her. 'I should have known this would happen. You put a woman in charge and give her a free hand and right away, she thinks it means she has a blank check!'

Hot tears burned her eyes. 'If that's what you think,' pain strangled her voice, 'why don't you take over? I never asked for the job in the first place! If you think a man can do so much better, go ahead!'

'And don't think I couldn't!'

'The great Blake Chandler. Oh, I'm sure you could do a lot better job,' Dina issued sarcastically, and turned away, hugging her arms in front of her in a mixture of disgust and hurt. 'I don't know what ever made me think I'd want your baby.'

'I don't know either!' Blake snarled behind her. 'It's a lucky thing you have a choice, isn't it?'

'That's the whole point! I don't have a choice any more,' she cried bitterly.

Her sentence hung in the air for a long, heavy second before Blake broke the silence with a low demand, 'What did you say?'

'Didn't I tell you?' She tossed the question over her shoulder, her chin quivering with the forced attempt at lightness. 'I'm going to have a baby.'

In the next second, his hands were on her shoulders to gently turn her around. Dina kept her chin lowered, still angry and hurt by his barbed attack.

'Are you sure?' he asked quietly.

'Yes, I'm sure.' She closed her eyes to try to force back the tears. 'Doctor Cosgrove called me a few minutes ago to confirm the test results.'

'Why didn't you tell me?' His tension was exhaled with the question.

'How could I when you've been yelling at me for the past five minutes?' Her eyes flared open to glare at him.

His fingers lightly touched her cheek before he cupped it in his hand. 'I was, wasn't I?' There was a rueful quirk to his mouth.

'Yes, you were.' But her assertion didn't carry any sting of anger.

'I lost my perspective for a moment, the order of importance. I could lose everything I have and it wouldn't matter as long as I didn't lose you.'

The glow radiating from his face was warm and powerful and Dina basked in the love light. That serene joy she had known before their argument returned with doubled strength.

'No, it doesn't matter as long as I have you,' she agreed, and turned her lips into his hand to press a kiss in his open palm.

His head lowered, his mouth claiming hers in a sweetly fierce kiss that rocked her senses. She clung to him, revelling in the possessive embrace that gathered her close to his male length. A wild, glorious melody raced through her veins, its tune timeless, the universal song of love.

She was breathless when the kiss ended, and the sensation remained as Blake buried his face in the silver-gold hair, his mouth trailing a blazing fire to the sensitive skin of her neck. She felt the tremors vibrating through his muscular form and knew she disturbed him as sensually as he disturbed her.

When he finally lifted his head, there was a disarming smile softening his roughly carved features. His hands moved to tangle his fingers in her hair and hold her face up for his gaze to explore. Dina knew this was a moment she would treasure forever in her heart.

'We're really going to have a baby?' There was a faintly marvelling look in his eyes as Blake turned the statement into a near question.

'Yes,' Dina nodded.

'Are you all right?' he frowned.

'I'm fine,' she smiled. With a sighing shake of her head, she asked, 'Why do we argue so much, Blake?'

'It's our nature, I guess,' he smiled wryly in return. 'We'd better get used to the fact, because we'll probably do it the rest of our lives.'

'Always testing to find out which of us is stronger.' Dina recalled Chet's explanation for their constant quarrels.

'Don't worry, honey, I'll let you be stronger once in a while,' he promised.

'Blake!' She started to protest indignantly at his superior remark.

'Can you imagine what our children are going to be like?' he laughed. 'Pigheaded, argumentative little rebels, more than likely.'

'More than likely,' Dina agreed. 'And we'll love every battling moment of raising them.'

'The same as every battling moment you and I have together.' He kissed her lightly and gazed into her eyes. 'When's the baby due?'

'July.'

'The new campaign will be in full swing by then.

I can just see you directing operations from the maternity ward,' Blake chuckled.

'You mean that I still have the job?' Dina arched a mocking brow at him.

'Of course,' he returned with an arrogant smile. 'Aren't you glad you have an understanding boss who will let you set your own hours or work at home, if that's more convenient?'

'I'm very lucky.' She slid her arms around his neck, rising on tiptoes. 'Lucky in more than one way.'

'Dina.' Blake spoke her name in an aching murmur against her lips.

RELENTLESS AMBITIONS, SHOCKING SECRETS AND POWERFUL DESIRES

Penny Jordan's stunning new novel is not to be missed!

The dramatic story of six very different people—irrevocably linked by ambition and desire, each must face private demons in a riveting struggle for power. Together they must find the strength to emerge from the lingering shadows of the past, into the dawning promise of the future.

WORLDWIDE

AVAILABLE NOW   PRICED AT £4.99

The truth often hurts...

Sometimes it heals

Critically injured in a car accident, Liz Danvers insists her family
read the secret diaries she has kept for years—revealing a lifetime
of courage, sacrifice and a great love. Liz knew the truth would be
painful for her daughter Sage to face, as the diaries would finally
explain the agonising choices that have so embittered her most
cherished child.

Available now priced at £4.99

W❍RLDWIDE

Revenge is a dangerous game...

Pepper Minesse has paid dearly for her success. For ten years her thirst for revenge has fuelled her ambition and made her rich. But now the four men responsible for her tragic past must pay too. She held files that could destroy each of them and together they must silence her—forever. Only one man's love can defuse the time bomb she has set ticking. . .

Available now priced at £3.99

WORLDWIDE

Bewitched in her dreams she awoke to discover the face of reality

The same dark hair, the same mocking eyes. The Regency rake in the portrait, the seducer of Jenna's dreams, had a living double. But James Allingham was no dream, he was a direct descendent of the black sheep of the Deveril family. They would fight for possession of the old ancestral home, but they would fight harder against their desire to be together.

Available now priced at £3.99

W🌐RLDWIDE

Purest Innocence, Deepest Passions and Love's Choices...

Determined and ruthless Comte Alexei Serivace would not be swayed from his cruel plan of revenge—a plan in which Hope Stanford was an unwilling pawn. Removed from her sheltered convent life, Hope quickly realised that she was no match for this arrogant sophisticate—but she didn't intend to be a pushover either.

Available now priced at £3.99

W⬤RLDWIDE